Fundamentals of Machine Component Design

Aer606 Engineering Drafting & Component Design

Instructors

Professor B. Tan

Authors

Juvinall

To order books or for customer service please,

call 1-800-CALL WILEY (225-5945).

Printed in the United States of America 10 9 8 7 6 5 4 3 2 1

List of Titles

Fundamentals of Machine Component Design
by Robert C. Juvinall and Kurt M. Marshek
Copyright © 2006, ISBN: 978-0-47166-177-1

Table of Contents

Symbols

A area, cross-sectional area, arm of planetary gear

A point A

A_0 original unloaded cross-sectional area

a, a acceleration

a crack depth, radius of contact area of two spheres

A_c effective clamped area

a_{cr} critical crack depth

A_f final area

A_r area reduction

A_t tensile stress area, tensile stress area of the thread

b section width, half width of contact area measured perpendicular to axes of two parallel contacting cylinders, gear face width, band width

C spring index, overall heat transfer coefficient, rated load capacity, heat transfer coefficient, constant (material property)

c distance from the neutral axis to the extreme fiber, half of crack length, radial clearance, center distance, distance between shafts, crack length

$\bar{c}$ distance from the centroidal axis to the extreme inner fiber

c_{cr} critical crack length

CR contact ratio

CG center of gravity

C_G gradient factor or gradient constant

c_i distance from the neutral axis to the extreme inner fiber

C_L load factor

C_{Li} life factor

c_o distance from the neutral axis to the extreme outer fiber

CP center of aerodynamic pressure

C_p elastic coefficient

C_R reliability factor

$c\rho$ volumetric specific heat

C_{req} required value of C

C_s surface factor

D diameter, mean coil diameter, velocity factor

d diameter, major diameter, nominal diameter, wire diameter

d_{av} average diameter

d_b diameter of base circle

d_c collar (or bearing) diameter

dc/dN crack propagation rate

$(dc/dN)_o$ crack propagation rate at $(\Delta K)_o$

d_g pitch diameter of gear

d_i minor diameter of the internal thread

d_m mean diameter

d_p pitch diameter, pitch diameter of pinion

d_r root (or minor) diameter

E modulus of elasticity, elastic proportionality constant, tensile elastic modulus

e distance between the neutral axis and the centroidal axis, efficiency, eccentricity, train value

E_b Young's modulus for the bolt

E_c Young's modulus for clamped member

F force, compressive force between the surfaces

f relative hardenability effectiveness, coefficient of friction

F, F force

F_a axial force

F_b bolt axial load

F_c clamping force

f_c collar (or bearing) coefficient of friction

F_d drag force, dynamic load

F_e equivalent radial load, equivalent static force, external force

F_{ga} gear axial force

F_{gr} gear radial force

F_{gt} gear tangential force

F_i initial tensile force, initial clamping force

F_n normal force

f_n natural frequency

F_r radial load, radial force

F_s strength capacity

F_{solid} force when solid

F_t thrust force, tendon force, tangential force, thrust load

F_w wear capacity

F_{wa} worm axial force

F_{wr} worm radial force

F_{wt} worm tangential force

G torsional or shear modulus of elasticity

g gravitational acceleration or acceleration of gravity, grip length

g_c constant of proportionality, 32.2 lbm-ft/lb-s^2

H surface hardness, time rate of heat dissipation

h section depth, height of fall, leg length, weld size, film thickness, height

h_0 minimum film thickness

H_B Brinell hardness number

I polar moment of inertia, moment of inertia, geometry factor

i integer

I_x moment of inertia about x axis

J polar moment of inertia, spur gear geometry factor

K curvature factor, spring rate for angular deflection, stress intensity factor, wear coefficient

k spring rate, thermal conductivity, spring rate for linear deflection, number of standard deviations, shaft spring rate

K' section property

K_1 stress intensity factor for tensile loading (mode I)

K_{1c} critical stress intensity factor for tensile loading (mode I)

K_a application factor

K_B constant of proportionality

k_b spring constant for the bolt

K_c fracture toughness or critical stress intensity factor

k_c spring constant for clamped members

KE kinetic energy

K_f fatigue stress concentration factor

K_i curvature factor for inner fiber, effective stress concentration factor for impact loading, constant used for calculating initial bolt-tightening force

K_m mounting factor

K_{max} stress intensity factor at σ_{max}

K_{min} stress intensity factor at σ_{min}

k_{ms} mean stress factor

K_o curvature factor for outer fiber, overload factor, critical stress intensity factor for infinite plate with central crack in uniaxial tension

K_r life adjustment reliability factor

k_r reliability factor

K_s stress concentration factor for static loading

K_t theoretical or geometric stress concentration factor

k_t temperature factor

K_v velocity or dynamic factor

K_w Wahl factor, material and geometry factor

L length, contact length measured parallel to the axis of contacting cylinder, lead, length of weld, life corresponding to radial load F_r, or life required by the application, pitch cone length

L_0 original unloaded length

L_e equivalent length

L_f final length, free length

L_R life corresponding to rated capacity

L_s solid height

M moment, internal bending moment, bending moment

M_0 redundant moment

m mass, strain-hardening exponent, module (used only with SI or metric units)

m' mass per unit length of belt

M_f moment of friction forces

M_n moment of normal forces

N fatigue life, total normal load, number of active coil turns, number of teeth, number of friction interfaces, number of cycles

n rotating speed, number of cycles, normal force, number of equally spaced planet gears, index (subscript)

N' virtual number of teeth

N.A. neutral axis

n_c critical speed

N_e number of teeth

N_t total number of turns, number of teeth in the sprocket

P load, cumulative probability of failure, bearing unit load, average film pressure, radial load per unit of projected bearing area, pitch point, diametral pitch (used only with English units), diameter or number of teeth of planet, band force, load (force), uniform load

p frequency of occurrence, probability of failure, surface interface pressure, pitch, film pressure, circular pitch, uniform level of interface pressure, pressure

p_0 maximum contact pressure

p_a axial pitch

p_b base pitch

P_c tension created by centrifugal force

P_{cr} critical load

PE potential energy

P_{max} allowable pressure, maximum normal pressure

p_n circular pitch measured in a plane normal to the teeth

Q heat energy transferred to the system, load, total tangential force, flow rate, mass flow rate

q number of revolutions, notch sensitivity factor, tangential force

Q_f volume of lubricant per-unit time flowing across

Q_s side leakage rate

R radius, transmission speed ratio, area ratio, radius of curvature, diameter or number of teeth of ring or annulus gear, ratio of gear and pinion diameter, load ratio

r radius, reliability

$\bar{r}$ radial distance to the centroidal axis

$r_{a(max)}$ maximum noninterfering addendum circle radius of pinion or gear

r_{ap}, r_{ag} addendum radii of the mating pinion and gear

r_b base circle radius

r_b back cone radius

r_{bp}, r_{bg} base circle radii of the mating pinion and gear

r_c chordal radius

r_f friction radius

r_i inner radius

R_m modulus of resilience

r_n radial distance to the neutral axis

r_o outer radius

S linear displacement, total rubbing distance, Saybolt viscometer measurement in seconds, bearing characteristic number or Sommerfeld variable, diameter or number of teeth of sun gear, slip

S_{cr} critical unit load

S_e elastic limit

SF safety factor

S_{fe} surface fatigue strength

S_H surface endurance strength

S_n endurance limit

S_n' standard fatigue strength for rotating bending

S_p proof load (strength)

S_{sy} shear yield strength

S_u ultimate strength, ultimate tensile strength

S_{uc} ultimate strength in compression

S_{us} ultimate shear strength, ultimate torsional shear strength

S_{ut} ultimate strength in tension

S_y yield strength

S_{yc} yield strength in compression

S_{yt} yield strength in tension

T torque, brake torque, band brake torque

t time, thickness, nut thickness, throat length

T_a alternating torque

t_a air temperature, ambient air temperature

T_e equivalent static torque

T_f friction torque

T_m modulus of toughness, mean torque

t_o average oil film temperature, oil temperature

t_s average temperature of heat-dissipating surfaces

U stored elastic energy, impact kinetic energy, laminar flow velocity

U' complementary energy

V internal transverse shear force, shear force, volume

V, v linear velocity, gear pitch line velocity

v velocity at impact, sliding velocity

V_{60} cutting speed in feet per minute for 60-min tool life under standard cutting conditions

V_{av} average velocity

V_g gear tangential velocity, pitch line velocity of the gear

V_{gt} velocity of gear at contact point in tangent direction

V_{pt} velocity of pinion at contact point in tangent direction

V_{ga} velocity of gear at contact point in normal direction

V_{pn} velocity of pinion at contact point in normal direction

V_s sliding velocity

V_w worm tangential velocity

W work done, weight, volume of material worn away, total axial load

$\dot{W}$ power

w load, load intensity, gravitational force, width

Y Lewis form factor based on diametral pitch or module, configuration factor

y distance from the neutral axis, Lewis form factor

Y_{cr} configuration factor at critical crack size

Z section modulus

Greek Letters

α angular acceleration, coefficient of thermal expansion, angles measured clockwise positive from the 0° gage to the principal strain axes numbers 1 and 2, factor by which the compressive strength is reduced through buckling tendencies, thread angle, contact angle, cone angle, normalized crack size

α_{cr} normalized critical crack size

α_1 normalized crack size at c_1

α_2 normalized crack size at c_2

α_n thread angle measured in the normal plane

Δ deflection, material parameter important in computing contact stress

δ, δ deflection

δ linear deflection, wear depth

ΔA change in area

ΔE change in total energy of the system

ΔKE change in kinetic energy of the system

ΔK stress intensity range

ΔK_o stress intensity range at the point o

ΔL change in length

ΔPE change in gravitational potential energy of the system

ΔN_{12} number of cycles during crack growth from c_1 to c_2

δ_s solid deflection

δ_{st} deflection caused by static loading (static deflection)

ΔT temperature change

ΔU change in internal energy of the system

ϕ angle between the principal axes and the x and y axes, angle giving position of minimum film thickness, pressure angle, angle of wrap

ϕ_n pressure angle measured in a plane normal to the teeth

γ pitch cone angle

$\gamma_{xy}, \gamma_{xz}, \gamma_{yz}$ shear strains

λ lead angle, helix angle

μ mean, viscosity

ν Poisson's ratio

ϵ normal strain

$\epsilon_1, \epsilon_2, \epsilon_3$ principal strains

ϵ_f strain at fracture

ϵ_T "true" normal strain

ϵ_{Tf} true normal strain at fracture

$\epsilon_x, \epsilon_y, \epsilon_z$ normal strains

θ angular displacement, angular deflection, slope

$\theta_{p_{max}}$ position of maximum film pressure

ρ mass density, radial distance

σ normal stress, standard deviation, uniform uniaxial tensile stress

$\sigma_1, \sigma_2, \sigma_3$ principal stresses in 1, 2, and 3 directions

σ_0 square root of strain-strengthening proportionality constant

σ_a alternating stress (or stress amplitude)

σ_e equivalent stress

σ_{ea} equivalent alternating bending stress

σ_{em} equivalent mean bending stress

σ_g gross-section tensile stress

σ_H surface fatigue stress

σ_i maximum normal stress in the inner surface

σ_m mean stress

σ_{max} maximum normal stress

σ_{min} minimum normal stress

σ_{nom} nominal normal stress

σ_o maximum normal stress in the outer surface

σ_T "true" normal stress

σ_x normal stress acting along x axis

σ_y normal stress acting along y axis

τ shear stress, natural period of vibration

τ_a alternating shear stress

τ_{av} average shear stress

$\tau_{initial}$ initial shear stress

τ_m mean shear stress

τ_{max} maximum shear stress

τ_{nom} nominal shear stress

τ_{solid} shear stress when solid

τ_{xy} shear stress acting on an x face in the y direction

ω angular velocity, impact angular velocity

ω_g angular velocity of gear

ω_n natural frequency

ω_p angular velocity of pinion

ψ helix angle, spiral angle

CHAPTER 1

Mechanical Engineering Design in Broad Perspective

1.1 *An Overview of the Subject*

The essence of engineering is *the* utilization of the resources and laws of nature to benefit humanity. Engineering is an applied science in the sense that it is concerned with understanding scientific principles and applying them to achieve a designated goal. Mechanical engineering design is a major segment of engineering; it deals with the conception, design, development, refinement, and application of machines and mechanical apparatus of all kinds.

For many students, mechanical engineering design is one of their first *professional engineering courses*—as distinguished from background courses in science and mathematics. Professional engineering is concerned with obtaining *solutions* to practical problems. These solutions must reflect an understanding of the underlying sciences, but usually this understanding is not enough; empirical knowledge and "engineering judgment" are also involved. For example, scientists do not completely understand electricity, but this does not prevent electrical engineers from developing highly useful electrical devices. Similarly, scientists do not completely understand combustion processes or metal fatigue, but mechanical engineers use the understanding available to develop highly useful combustion engines. As more scientific understanding becomes available, engineers are able to devise better solutions to practical problems. Moreover, the engineering process of solving problems often highlights areas particularly appropriate for more intensive scientific research. There is a strong analogy between the engineer and the physician. Neither is a scientist whose primary concern is with uncovering basic knowledge, but both *use* scientific knowledge—supplemented by empirical information and professional judgment—in solving immediate and pressing problems.

Because of the professional nature of the subject, most problems in mechanical engineering design do not have a *single* right answer. Consider, for example, the problem of designing a household refrigerator. There is a nearly endless number of workable designs, none of which could be called an "incorrect" answer. But of the "correct" answers, some are obviously *better* than others because they reflect a more sophisticated knowledge of the underlying technology, a more ingenious concept of basic design, a more effective and economical utilization of existing production technology, a more pleasing aesthetic appearance, and so on. It is precisely at this point, of course, that one finds the challenge and excitement of modern engineering. Engineers today are concerned with the design and development of products for a society different from any that existed previously, and they have more knowledge available to them than did engineers in the past. Hence, they are able to produce distinctly *better* solutions to meet today's needs. How much better depends on their ingenuity, imagination, depth of understanding of the need involved, and of the technology that bears on the solutions, and so on.

This book is primarily concerned with the design of specific *components* of machines or mechanical systems. Competence in this area is basic to the consideration and synthesis of complete machines and systems in subsequent courses and in professional practice. It will be seen that even in the design of a single bolt or spring, the engineer must use the best available scientific understanding together with empirical information, good judgment, and often a degree of ingenuity, in order to produce the best product for today's society.

The technical considerations of mechanical component design are largely centered around two main areas of concern: (1) stress–strain–strength relationships involving the *bulk* of a solid member and (2) surface phenomena including friction, lubrication, wear, and environmental deterioration. Part One of the book is concerned with the fundamentals involved, and Part Two with applications to specific machine components. The components chosen are widely used and will be somewhat familiar to the student. It is not feasible or desirable for the student to study the detailed design considerations associated with *all* machine elements. Hence, the emphasis in treating those selected here is on the *methods* and *procedures* used so that the student will gain competence in applying these methods and procedures to mechanical components in general.

When considering a complete machine, the engineer invariably finds that the requirements and constraints of the various components are interrelated. The design of an automotive engine valve spring, for example, depends on the space available for the spring. This, in turn, represents a compromise with the space requirements for the valve ports, coolant passages, spark plug clearance, and so on. This situation adds a whole new dimension to the imagination and ingenuity required of engineers as they seek to determine an optimum design for a combination of related components. This aspect of mechanical engineering design is illustrated by a "case study" at http://www.wiley.com/college/juvinall.

In addition to the traditional technological and economic considerations fundamental to the design and development of mechanical components and systems, the modern engineer has become increasingly concerned with the broader considerations of safety, ecology, and overall "quality of life." These topics are discussed briefly in the following sections.

1.2   *Safety Considerations*

It is natural that, in the past, engineers gave first consideration to the functional and economic aspects of new devices. After all, unless devices can be made to function usefully, they are of no further engineering interest. Furthermore, if a new device cannot be produced for a cost that is affordable by contemporary society, it is a waste of engineering time to pursue it further. But the engineers who have gone before us have succeeded in developing a multitude of products that do function usefully, and that can be produced economically. Partly because of this, increasing engineering effort is now being devoted to broader considerations relating to the influence of engineered products on people and on the environment.

Personnel safety is a consideration that engineers have always kept in mind but now demands increasing emphasis. In comparison with such relatively straightforward computations as stress and deflection, determination of safety is likely to be an elusive and indefinite matter, complicated by psychological and sociological factors. But this should only add to the appeal of the task for an engineer. It challenges him or her to assemble all pertinent facts, and then to make good decisions reflecting understanding, imagination, ingenuity, and judgment.

The important first step in developing engineering competence in the safety area is cultivating an *awareness* of its importance. Product safety is of great concern to legislators, attorneys, judges, jurors, insurance executives, and so forth. But none of these individuals can contribute directly to the safety of a product; they can only underscore the urgency of giving appropriate emphasis to safety in the *engineering development* of a product. It is the *engineer* who must carry out the development of safe products.

Safety is inherently a *relative* matter, and value judgments must be made regarding trade-offs between safety, cost, weight, and so on. Some years ago the first author was associated with a particularly safety-conscious company and was in the position of frequently admonishing the staff safety engineer to reduce further the inevitable hazards associated with the company's equipment. When pushed a little too far one day, this engineer responded, "Look, I have made this model foolproof, but I can never make it *damn* foolproof! If someone tries hard enough, he can hurt himself with this machine!" The next day this gentleman inadvertently proved his point when he accidentally dropped the new model prototype on his foot and broke a toe! But the point to be made here is that when society makes decisions relative to safety requirements, engineers should contribute important input.

1.2.1 Imagination and Ingenuity

Following awareness, the second main point of safety engineering is *ingenuity*. The engineer must be imaginative and ingenious enough to *anticipate* potentially hazardous situations relating to a product. The old maxim that anything that *can* happen probably *will* happen sooner or later is relevant. The following are four cases in point, all involving costly liability suits.

1. A large open area with a high ceiling was to be heated and cooled with three cubical units, each suspended from the ceiling by long steel rods at four corners. The cubicles were being fitted with heat exchangers, blowers, and filters by workers inside and on top of the enclosures. The flexibility of the long support rods permitted the cubicles to swing back and forth, and the workers sometimes enjoyed getting their cubicle swinging with considerable amplitude. Fatigue failure of a support rod caused the death of one worker. Since large steam pipes (not yet installed at the time of the accident) prevented significant sway of the completed units, and the rods were designed with a

safety factor of 17 (based on static weight of the completed cubicles), no further thought was given to safety. No one responsible for the design and installation of the units had reviewed the installation sequence with the imagination and ingenuity needed to foresee this hazard.

2. A boy was seriously injured by collision with a car when the brakes on his new bicycle failed to respond in an emergency. The cause was discovered to be interference between a fitting on the three-speed shift mechanism and a sharp edge on the caliper brake handle. Both the shift control mechanism and the brake handle were of unusual design. Both were safe within themselves and were safe when used in combination with a conventional design of the other member. But when these two unusual members were used together, it was easy for them to be mounted on the handlebar in such a position that the travel of the brake handle was limited, thereby preventing full application of the brake. Again, no one responsible for the overall design of the bicycle foresaw this hazardous situation.

3. A worker lost a hand in a 400-ton punch press despite wearing safety cuffs that were cam-actuated to pull the hands out of the danger zone before the ram came down. The cause was a loosened setscrew that permitted the cam to rotate with respect to its supporting shaft, thereby delaying hand retraction until *after* the ram came down. This case illustrates the old adage that "A chain is no stronger than its weakest link." Here, an otherwise very positive and strong safety device was nullified because of the inexcusably weak link of the setscrew. A very little imagination and ingenuity on the part of the engineer responsible for this design would have brought this hazard to light before the unit was released for production.

4. A crawling infant lost the ends of three fingers as he attempted to climb up an "exercycle" being ridden by an older sister. When placed on the bottom chain, the infant's hand was immediately drawn into the crank sprocket. In order to minimize cost, the exercycle was very properly designed to take advantage of many high-production, low-cost parts used on a standard bicycle. Unfortunately, however, the chain guard, which provides adequate protection for a bicycle, is totally inadequate for the exercycle. Was it too much to expect that the engineer responsible for this design would have enough imagination to foresee this hazard? Should he or she not have been sufficiently ingenious to devise an alternative guard design that would be economically and otherwise feasible? Should it be necessary for this kind of imagination and ingenuity to be forced upon the engineer by legislation devised and enacted by nonengineers?

1.2.2 Techniques and Guidelines

Once the engineer is suffciently *aware* of safety considerations, and accepts this challenge to his or her *imagination and ingenuity*, there are certain techniques and guidelines that are often helpful. Six of these are suggested in the following.

1. *Review the total life cycle* of the product from initial production to final disposal, with an eye toward uncovering significant hazards. Ask yourself what kinds of situations can reasonably develop during the various stages of manufacturing, transporting, storing, installing, using, servicing, and so on.

2. Be sure that the safety provisions represent a *balanced approach*. Do not accept a dollar penalty to eliminate one hazard and overlook a twenty-cent possibility for eliminating an equal hazard. And, like the punch press example just given, do not focus attention on how strong the wrist cuffs are while overlooking how weak the cam attachment is.

3. *Make safety an integral feature* of the basic design wherever possible, rather than "adding on" safety devices after the basic design has been completed. An example of this was the development of an electrostatic hand-operated paint gun. Earlier stationary-mounted electrostatic paint guns had metal atomizing heads operating at 100,000 volts. A handgun version, incorporating elaborate guards and shields, was quickly recognized as impractical. Instead, a fundamentally new electric circuit design combined with a nonmetallic head was developed so that even if the operator came in contact with the high-voltage head, he or she would receive no shock; the voltage automatically dropped as a hand approached the head, and the head itself had a low enough capacitance to avoid significant discharge to the operator.

4. Use a *"fail-safe" design* where feasible. The philosophy here is that precaution is taken to avoid failure, but if failure *does* occur, the design is such that the product is still "safe"; that is, the failure will not be catastrophic. For example, the first commercial jet aircraft were the British Comets. Some of these experienced catastrophic failure when fatigue cracks started in the outer aluminum "skin" at the corners of the windows (caused by alternately pressurizing the cabin at high altitude and relieving the pressurizing stresses at ground level). Soon after the cracks were initiated, the fuselage skin ripped disastrously (somewhat like a toy rubber balloon). After the cause of the crashes was determined, subsequent commercial jet aircraft incorporated the fail-safe feature of bonding the outer panels to the longitudinal and circumferential frame members of the fuselage. Thus, even if a crack does start, it can propagate only to the nearest bonded seam. The relatively short cracks in no way impair the safety of the aircraft. (This particular fail-safe feature can be illustrated by ripping an old shirt. Once a tear has been started, it is easily propagated to a seam, but it is extremely difficult to propagate the tear through the seam, or "tear stopper.") Fail-safe designs often incorporate *redundant* members so that if one load-carrying member fails, a second member is able to assume the full load. This is sometimes known as the "belt *and* suspenders" design philosophy. (In extreme cases, a "safety pin" may be employed as a third member.)

5. Check *government and industry standards* (such as OSHA and ANSI) and the pertinent technical literature to be sure that legal requirements are complied with, and that advantage is taken of the relevant safety experience of others. The OSHA regulations may be downloaded from the government's web site at http://www.osha.gov. A search for specific titles of ANSI standards can be conducted at http://www.ansi.org. For national, foreign, regional, and international standards and regulatory documents, see http://www.nssn.org.

6. Provide *warnings* of all significant hazards that remain after the design has been made as safe as reasonably possible. The engineers who developed the product are in the best position to identify these hazards. The warnings should be designed to bring the information to the attention of the persons in jeopardy in the most positive manner feasible. Conspicuous warning signs attached permanently

to the machine itself are usually best. There are OSHA and ANSI standards pertaining to warning signs. More complete warning information is often appropriately included in an instruction or operating manual that accompanies the machine.

To apply these techniques and guidelines in an alternative procedural form, consider the following list from [9]:

1. Delineate the scope of product uses.
2. Identify the environments within which the product will be used.
3. Describe the user population.
4. Postulate all possible hazards, including estimates of probability of occurrence and seriousness of resulting harm.
5. Delineate alternative design features or production techniques, including warnings and instructions, that can be expected to effectively mitigate or eliminate the hazards.
6. Evaluate such alternatives relative to the expected performance standards of the product, including the following:
   a. Other hazards that may be introduced by the alternatives.
   b. Their effect on the subsequent usefulness of the product.
   c. Their effect on the ultimate cost of the product.
   d. A comparison to similar products.
7. Decide which features to include in the final design.

The National Safety Council publishes a hierarchy of design that sets guidelines for designing equipment that will minimize injuries. The order of design priority is [10]:

1. **Design to eliminate hazards and minimize risk.** From the very beginning, the top priority should be to eliminate hazards in the design process.
2. **Incorporate safety devices.** If hazards cannot be eliminated or the risks adequately reduced through design selection, the next step is to reduce the risks to an acceptable level. This can be achieved with the use of guarding or other safety devices.
3. **Provide warning devices.** In some cases, identified hazards cannot be eliminated or their risks reduced to an acceptable level through initial design decisions or through the incorporated safety devices. Warnings are a potential solution.
4. **Develop and implement safe operating procedures and employee safety training programs.** Safe operating procedures and training are essential in minimizing injuries when it is impractical to eliminate hazards or reduce their risks to an acceptable level through design selection, incorporating safety devices, or with warning devices.
5. **Use personal protective equipment.** When all other techniques cannot eliminate or control a hazard, employees should be given personal protective equipment to prevent injuries and illnesses.

1.2.3 Documentation

The documentation of a product design is costly yet necessary to support possible litigation. Such documentation has been categorized in [9] as:

1. Hazard and risk data—historical, field, and/or laboratory testing, causation analyses.
2. Design safety formulation—fault-tree, failure modes, hazard analyses.
3. Warnings and instruction formulations—methodology for development and selection.
4. Standards—the use of in-house, voluntary, and mandated design or performance requirements.
5. Quality assurance program—methodology for procedure selection and production records.
6. Product performance—reporting procedures, complaint file, follow-up data acquisition and analysis, recall, retrofit, instruction, and warning modification.
7. Decision making—the "how," "who," and "why" of the process.

By documenting a design during the process, a safer product is generally produced. Also, imagination and ingenuity can sometimes be stimulated by requiring documentation of a product design.

1.2.4 Nontechnical Aspects

Safety engineering inherently includes important *nontechnical aspects* that are related to the *individuals* involved. Engineers must be aware of these if their safety-related efforts are to be effective. Three specific points within this category are suggested.

1. *Capabilities* and *characteristics* of individuals, both physiological and psychological. When the device is used or serviced, the strength, reach, and endurance requirements must be well within the physiological limitations of the personnel involved. The arrangement of instruments and controls, and the nature of the mental operating requirements, must be compatible with psychological factors. Where the possibility of accident cannot be eliminated, the design should be geared to limiting personnel accident-imposed loads to values minimizing the severity of injury.

2. *Communication*. Engineers must communicate to others the rationale and operation of the safety provisions incorporated in their designs, and in many situations they must involve themselves in "*selling*" the proper use of these safety provisions. What good does it do, for example, to develop an effective motorcycle helmet if it is not used? Or to provide a punch press with safety switches for both hands if the operator blocks one of the switches closed in order to have a hand free for smoking? Unfortunately, even the most effective communication does not always guarantee intelligent use by the operator. This unresponsiveness may cause controversies, such as that surrounding the requirement that air bags be installed in cars, because a significant segment of

the public cannot be persuaded to use seat belts voluntarily. Resolution of such controversies requires intelligent input from many quarters, one of which is certainly the engineering profession.

3. *Cooperation*. The controversy just mentioned illustrates the need for engineers to cooperate effectively with members of other disciplines—government, management, sales, service, legal, and so on—in order that joint safety-directed efforts may prove effective.

1.3   *Ecological Considerations*

People inherently depend on their environment for air, water, food, and materials for clothing and shelter. In primitive society, human-made wastes were naturally recycled for repeated use. When open sewers and dumps were introduced, nature became unable to reclaim and recycle these wastes within normal time periods, thus interrupting natural ecological cycles. Traditional economic systems enable products to be mass-produced and sold at prices that often do not reflect the true cost to society in terms of resource consumption and ecological damage. Now that society is becoming more generally aware of this problem, legislative requirements and more realistic "total" cost provisions are having increasing impact upon engineering design. Certainly, it is important that the best available engineering input go into societal decisions involving these matters.

We can perhaps state the basic ecological objectives of mechanical engineering design rather simply: (1) to utilize materials so that they are economically recyclable within reasonable time periods without causing objectionable air and water pollution and (2) to minimize the rate of consumption of nonrecycled energy sources (such as fossil fuels) both to conserve these resources and to minimize thermal pollution. In some instances, the minimization of noise pollution is also a factor to be considered.

As with safety considerations, ecological factors are much more difficult for the engineer to tie down than are such matters as stress and deflection. The following is a suggested list of points to be considered.

1. Consider all aspects of the *basic design objective* involved, to be sure that it is sound. For example, questions are raised about the overall merits of some major dam constructions. Are there ecological side effects that might make it preferable to follow an alternative approach? Before undertaking the design of an expanded highway system or a specific mass-transit system, the engineer must determine whether the best available knowledge and judgment indicate that the proposed project represents the best alternative.

2. After accepting the basic design objective, the next step is a review of the *overall concepts* to be embodied into the proposed design. For example, a modular concept may be appropriate, wherein specific components or modules most likely to wear out or become obsolete can be replaced with updated modules that are interchangeable with the originals. The motor and transmission assembly of a domestic automatic washing machine might be an example for which this approach would be appropriate. Another example is the provision of replaceable exterior trim panels on major kitchen appliances that permit the

exterior surfaces to be changed to match a new decorating scheme without replacing the entire appliance.

3. An important consideration is *designing for recycling*. At the outset of a new design, it is becoming increasingly important that the engineer consider the full ecological cycle including the disposal and reuse of the entire device and its components. Consider an automobile. Parts appropriate for reuse (either with or without rebuilding) should be made so that they can be easily removed from a "junk" car. Dismantling and sorting of parts by material should be made as easy and economical as possible. It has been somewhat facetiously suggested that cars be made so that all fasteners break when dropping a junk car from, say, a height of 30 feet. Automatic devices would then sort the pieces by material for reprocessing. A more realistic proposal is that of attaching the wiring harness so that it can be quickly ripped out in one piece for easy salvaging of the copper.

   In developing recycling procedures along these lines it is obviously desirable that the costs to a company for recycling versus costs for abandoning the old parts and using virgin materials reflect total real costs to society. No individual company could stay in business if it magnanimously undertook a costly recycling program in order to conserve virgin materials and reduce processing pollution if its competitors could utilize inexpensive new materials obtained at a price that did not reflect these total costs.

4. Select *materials* with ecological factors in mind. Of importance here are the known availability in nature of the required raw materials, processing energy requirements, processing pollution problems (air, water, land, thermal, and noise), and recyclability. Ideally, all these factors would be appropriately reflected within the pricing structure, and this will more likely happen in the future than it has in the past.

   Another factor to be considered is the relative durability of alternative materials for use in a perishable part. For example, consider the great reduction in the number of razor blades required (and in the number of scrap razor blades) made by changing the material to stainless steel. (But would it be better, overall, to devise a convenient and effective way to resharpen the blades rather than throwing them away?)

   The engineer should also consider the *compatibility* of materials with respect to recycling. For example, zinc die castings deteriorate the quality of the scrap obtained when present junked cars are melted.

5. Consider ecological factors when specifying *processing*. Important here are pollution of all kinds, energy consumption, and efficiency of material usage. For example, forming operations such as rolling and forging use less material (and generate less scrap) than cutting operations. There may also be important differences in energy consumption.

6. *Packaging* is an important area for resource conservation and pollution reduction. Reusable cartons, and the use of recycled materials for packaging, are two areas receiving increasing attention. Perhaps the ultimate in ecologically desirable packaging is that commonly used ice cream container, the cone.

As a concluding example of the importance of introducing sound engineering thinking into societal ecological decisions, consider the suggestion made by a highly vocal (nonengineering) student that power plant pollution be virtually eliminated by requiring the power companies to drive their generators with electric motors! But the matter of protecting our environment is a deadly serious one. As the late Adlai Stevenson once said, "We travel together, passengers on a little space ship, dependent on its vulnerable supplies of air and soil . . . preserved from annihilation only by the care, the work, and I will say the love, we give our fragile craft."

1.4   *Societal Considerations*

As the reader well knows, the solution to any engineering problem begins with its clear definition. Accordingly, let us define, in the broadest terms, the problem to be addressed when undertaking mechanical engineering design. The opening sentence in this chapter suggests a definition: The basic objective of any engineering design is to provide a machine or device that will benefit humanity. In order to apply this definition, it is necessary to think in more specific terms. Just how does an individual benefit humanity? What "yardstick" (meterstick?) can be used to measure such benefits? The formulation of precise definitions of problem objectives, and the devising of means for measuring results, *fall within the special province of the engineer.*

The writer has suggested [2][1] that the basic objective of engineering design as well as other human pursuits is to improve the quality of life within our society, and that this might be measured in terms of a life quality index (LQI). This index is in some ways similar to the familiar "gross national product," but very much broader. Judgments about the proper composition of the LQI would, of course, vary somewhat in the many segments of society and also with time.

To illustrate the LQI concept, Table 1.1 lists some of the important factors most people would agree should be included. Perhaps we might arbitrarily assign a value of 100 to the factor deemed most important, with other factors being weighed accordingly. Each factor might then be multiplied by the same fraction so that the total would add up to 100.

The list in the table is admittedly a very rough and oversimplified indication of the direction of thought that would be involved in arriving at an LQI for a given

TABLE 1.1   Preliminary List of Factors Constituting the Life Quality Index (LQI)

1. *Physical health*
2. *Material well-being*
3. *Safety* (crime and accident rates)
4. *Environment* (air, water, land, and natural resource management)
5. *Cultural–educational* (literacy rate, public school quality, college attendance among those qualified, adult educational opportunities, library and museum facilities, etc.)
6. *Treatment of disadvantaged groups* (physically and mentally handicapped, aged, etc.)
7. *Equality of opportunity* (and stimulation of initiative to use opportunities)
8. *Personal freedom*
9. *Population control*

---

[1] Bracketed numbers in the text correspond to numbered references at the end of the chapter.

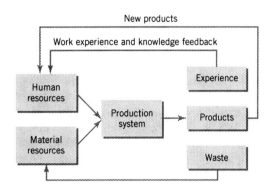

FIGURE 1.1
Societal relationships involving
engineered products.

segment of society at a given time. But this *kind* of thinking must be done in order
to provide a sound basis for judgment with respect to the fulfillment of the engineering mission of service to humanity.

The professional contribution of engineers engaged in the broad area of engineering design and development plays a major role in determining the LQI of a population. Figure 1.1 depicts the societal relationships involving engineered products. A
major segment of the population works within organizations whose function is to do
one or more of the following: research, design, develop, manufacture, market, and service engineered products. The efforts of these people, together with appropriate natural
resources, go into production systems that yield useful products, waste materials, and
experience. The experience is of two kinds: (1) direct working experience of the individuals, which is hopefully constructive and satisfying, and (2) empirical knowledge
gained about the effectiveness of the overall system, with implications for its future improvement. The products made serve all people until discarded, when they constitute
long- and short-term recyclable material resources, and possibly pollution.

A valid LQI must take into account psychological factors. A book of this kind can
include only the briefest introduction to this vast subject. But hopefully this will aid
in stimulating the student toward a life-long interest and concern with this fundamental area.

We know that people exhibit an infinitely varying and often baffling set of characteristics. But we also know that there are certain inherent human characteristics and
needs that remain fixed—for all individuals and presumably for all time. These have
been expressed as proposed *levels of human need* by the late Abraham Maslow, a psy-
chologist at Brandeis University [4,5]. As an aid to memory, these are expressed in
Table 1.2 in terms of five key words beginning with "S" [3].

The first level, obviously, is the need for immediate *survival*—food, shelter, clothing, and rest—here and now.

The second level involves *security*—ensuring one's safety and future survival.

The third level is *social acceptance*. People need to belong to and interact with
a family, clan, or other group; they need love and acceptance.

TABLE 1.2   **Maslow's Hierarchy
of Needs**

1. Survival	4. Status
2. Security	5. Self-fulfillment
3. Social acceptance	

The fourth level is status or recognition—a need not only to fit into a social group but also to earn and receive peer respect and admiration.

The highest level is *self-fulfillment*—growth toward reaching one's full potential, and achievement of the resulting inner satisfaction.

At any given time, both people and nations operate on more than one of these levels; yet the levels define a general path or ladder of advancement that leads from primitive existence to a mature, rich quality of life.

Historically, engineering effort has been directed primarily toward satisfying needs 1 and 2. More recently, an increased percentage of the production systems have been designed to provide society with products going beyond the basic survival and security needs, presumably contributing to satisfying the legitimate higher needs of the consumer. As for the workers, it is interesting to note that recent "job enlargement" and "job enrichment" programs are directed toward the workers' higher needs, 3, 4, and 5.

A basic ingredient of human society is *change*. Engineers must seek to understand not only the needs of society today, but also the direction and rapidity of the societal changes that are occurring. Moreover, we must seek to understand the influence of technology—and of mechanical products and associated production systems in particular—on these changes. Perhaps the engineering profession's most important objective is to make its input to society such that it *promotes changes in the direction of increasing the life quality index.*

1.5   *Overall Design Considerations*

Most engineering designs involve a multitude of considerations, and it is a challenge to the engineer to recognize all of them in proper proportion. Although no simple checklist given here can be adequate or complete, it may be helpful to list in some organized fashion the major categories involved (see Table 1.3).

Traditional considerations for the bulk or body of the component include: (a) strength, (b) deflection, (c) weight, and (d) size and shape. Traditional considerations for the surfaces of the component are (a) wear, (b) lubrication, (c) corrosion, (d) frictional forces, and (e) frictional heat generated.

Often various design considerations are seemingly incompatible until the engineer devises a sufficiently imaginative and ingenious solution. The design of the lift truck pictured in Figure 1.2 provides a simple example.

TABLE 1.3   **Major Categories of Design Considerations**

Traditional Considerations	Modern Considerations
1. Materials	1. Safety
2. Geometry	2. Ecology
3. Operating conditions	3. Quality of life
4. Cost	
5. Availability	**Miscellaneous Considerations**
6. Producibility	1. Reliability and maintainability
7. Component life	2. Ergonomics and aesthetics

FIGURE 1.2
Lift truck designed for functional, attractive, and unique appearance together with low cost.
(Courtesy Clark Material Handling Company.)

Here, the objective of achieving a desired aesthetic appearance was seemingly incompatible with cost limitations. Matched metal forming dies were too costly, and inexpensive tooling resulted in unattractive mismatches of mating parts. The solution here was to work deliberate mismatches into the design and eliminate the need for precision fitting. The mismatches were used to give the truck a rugged look. The gap under the hood, for example, creates a strong horizontal line while disguising the fit-up of several frame and fender weldments. It also provides a handhold for lifting the hood. Another gap (not shown) makes the instrument pod appear to "float" from a steel pylon, again disguising a large tolerance. The large hood simplifies maintenance by providing wide-open access to the engine. By serving also as the seat support, it further reduces cost, while adding to the clean, uncluttered appearance.

1.6   *Systems of Units*[2]

Because the present generation of American engineers seems destined to suffer the inconvenience of having to deal with different systems of units, three types are discussed in this book. Appendix A-1 lists units associated with these systems, conversion factors relating them, and their standard abbreviations.

The *units* of the physical quantities used in engineering calculations are of major importance. A unit is a specified amount of a physical quantity by which through comparison another quantity of the same kind is measured. For example, inches, feet,

---

[2]This section is adapted from [1].

miles, centimeters, meters, and kilometers are all *units of length*. Seconds, minutes, and hours are *units of time*.

Because physical quantities are related by laws and definitions, a small number of physical quantities, called *primary dimensions*, are sufficient to conceive of and measure all others. *Secondary dimensions* are those quantities measured in terms of the primary dimensions. For example, if mass, length, and time are primary dimensions, area, density, and velocity would be secondary dimensions.

Equations from physics and engineering that relate physical quantities are dimensionally homogeneous. *Dimensionally homogeneous* equations must have the same dimensions for each term. Newton's second law ($\mathbf{F} \propto m\mathbf{a}$) relates the dimensions *force, mass, length*, and *time*. If length and time are primary dimensions, Newton's second law, being dimensionally homogeneous, requires that both force and mass cannot be primary dimensions without introducing a constant of proportionality that has dimensions (and units).

Primary dimensions in all systems of dimensions in common use are length and time. Force is selected as a primary dimension in some systems. Mass is taken as a primary dimension in others. For application in mechanics, we have three basic systems of dimensions.

1. Force [F], mass [M], length [L], time [t]
2. Force [F], length [L], time [t]
3. Mass [M], length [L], time [t]

In system 1, length [L], time [t], and both force [F] and mass [M] are selected as primary dimensions. In this system, in Newton's second law ($\mathbf{F} = m\mathbf{a}/g_c$), the constant of proportionality, g_c, is not dimensionless. For Newton's law to be dimensionally homogeneous, the dimensions of g_c must be [ML/Ft^2]. In system 2, mass [M] is a secondary dimension, and in Newton's second law the constant of proportionality is dimensionless. In system 3, force [F] is a secondary dimension, and in Newton's second law the constant of proportionality is again dimensionless. The units of measure selected for each of the primary physical quantities determine the numerical value of the constant of proportionality.

In this text we will use the SI, British Gravitational, and English Engineering systems of units. The *base units* employed for these are listed in Table 1.4 and discussed in the following paragraphs. Newton's second law is written as $\mathbf{F} = m\mathbf{a}$ for the SI and British systems, and as $\mathbf{F} = m\mathbf{a}/g_c$ for the English Engineering system. For each system, the constant of proportionality in Newton's second law is given in Figure 1.3 which

TABLE 1.4   English, British, and SI Units for Length, Time, Mass, and Force

Quantity	English Engineering [*FMLt*]		British Gravitational [*FLt*]		SI [*MLt*]	
	Unit	Symbol	Unit	Symbol	Unit	Symbol
Mass	pound mass	lbm	slug	slug	kilogram	kg
Length	foot	ft	foot	ft	meter	m
Time	second	s	second	s	second	s
Force	pound force ($=32.1740$ lbm · ft/s^2)	lb (or lbf)	pound ($=1$ slug · ft/s^2)	lb	newton ($=1$ kg · m/s^2)	N

System of Units	Standard Objects	Mass (of standard object)	Weight (standard earth gravitational field)	Constant of Proportionality	Newton's Second Law
English Engineering [FMLt]		1 lbm	1 lb	$g_c = 32.1740 \dfrac{\text{ft} \cdot \text{lbm}}{\text{lb} \cdot \text{s}^2}$	$\mathbf{F} = ma/g_c$
British Gravitational [FLt]	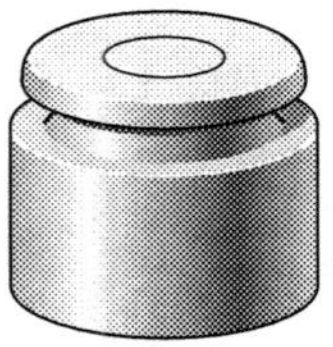	1 slug (=32.2 lbm)	32.2 lb	1	$\mathbf{F} = ma$
SI [MLt]	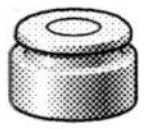	1 kg (=2.2046 lbm)	9.81 N (=2.2046 lb)	1	$\mathbf{F} = ma$

Figure 1.3

Comparison of units for force (or weight) and mass. Note that the weight for each of the standard masses is valid only for the standard earth gravitational field (g = 9.81 m/s^2 or g = 32.2 ft/s^2).

also compares the three systems of units. In both the SI and British systems, the constant of proportionality is dimensionless and has a value of unity. The gravitational force (the weight) on an object of mass, m, is given by $W = mg$ for the SI and the British systems and as $W = mg/g_c$ for the English Engineering system.

1. *English Engineering (FMLt).* The English Engineering system takes force, mass, length, and time as primary dimensions. The base units employed for these primary dimensions are listed in Figure 1.3. The base units are the pound force (lb), the pound mass (lbm), the foot (ft), and the second (s).

   A force of one pound (lb) accelerates a mass of one pound (lbm) at a rate equal to the standard earth acceleration of gravity of 32.2 ft/s^2.

   Newton's second law is written as

$$\mathbf{F} = m\mathbf{a}/g_c \qquad\qquad (1.1a)$$

   From Newton's law we have

$$1 \text{ lb} \equiv \frac{\text{lbm} \times 32.2 \text{ ft/s}^2}{g_c}$$

   or

$$g_c \equiv 32.2 \text{ ft} \cdot \text{lbm/lb s}^2$$

   The constant of proportionality, g_c, has units and dimensions.

2. *British Gravitational (FLt).* The British Gravitational system takes force, length, and time as primary dimensions. The base units are the pound (lb) for force, the foot (ft) for length, and the second (s) for time. Mass is a secondary dimension. Newton's second law is written as

$$\mathbf{F} = m\mathbf{a} \qquad\qquad (1.1b)$$

   The unit of mass, the slug, is defined, using Newton's second law, as

$$1 \text{ slug} \equiv 1 \text{ lb} \cdot \text{s}^2/\text{ft}$$

   Since a force of 1 lb accelerates 1 slug at 1 ft/s^2, it would accelerate 1/32.2 slug at 32.2 ft/s^2. One pound mass also is accelerated at 32.2 ft/s^2 by a force of 1 lb. Therefore,

$$1 \text{ lbm} = 1/32.2 \text{ slug}$$

3. *SI (MLt).* The SI (Système International d'Unités) takes mass, length, and time as primary dimensions. The base units are the kilogram (kg) for mass, the meter (m) for length, and the second (s) for time. Force is a secondary dimension. Newton's second law is written as

$$\mathbf{F} = m\mathbf{a} \qquad\qquad (1.1c)$$

   The unit of force, the newton (N), is defined using Newton's second law as

$$1 \text{ N} \equiv 1 \text{ kg} \cdot \text{m/s}^2$$

The unit of force is of particular significance in mechanical engineering design and analysis because it is involved in calculations of force, torque, stress (and pressure), work (and energy), power, and elastic moduli. In SI units, it is interesting to note that a *newton* is approximately the weight of (or earth's gravitational force on) an average apple.

Appendix A-2 lists standard prefixes for SI units. Appendixes A-3, A-4, and A-5 list compatible combinations of SI prefixes that will be found convenient in solving stress and deflection equations.

1.7   *Methodology for Solving Machine Component Problems*[3]

An essential method of attack for machine component problems is to formulate them precisely and to present their solutions accurately. Formulating the problem requires consideration of the physical situation and the matching mathematical situation. The mathematical representation of a physical situation is an ideal description or model that approximates but never matches the actual physical problem.

The first step in solving machine component problems is to define (or understand) the problem. The next steps are to define (or synthesize) the structure, identify the interactions with the surroundings, record your choices and decisions, and draw the relevant diagrams. Attention then turns to analyzing the problem, making appropriate assumptions by using pertinent physical laws, relationships, and rules that parametrically relate the geometry and behavior of the component or system. The last step is to check the reasonableness of the results and when appropriate comment about the solution. Most analyses use, directly or indirectly,

- Statics and dynamics
- Mechanics of materials
- Formulas (tables, diagrams, charts)
- The conservation of mass principle
- The conservation of energy principle

In addition, engineers need to know how the physical characteristics of the materials of which components are fabricated relate to one another. Newton's first and second laws of motion as well as the third law and relations such as the convective heat transfer equations and Fourier's conduction model may also play a part. Assumptions will usually be necessary to simplify the problem and to make certain that equations and relationships are appropriate and valid. The last step involves checking the reasonableness of the results.

A major goal of this textbook is to help students learn how to solve engineering problems that involve mechanical components. To this end numerous solved examples and end-of-chapter problems are provided. It is extremely important to study the examples *and* solve the problems, for mastery of the fundamentals comes only through practice.

---

[3]This section is adapted from [6].

To maximize the results and rewards in solving problems, it is necessary to develop a systematic approach. We recommend that problem solutions be organized using the following seven steps, which are employed in the solved examples of this text. Problems should be started by recording what is known and completed by commenting on what was learned.

SOLUTION

Known: State briefly what is known. This requires that you read the problem carefully and understand what information is given.

Find: State concisely what is to be determined.

Schematic and Given Data: Sketch the component or system to be considered. Decide whether a free-body diagram is appropriate for the analysis. Label the component or system diagram with relevant information from the problem statement.

Record all material properties and other parameters that you are given or anticipate may be required for subsequent calculations. If appropriate, sketch diagrams that locate critical points and indicate the possible mode of failure.

The importance of good sketches of the system and free-body diagrams cannot be overemphasized. They are often instrumental in enabling you to think clearly about the problem.

Decisions: Record your choices and selections. Design problems will require you to make subjective decisions. Design decisions will involve selection of parameters such as geometric variables and types of materials. Decisions are individual choices.

Assumptions: To form a record of how you *model* the problem, list all simplifying assumptions and idealizations made to reduce it to one that is manageable. Sometimes this information can also be noted on the sketches. In general, once a design is complete, assumptions are still beliefs whereas decisions are true. Assumptions are theories about reality.

Analysis: Using your decisions, assumptions, and idealizations, apply the appropriate equations and relationships to determine the unknowns.

It is advisable to work with equations as long as possible before substituting in numerical data. Consider what additional data may be required. Identify the tables, charts, or relationships that provide the required value. Additional sketches may be helpful at this point to clarify the problem.

When all equations and data are in hand, substitute numerical values into the equations. Carefully check that a consistent and appropriate set of units is being employed to ensure dimensional homogeneity. Then perform the needed calculations.

Finally, consider whether the magnitudes of the numerical values seem reasonable and the algebraic signs associated with the numerical values are correct.

Comments: When appropriate, discuss your results briefly. Comment on what was learned, identify key aspects of the solution, discuss how better results might be obtained by making different design decisions, relaxing certain assumptions, and so on.

Approximations will be required for mathematical models of physical systems. The degree of accuracy required and the information desired determine the degree of approximation. For example, the weight of a component can usually be neglected if the loads on the component are many times greater than the component's total weight. The ability to make the appropriate assumptions in formulating and solving a machine component problem is a requisite engineering skill.

As a particular solution evolves, you may have to return to an earlier step and revise it in light of a better understanding of the problem. For example, it might be necessary to add or delete an assumption, modify a decision, revise a sketch, or seek additional information about the properties of a material.

The problem solution format used in this text is intended to *guide* your thinking, not substitute for it. Accordingly, you are cautioned to avoid the rote application of these seven steps, for this alone would provide few benefits. In some of the earlier sample problems and end-of-chapter problems, the solution format may seem unnecessary or unwieldy. However, as the problems become more complicated, you will see that it reduces errors, saves time, and provides a deeper understanding of the problem at hand.

1.8 Work and Energy

All mechanical apparatus involves *loads* and *motion*, which, in combination, represent *work*, or *energy*. Thus, it is appropriate to review these basic concepts.

The work done by the force **F** acting at a point on a component as the point moves from initial point s_1 to final point s_2 is

$$W = \int_{s_1}^{s_2} \mathbf{F} \cdot d\mathbf{s} \tag{a}$$

where the expression for work has been written in terms of the scalar product of the force vector **F** and the displacement vector $d\mathbf{s}$.

To evaluate the integral we need to know how the force varies with the displacement. The value of W depends on the details of the interactions taking place between the component and the surroundings during a process. The limits of the integral mean "from position 1 to position 2" and cannot be interpreted as the values of work at 1 and 2. The notion of work at 1 or 2 has no meaning, so the integral should never be indicated as $W_2 - W_1$.

Figure 1.4 shows a wheel being turned by the application of tangential force F acting at radius R. Let the wheel rotate through q revolutions. Then the work done, W, is given by

$$W = F(2\pi R)(q) = FS \tag{b}$$

where S is the distance through which the force F is applied.

Suppose that the wheel is turned through an angle θ by applying a torque T (equal to the product of F times R). Then the work done, W, is given by

$$W = F(R\theta) = T\theta \tag{c}$$

The work done by the force or torque can be considered as a transfer of energy to the component, where it is stored as gravitational potential energy, kinetic energy, or

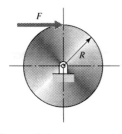

FIGURE 1.4

Wheel being turned by a tangential force.

internal energy, or both or all three; or it may be dissipated as heat energy. The total amount of energy is conserved in all transfers.

Work has units of force times distance. The units of kinetic energy, potential energy, and internal energy are the same as that for work. In SI units, the work unit is the newton · meter (N · m), called the joule (J). Commonly used English or British units for work and energy are the foot-pound force (ft · lb) and the British thermal unit (Btu).

SAMPLE PROBLEM 1.1   Camshaft Torque Requirement

Figure 1.5*a* shows a rotating *cam* that causes a *follower* to move vertically. For the position shown, the follower is being moved upward with a force of 1 N. In addition, for this position it has been determined that a rotation of 0.1 radian (5.73°) corresponds to a follower motion of 1 mm. What is the average torque required to turn the camshaft during this interval?

SOLUTION

Known: A cam exerts a given force on a cam follower through a known distance.

Find: Calculate the average torque required.

Schematic and Given Data:

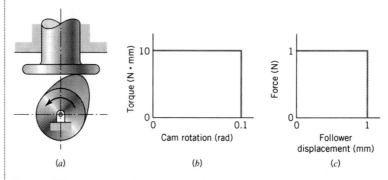

(a)   (b)   (c)

FIGURE 1.5
Cam and follower for Sample Problem 1.1.

Assumptions:

1. The torque can be regarded as remaining constant through the rotation.
2. The friction losses can be neglected.

Analysis:

1. The work done on the camshaft is equal to the work done by the follower, if friction can be neglected.
2. Work in = $T\theta$ = $T(0.1 \text{ rad})$
3. Work out = FS = $(1 \text{ N})(0.001 \text{ m})$

4. Equating the work in to the work out and solving for T gives

$$T = \frac{1\ \text{N} \times 0.001\ \text{m}}{0.1\ \text{rad}} = 0.01\ \text{N} \cdot \text{m} = 10\ \text{N} \cdot \text{mm}$$

Comment: For constant friction, if the cam contact "point" moves across the follower face a distance Δ, the work done to overcome the contact point frictional force would be $\mu F \Delta$, where μ is the coefficient of friction between the cam and the follower and F is the upward force.

1.9 *Power*

Many machine design analyses are concerned with the time rate at which energy is transferred. The rate of energy transfer by work is called *power* and is denoted by $\dot{W}$. When work involves a force, as in Eq. a, the rate of energy transfer is equal to the product of the force and the velocity at the point of application of the force:

$$\dot{W} = \mathbf{F} \cdot \mathbf{V} \tag{d}$$

The dot over W indicates a time rate. Equation d can be integrated from time t_1 to time t_2 to get the total work done during the time interval:

$$W = \int_{t_1}^{t_2} \dot{W}\, dt = \int_{t_1}^{t_2} \mathbf{F} \cdot \mathbf{V}\, dt \tag{e}$$

Since power is the time rate of doing work, it can be expressed in terms of any units of energy and time. In the SI system, the unit for power is joules per second (J/s), called the watt (W). In this book the kilowatt, (kW) is also used. Commonly used English and British units for power are ft · lb/s, British thermal units per second (Btu/s), and horsepower (hp).

The power transmitted by a rotating machine component such as a shaft, flywheel, gear, or pulley is of keen interest in the study of machines. A rotating shaft is a commonly encountered machine element. Consider a shaft subjected to a torque T from its surroundings and rotating with angular velocity ω. Let the torque be expressed in terms of a tangential force F and radius R; then $T = FR$. The velocity at the point of application of the force is $V = R\omega$, where ω is in radians per unit of time. Using these relations and Eq. d gives an expression for the power transmitted to the shaft from the surroundings:

$$\dot{W} = FV = (T/R)(R\omega) = T\omega$$

In SI units, the watt (W) is defined as 1 J/s, which is the same as 1 N · m/s. In addition, 1 revolution $= 2\pi$ radians, 60 s $=$ 1 minute, and 1000 W $=$ 1 kW. The power in kilowatts is

$$\dot{W} = \frac{FV}{1000} = \frac{T\omega}{1000} = \frac{T(2\pi n)}{1000(60)} = \frac{Tn}{1000(60)/2\pi} = \frac{Tn}{9549} \tag{1.2}$$

where $\dot{W}$ = power (kW), T = torque (N·m), n = shaft speed (rpm), F = force (N), V = velocity (m/s), and ω = angular velocity (rad/s).

In English and British units, the horsepower (hp) is defined as a work rate of 33,000 ft·lb/min. In addition, 1 rev = 2π rad. The power in horsepower is thus

$$\dot{W} = \frac{FV}{33,000} = \frac{2\pi Tn}{33,000} = \frac{Tn}{33,000/2\pi} = \frac{Tn}{5252} \tag{1.3}$$

where $\dot{W}$ = power (hp), T = torque (lb·ft), n = shaft speed (rpm), F = force (lb), and V = velocity (fpm).

1.10 *Conservation of Energy*

For a system in which there is no transfer of mass across its boundary, conservation of energy requires that

$$\Delta E = \Delta \mathrm{KE} + \Delta \mathrm{PE} + \Delta U = Q + W \tag{1.4}$$

where

ΔE = change in total energy of the system

$\Delta \mathrm{KE} = \frac{1}{2}m(V_2^2 - V_1^2)$ = change in kinetic energy of the system

$\Delta \mathrm{PE} = mg(z_2 - z_1)$ = change in gravitational potential energy of the system

ΔU = change in internal energy of the system

Q = heat energy transferred to the system

W = work done on the system

Various special forms of the energy balance can be written. The instantaneous time rate of the energy balance is

$$\frac{dE}{dt} = \frac{d(KE)}{dt} + \frac{d(PE)}{dt} + \frac{dU}{dt} = \dot{Q} + \dot{W} \tag{1.5}$$

Equation 1.4 may be used to apply the conservation of energy principle. This principle states that although energy may be changed from one form to another, it cannot be destroyed or lost; it may pass out of control and be unusable yet it still exists.

There are several facets associated with work, energy, and power, some of which are illustrated in the following examples. In studying these examples, the following unit conversions are helpful to remember: 1.34 hp/kW = 1; 0.746 kW/hp = 1; 1.356 J/ft·lb = 1; 1 N·m/J = 1; 6.89 MPa/ksi = 1; 145 psi/MPa = 1.

SAMPLE PROBLEM 1.2   Camshaft Power Requirement

If the camshaft shown in Figure 1.6 and discussed in the previous example rotates at a uniform rate of 1000 rpm, what is the average power requirement during the time interval involved?

SOLUTION

Known: The camshaft in Sample Problem 1.1 rotates at 1000 rpm and exerts a force on the cam follower.

Find: Determine the average power requirement.

Schematic and Given Data:

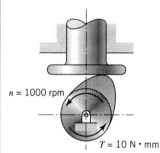

$n = 1000$ rpm

$T = 10$ N · mm

FIGURE 1.6
Cam and follower for Sample Problem 1.2.

Assumptions:

1. The torque can be regarded as remaining constant through the rotation.
2. The friction losses can be neglected.

Analysis:

1. The rotating speed of 1000 rpm corresponds to 2000π rad/min or 33.3π rad/s.
2. Thus, a rotation of 0.1 rad requires $(0.1/33.3\pi)$ seconds.
3. During this time interval the work done on the shaft is 0.001 N · m.
4. Power, therefore, being the time rate of doing work, is 0.001 N · m per $(0.1/33.3\pi)$ s, or 1.05 N · m/s. This is the same as 1.05 W.
5. The horsepower equivalent (Appendix A-1) is

$$1.05 \text{ W} \times 0.00134 \text{ hp/W} \quad \text{or} \quad 0.0014 \text{ hp}$$

SAMPLE PROBLEM 1.3	Punch Press Motor Power Requirement Without Flywheel

The crankshaft of a punch press rotates 60 rpm, causing holes to be punched in a steel part at the rate of 60 punches per minute. The crankshaft torque requirement is shown in Figure 1.7. The press is driven (through suitable speed reducers) by a 1200-rpm motor. Neglecting any "flywheel effect," what motor power is required to accommodate the peak crankshaft torque?

SOLUTION

Known: The crankshaft of a punch press with a known torque requirement rotates at a given rpm creating holes in a part at a given rate.

Find: Determine the motor power to provide the peak crankshaft torque.

Schematic and Given Data:

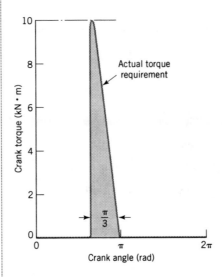

FIGURE 1.7
Punch press torque requirement for Sample Problem 1.3.

Assumptions:

1. Friction losses are negligible.

2. No energy is stored as rotational kinetic energy.

3. The motor delivers maximum torque continuously.

Analysis:

1. Neglecting friction losses, "motor power in" equals "crankshaft power out," and the 20:1 speed reduction (1200 rpm/60 rpm) is associated with a 20:1 torque increase. Hence, the motor must provide a torque of 10 kN·m/20, or 500 N·m.

2. On the basis that the motor has the capacity to deliver this torque *continuously*, the work capacity corresponding to 1 revolution of the shaft is $2\pi(500$ N·m$) = 1000\pi$ J

3. In 1 s, during which time the shaft turns 20 revolutions, the work capacity is 20π kJ. This is a work rate (power) of 20π kW, or 62.8 kW. The horsepower equivalent (see Appendix A-1) is 62.8 kW $\times$ 1.34 hp/kW, or 84.2 hp.

Comment: It is obviously wasteful to provide such a large motor when its full capacity is needed but a small fraction of the time. Providing a suitable *flywheel* allows a much smaller motor to be used. During the actual punch stroke, energy will be taken from the flywheel, slowing it down. During the relatively long period of time between punch strokes, the motor will accelerate the flywheel back to its original speed. This is illustrated in the next sample problem.

SAMPLE PROBLEM 1.4   Punch Press Motor Power Requirement With Flywheel

For the punch press in Sample Problem 1.3 determine the motor power capacity required if use is made of a flywheel. The energy required for the press is represented by the area under the actual crank torque versus the crank angle curve of Figure 1.8 which is 2π kN·m, or 6283 J.

SOLUTION

Known: A flywheel is used in the punch press of Sample Problem 1.3.

Find: Estimate the motor power capacity.

Schematic and Given Data:

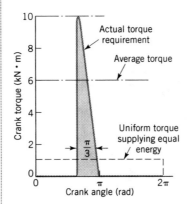

FIGURE 1.8
Punch press torque requirement.

Assumption: Friction losses are negligible.

Analysis:

1. Figure 1.8 shows that the *average* torque requirement during the actual punch stroke is 6 kN·m, and that the punch stroke lasts for $\pi/3$ rad. (The energy involved is the area under the curve; 2π kN·m, or 6283 J.) By using a flywheel that permits the motor to deliver a constant torque over the entire 2π rad we reduce the torque requirement to 1 kN·m. This is shown in Figure 1.8 as "uniform torque supplying equal energy."

2. Since, at the same shaft speed, motor torque and motor power are proportional, the 10 : 1 reduction in motor torque requirement (1 kN·m with flywheel; 10 without) corresponds to a like reduction in power rating required. Hence, the answer, rounded off to two significant figures, is 6.3 kW or 8.4 hp.

Comment: The next question that arises is how large a flywheel is required. If the flywheel is too small (or, more precisely, if the flywheel has too small a polar moment of inertia), the speed fluctuation will be excessive. If the flywheel is too large, it will involve an excess of weight, bulk, and cost, and there may be problems in getting it up to speed when starting. The next sample problem illustrates a typical flywheel calculation.

SAMPLE PROBLEM 1.5   Design of Punch Press Flywheel

Continuing with the previous problem, we choose to design a flywheel that rotates at $\frac{1}{3}$ motor speed and that limits motor speed fluctuation to the range of 900 to 1200 rpm. The flywheel is to be made of steel and have the geometric proportions shown in Figure 1.9. To simplify the calculation, assume that the inertia contributed by the hub and arms is negligible. Determine the required flywheel polar moment of inertia, I, and diameter, d.

SOLUTION

Known: A flywheel of given configuration and material is to be designed to rotate at a specified speed while maintaining motor speed in a specified speed range.

Find: Determine I and d for the flywheel.

Schematic and Given Data:

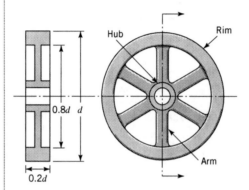

FIGURE 1.9
Punch press flywheel proportions.

Assumptions/Decisions:

1. The flywheel rotates at $\frac{1}{3}$ motor speed.
2. Motor speed fluctuation is limited to the range of 900 to 1200 rpm.
3. The flywheel is made of steel.
4. Geometric proportions for the flywheel are as shown in Figure 1.9.
5. The inertia contributed by the hub and arms is negligible.
6. Friction losses are negligible.

Design Analysis:

1. Figure 1.8 shows that during the *actual punch stroke*, energy provided by the *motor* is represented by an approximate rectangle 1 kN·m high and $\pi/3$ rad wide. Thus, the motor provides 1047 J of the total of 6283 J required. The flywheel must provide the remaining 5236 J.

2. Recalling that kinetic energy is $\frac{1}{2}mv^2$ for linear motion, and $\frac{1}{2}I\omega^2$ for rotational motion, it is evident that the flywheel inertia must be such that

$$5236 = \tfrac{1}{2}I(\omega_{max}^2 - \omega_{min}^2)$$

(Units: I expressed in kg·m^2 and ω_{max} and ω_{min} expressed in rad/s.)

$$5236 = \tfrac{1}{2}I[(13.3\pi)^2 - (10\pi)^2], \quad \text{or} \quad I = 13.80 \text{ kg·m}^2$$

3. The moment of inertia for a hollow cylinder is

$$I = \pi(d_o^4 - d_i^4)L\rho/32 \quad \text{(see Appendix B-2)}$$

where ρ = mass density = 7700 kg/m^3 for steel (Appendix C-1). Substituting, we have

$$13.80 = \pi[(d)^4 - (0.8d)^4](0.2d)(7700)/32$$

from which $d = 0.688$ m.

Comment: If the inertia contributed by the hub and arms is included in the analysis, we would find that a smaller d is required.

SAMPLE PROBLEM 1.6   Automotive Performance Analysis

Figure 1.10 shows a representative engine power requirement curve for constant speed, level road operation of a 4000-lb automobile. Figure 1.11 shows the wide-open-throttle horsepower curve of its 350-in.[3] V-8 engine. Figure 1.12 gives specific fuel consumption curves for the engine for the vehicle shown in Figure 1.13. The extreme right-hand point of each curve represents wide-open-throttle operation. The rolling radius of the wheels varies a little with speed, but can be taken as 13 in. The transmission provides direct drive in high gear.

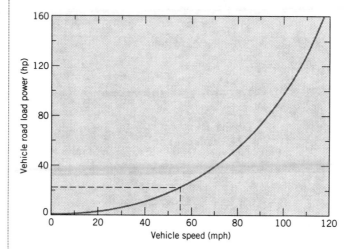

FIGURE 1.10

Vehicle power requirement. Typical 4000-lb sedan (level road, constant speed, no wind).

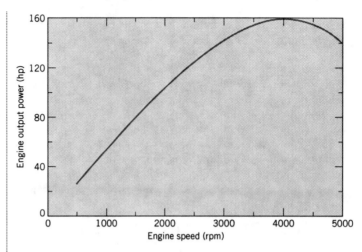

FIGURE 1.11

Engine output power versus engine speed. Typical 350-in.[3] V-8 engine.

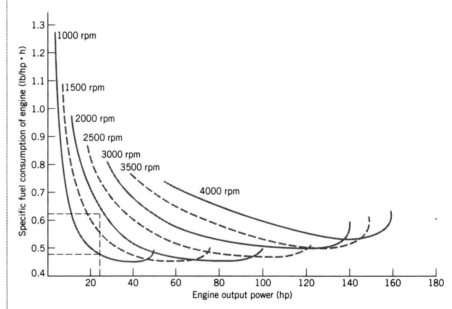

FIGURE 1.12

Specific fuel consumption versus engine output power. Typical 350-in.[3] V-8 engine.

1. What axle ratio would result in the highest top speed, and what is that speed?

2. Estimate the gasoline mileage at a constant 55 mph, using this axle ratio.

3. Describe briefly the nature of a theoretically "ideal" automatic transmission. How would it change the 55-mph fuel consumption and the vehicle performance (i.e., acceleration and hill climbing ability)?

SOLUTION

Known: We know the vehicle horsepower–speed curve, the engine horsepower–speed curve, and the brake-specific fuel consumption for the engine.

Find: (1) Determine the axle ratio for highest vehicle speed, (2) estimate gasoline mileage, (3) describe an ideal automatic transmission.

Schematic and Given Data:

FIGURE 1.13
Vehicle for Sample Problem 1.6.

Assumptions:

1. The vehicle operates on a level road, at constant velocity, without external wind.
2. The change in rolling radius of the wheels with speed is negligible.

Analysis:

1. Figure 1.11 shows the maximum engine power to be 160 hp at 4000 rpm. Figure 1.10 shows that 160 hp will drive the car 117 mph. The axle ratio must be such that the engine rotates 4000 rpm when the vehicle speed is 117 mph. At 117 mph, wheel speed is

$$\frac{5280 \text{ ft/mi} \times 117 \text{ mi/h}}{60 \text{ min/h} \times 2\pi(13/12) \text{ ft/rev}} = 1513 \text{ rpm}$$

   The axle ratio required is

$$\frac{4000 \text{ rpm (engine)}}{1513 \text{ rpm (wheels)}} = 2.64$$

2. At 55 mph, engine speed is

$$4000 \text{ rpm } (55 \text{ mph}/117 \text{ mph}) = 1880 \text{ rpm}$$

   From Figure 1.10, the 55-mph power requirement is 23 hp. With engine output power equal to the vehicle road power, Figure 1.12 gives a specific fuel consumption of about 0.63 lb/hp·h. Hence the hourly fuel consumption is $0.63 \times 23 = 14.5$ lb/h.

   With 5.8 lb/gal as the specific weight of gasoline, the fuel mileage is

$$\frac{55 \text{ mi/h} \times 5.8 \text{ lb/gal}}{14.5 \text{ lb/h}} = 22 \text{ mi/gal}$$

3. An "ideal" automatic transmission would permit the engine to slow down until either minimum specific fuel consumption (about 0.46 lb/hp·h) or minimum satisfactory operating engine speed was reached. To provide 23 hp at 0.46 lb/hp·h would require the engine to operate below 1000 rpm. Let us conservatively

assume that 1000 rpm is the slowest satisfactory engine speed. At 1000 rpm, 23 hp can be had with a fuel consumption of 0.48 lb/hp · h. In comparison with getting the 23 hp at 1880 rpm, gasoline mileage is increased by the ratio of 0.63/0.48 = 1.31. Thus, with the "ideal" transmission, 55 mph fuel mileage is 22 mpg × 1.31 = *28.9 mpg*.

Comments:

1. Regarding vehicle performance, an "ideal" transmission would, with fully depressed accelerator, allow the engine to speed up to 4000 rpm and deliver its full 160 hp at *all vehicle speeds* and under all road conditions when this speed did not cause wheel "spin" and loss of traction. Under the latter conditions, engine speed would be increased just to the point of providing sufficient power to the driving wheels to *almost* overcome driving friction.

2. The "ideal" transmission would enable a *smaller* (and lighter) engine to be used and still match the normal-speed-range performance of the original engine and transmission. The smaller engine plus "ideal" transmission would presumably give 55 mph operation at 0.46 lb/hp · h and an estimated *30.1 mpg*.

References

1. Fox, Robert W., and Alan T. McDonald, *Introduction to Fluid Mechanics*, 4th ed., Wiley, New York, 1992.

2. Juvinall, Robert C., *Production Research—Basic Objectives and Guidelines*, Second International Conference on Production Research, Copenhagen, August, 1973. (Reproduced in full in *Congressional Record—Senate*, May 29, 1974, pp. S9168–S9172.)

3. Juvinall, Robert C., "The Mission of Tomorrow's Engineer: Mission Impossible?," *Agricultural Engineering* (April 1973).

4. Maslow, Abraham H., "A Theory of Human Motivation," *Psychological Review*, **50** (1943).

5. Maslow, Abraham H., *Motivation and Personality*, Harper, New York, 1954.

6. Moran, Michael J., and Howard N. Shapiro, *Fundamentals of Engineering Thermodynamics*, 5th ed., Wiley, New York, 2004.

7. Newton, K., W. Steeds, and T. K. Garrett, *The Motor Vehicle*, 12th ed., Butterworths, London, 1996.

8. U.S. Dept. of Commerce, National Bureau of Standards, "The International System of Units (SI)," Special Publication 330, 1980.

9. Weinstein, Alvin S., et al., *Products Liability and the Reasonably Safe Product: A Guide for Management, Design, and Marketing*, Wiley, New York, 1978.

10. Krieger, G. R., and J. F. Montgomery (eds.), *Accident Prevention Manual for Business and Industry: Engineering and Technology*, 11th ed., National Safety Council, Itasca, Illinois, 1997.

Problems

Sections 1.1–1.5

1.1D Write definitions of the words *science, engineering, art*, and *design* using a dictionary and compare with those given in Section 1.1.

1.2D Search online at http://www.osha.gov and from 29 CFR 1910.211 *Definitions*, define the following power press terms: *brake, clutch, two-hand control device, die, foot pedal, pinch point, point of operation*. Regulations for power presses are presented in 29 CFR 1910.217. Show a power press and identify the location of each item.

1.3D Search online at http://www.osha.gov and print a copy of 29 CFR 1910.212, *General requirements for all machines*. With these requirements in mind, identify a machine you have used that had a machine guard to protect the operator or other person in the machine area from hazards. Sketch the machine and label the guarding device, power source, point of operation, and danger zone.

1.4D Many machines that are used in automatic production operations are equipped with safety devices that stop the machine when a faulty machine operation takes place. Search the patent literature at http://www.uspto.gov for mechanical devices that stop operation of a machine when a problem occurs. Describe and sketch several such devices.

1.5D Search the OSHA regulations at http://www.osha.gov and review the section related to machine guarding. List the general methods used to guard known machine hazards. Give specific examples of conditions where guards should be used.

1.6D Search online at http://www.nssn.org and prepare a list of the titles and organizations for standards on:

(a) machine guarding

(b) refuse vehicles (garbage trucks)

(c) portable grinders

1.7D The unexpected or unintentional energization or start up of machinery, or the release of stored energy, during servicing or maintenance of the machine can result in employee injury or death. Review the regulation 29 CFR 1910.147 entitled *The control of hazardous energy (lockout/tagout)* at http://www.osha.gov and write a paragraph explaining the procedure of lockout/tagout for machines or equipment.

1.8D Design a danger sign and a caution sign for a power press. For specifications search online at http://www.osha.gov for 29 CFR 1910.145 entitled *Specifications for accident prevention signs and tags*. Describe the difference between a danger sign and a caution sign. When is the signal word "Warning" used?

1.9D From your own experience and observation, describe briefly (perhaps one or two typed pages, double-spaced) a specific example of mechanical engineering design that you regard as *excellent* from a *safety* standpoint. (Preferably, choose an example reflecting your own observation and safety consciousness rather than one featured in the news media.) Your write-up should reflect the professional appearance expected of an engineer. Use illustrations if and where appropriate.

1.10D Repeat Problem 1.9D, except describe an example of mechanical engineering design that you regard as *poor* from the standpoint of safety.

1.11D Repeat Problem 1.9D, except describe an example of mechanical engineering design that you regard as *good* from an *ecological* standpoint.

1.12D Repeat Problem 1.9D, except describe an example of mechanical engineering design that you regard as *poor* from an ecological standpoint.

1.13D Repeat Problem 1.9D, except describe an example of mechanical engineering design that you regard as *good* from a *sociological* standpoint. (This should represent the kind of engineering activity with which you would feel proud to be associated.)

1.14D Repeat Problem 1.9D, except describe a mechanical engineering design that you regard as *questionable* from a sociological standpoint.

1.15D Describe briefly a mechanical engineering design wherein you recognize compromises that had to be made among the various considerations discussed in Sections 1.2 through 1.5.

1.16D   Search for information on the organization, *Engineers Without Borders*, and describe briefly (one or two typed pages, double spaced) your own observation of the ability of this group to improve the quality of life within our society.

1.17D   Write a report reviewing the web site http://www.uspto.gov. From a mechanical engineer's viewpoint, discuss the *contents, usefulness, cost, ease of use*, and *clarity of the site*. Identify the search tools available.

1.18D   Repeat Problem 1.17D, except use the website http://www.osha.gov.

1.19D   Repeat Problem 1.17D, except use the websites http://www.ansi.org and http://www.iso.ch.

Sections 1.6 and 1.7

1.20   Check the dimensional homogeneity of the following equations: (a) $F = ma$, (b) $W = Fs$, and (c) $\dot{W} = T\omega$, where m = mass, a = acceleration, F = force, W = work, s = distance, ω = angular velocity, T = torque, and $\dot{W}$ = power.

1.21   An object has a mass of 10 kg at a location where the acceleration of gravity is 9.81 m/s^2. Determine its weight in (a) English Engineering units, (b) British Gravitational units, and (c) SI units.

1.22   An object whose mass is 7.8 kg occupies a volume of 0.7 m^3. Determine its (a) weight, in newtons, and average density, in kg/m^3, at a location on the earth where $g = 9.55$ m/s^2, (b) weight, in newtons, and average density, in kg/m^3, on the moon where $g = 1.7$ m/s^2.

1.23   A spacecraft component occupies a volume of 8 ft^3 and weighs 25 lb at a location where the acceleration of gravity is 31.0 ft/s^2. Determine its weight, in pounds, and its average density, in lbm/ft^3, on the moon, where $g = 5.57$ ft/s^2.

1.24   A spring stretches 5 mm per newton of applied force. An object is suspended from the spring, and a deflection of 30 mm is observed. If $g = 9.81$ m/s^2, what is the mass of the object (kg)?

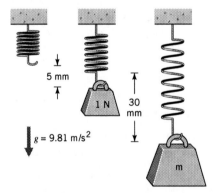

5 mm

1 N

30 mm

$g = 9.81$ m/s^2

m

FIGURE P1.24

1.25   An object weighs 20 lb at a location where the acceleration of gravity is $g = 30.5$ ft/s^2. Determine the magnitude of the net force (lb) required to accelerate the object at 25 ft/s^2.

1.26   The British Gravitational System uses the mass unit slug. By definition, a mass of 1 slug is accelerated at a rate of 1 ft/s^2 by a force of 1 lb. Explain why this is a convenient mass unit.

1.27   Deceleration is sometimes measured in g's or multiples of the standard acceleration of gravity. Determine the force, in newtons, that an automobile passenger whose mass is 68 kg experiences if the deceleration in a head-on crash is $50g$.

1.28 An object has a mass of 8 kg. Determine (a) its weight at a location where the acceleration of gravity is $g = 9.7$ m/s^2, (b) the magnitude of the net force, in N, required to accelerate the object at 7 m/s^2.

1.29 A truck weighs 3300 lb. What is the magnitude of the net force (lb) required to accelerate it at a constant rate of 5 ft/s^2? The acceleration of gravity is $g = 32.2$ ft/s^2.

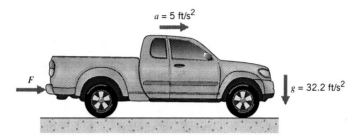

FIGURE P1.29

1.30D A solid metal object has a volume of 0.01 m^3. Select a metal from Appendix C-1. Use the density of the metal to determine: (a) the weight of the objects at a location where the acceleration of gravity is $g = 9.7$ m/s^2, and (b) the magnitude of the net force, in N, required to accelerate the object at 7 m/s^2 in a horizontal direction.

Sections 1.8–1.10

1.31D A vertically suspended wire has a cross-sectional area of 0.1 in.^{2}. A downward force, applied to the end of the wire, causes the wire to stretch. The force is increased linearly from initially zero to 2500 lb, and the length of the wire increases by 0.1%. Select a wire length and use it to determine (a) the normal stress, in lb/in.^{2}, and (b) the work done in stretching the wire, in ft · lb.

1.32 Figure P1.32 shows an object whose mass is 5 lbm attached to a rope wound around a pulley. The radius of the pulley is 3 in. If the mass falls at a constant velocity of 5 ft/s, determine the power transmitted to the pulley, in horsepower, and the rotational speed of the pulley, in revolutions per minute (rpm). The acceleration of gravity is $g = 32.2$ ft/s^2.

[Ans.: 0.045 hp, 191 rpm]

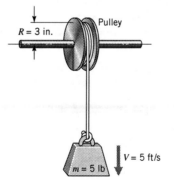

FIGURE P1.32

1.33 The input shaft to a gearbox rotates at 2000 rpm and transmits a power of 40 kW. The output shaft power is 36 kW at a rotational speed of 500 rpm. Determine the torque of each shaft, in N · m.

1.34   An electric motor draws a current of 10 amperes (A) with a voltage of 110 V. The output shaft develops a torque of 9.5 N·m and a rotational speed of 1000 rpm. All operating data are constant with time. Determine (a) the electric power required by the motor and the power developed by the output shaft, each in kilowatts; (b) the net power input to the motor, in kilowatts; (c) the amount of energy transferred to the motor by electrical work and the amount of energy transferred out of the motor by the shaft in kW·h and Btu, during 2 h of operation.

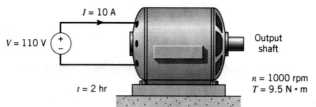

$I = 10$ A

$V = 110$ V

Output shaft

$n = 1000$ rpm

$t = 2$ hr

$T = 9.5$ N·m

FIGURE P1.34

1.35   An electric heater draws a constant current of 6 A, with an applied voltage of 220 V, for 10 h. Determine the total amount of energy supplied to the heater by electrical work, in kW·h.

1.36D The drag force, F_d, imposed by the surrounding air on an automobile moving with velocity V is given by

$$F_d = C_d A \tfrac{1}{2} \rho V^2$$

where C_d is a constant called the drag coefficient, A is the projected frontal area of the vehicle, and ρ is the air density. For $C_d = 0.42$, A $= 2$ m², and $\rho = 1.23$ kg/m³, (a) calculate the power required (kW) to overcome drag at a constant velocity of 100 km/h, (b) compute and plot the required power (kW) to overcome drag as a function of velocity, for V ranging from 0 to 120 km/h.

1.37   A solid cylindrical bar of 5-mm diameter is slowly stretched from an initial length of 100 mm to a final length of 101 mm. The normal stress acting at the end of the bar varies according to $\sigma = E(x - x_1)/x_1$, where x is the position of the end of the bar, x_1 is the initial length, and E is a material constant (Young's modulus). For $E = 2 \times 10^7$ kPa, determine the work done on the bar (J).

1.38   A steel wire suspended vertically has a cross-sectional area of 0.1 in.² and an initial length of 10 ft. A downward force applied to the end of the wire causes the wire to stretch. The force varies linearly with the length of the wire from zero initially to 2500 lb when the length has increased by 0.01 ft. Determine (a) the normal stress, in lb/in.², at the end of the wire as a function of the length of the wire and (b) the work done in stretching the wire, in ft·lb.

1.39   The crankshaft of a single-cylinder air compressor rotates 1800 rpm. The piston area is 2000 mm², and the piston stroke is 50 mm. Assume a simple "idealized" case where the average gas pressure acting on the piston during the compression stroke is 1 MPa, and pressure during the intake stroke is negligible. The compressor is 80% efficient. A flywheel provides adequate control of speed fluctuation.

(a) What motor power (kW) is required to drive the crankshaft?

(b) What torque is transmitted through the crankshaft?

[Ans.: 3.75 kW, 19.9 N·m]

1.40   What is the rate of work output of a press that delivers 120 strokes per minute, each stroke providing a force of 8000 N throughout a distance of 18 mm? If the press efficiency is 90%, what average torque must be provided by a 1750-rpm driving motor?

1.41D A press delivers a force of 8000 N throughout a distance of 18 mm each stroke. Select a number of strokes per minute and determine the rate of work output per second. If the press efficiency is 90%, what average torque must be provided by a 1750-rpm driving motor?

1.42 A punch press with flywheel adequate to minimize speed fluctuations produces 120 punching strokes per minute, each providing an average force of 2000 N over a stroke of 50 mm. The press is driven through a gear reducer by a shaft rotating 300 rpm. Overall efficiency is 80%.

(a) What power (W) is transmitted through the shaft?

(b) What average torque is applied to the shaft?

[Ans.: 250 W, 8.0 N · m]

1.43 Repeat Problem 1.42 except change the punch force to 10,000 N, stroke to 50 mm, and drive shaft speed to 900 rpm.

[Ans.: 1250 W, 13.26 N · m]

1.44 An 1800-rpm motor drives a camshaft 360 rpm by means of a belt drive. During each revolution of the cam, a follower rises and falls 20 mm. During each follower upstroke, the follower resists a constant force of 500 N. During the downstrokes, the force is negligible. The inertia of the rotating parts (including a small flywheel) provides adequate speed uniformity. Neglecting friction, what motor power is required? You should be able to get the answer in three ways: by evaluating power at the (a) motor shaft, (b) camshaft, and (c) follower.

[Ans.: 60 W]

1.45 Repeat Problem 1.44 except work with English units and use a follower displacement of 1 in. and a follower force (during the upstroke) of 100 lb.

1.46D Search online at http://www.pddnet.com and http://www.powertransmission.com, and copy speed torque curves and give typical applications for various types of fractional and subfractional motors (e.g., split phase, capacitor-start, induction, shaded pole, synchronous, universal, shunt, split-series field, compound, etc.).

1.47 The crankshaft of a small punch press rotates 100 rpm, with the shaft torque fluctuating between 0 and 1000 N · m in accordance with curve A of Figure P1.47. The press is driven (through a gear reducer) by a 1200-rpm motor. Neglecting friction losses, what motor power would theoretically be required:

(a) With a flywheel adequate to minimize speed fluctuations.

(b) With no flywheel.

[Ans.: (a) 2618 W, (b) 10,472 W]

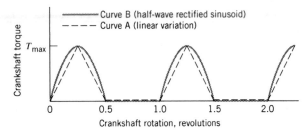

FIGURE P1.47

1.48   Repeat Problem 1.47 except use curve B of Figure P1.47.

[Ans.: (a) 3333 W, (b) 10,472 W]

1.49   A piston-type air compressor with an inlet pressure of 1 atm (100 kPa) rotates 1800 rpm and delivers 0.1 m³/min of air compressed to a gage pressure of 4 atms. For simplicity, assume that the compression is isothermal, and that the compressor efficiency is 50%.

(a)   What average torque must be supplied to the crankshaft?

(b)   Assuming an adequate flywheel, what motor power is required?

[Ans.: 14.24 N · m, 2.68 kW]

1.50   Assume in Problem 1.49 that the rotating inertia of the crankshaft, piston, connecting rod, and flywheel all taken together is equivalent to a steel flywheel of 0.3-m diameter (rotating at crankshaft speed) with proportions as shown in Figure 1.9, and assume that the instantaneous torque requirement varies as in curve A of Figure P1.47. If 1800 rpm is the maximum rotating speed, what is the minimum rotating speed?

[Ans.: 1788 rpm]

1.51   Repeat Problem 1.50 except assume that instantaneous torque varies as in curve B of Figure P1.47.

1.52   A steel flywheel has the proportions shown in Figure 1.9. The hub and arms add 10 percent to the inertia of the rim. How much energy does the flywheel give up in slowing from 1800 to 1700 rpm:

(a)   If diameter d is 500 mm (use SI units)?

(b)   If diameter d is 12 in. (use English units)?

1.53   Repeat Problem 1.52 except use a diameter, d, of (a) 30 mm (use SI units) and (b) 20 in. (use English units).

1.54   How steep a grade can be climbed by the automobile in Sample Problem 1.6 (with a 2.64 axle ratio) while maintaining a constant 55 mph:

(a)   With transmission in direct drive?

(b)   With a transmission reduction ratio of 1.6?

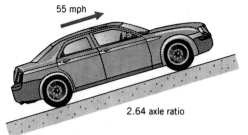

FIGURE P1.54

1.55   How great a speed can the car in Sample Problem 1.6 (with 2.64 axle ratio) maintain when going up a continuous 10 percent grade (1-ft rise in 10-ft horizontal travel)?

[Ans.: 73 mph]

1.56   How great a reduction in the Figure 1.10 "road load" horsepower requirement would be necessary to enable a car with an "ideal" transmission to get 30 miles per gallon (mpg) at 70 mph? (Assume that the engine would have a minimum brake-specific fuel consumption of 0.45 lb/hp · h, as shown in Figure 1.12.)

[Ans.: About 25 percent]

CHAPTER 2

Load Analysis

2.1   *Introduction*

This book is concerned with the design and analysis of machine and structural components. Since these are *load-carrying* members, an analysis of loads is of fundamental importance. A sophisticated stress or deflection analysis is of little value if it is based on incorrect loads. A mechanical component cannot be satisfactory unless its design is based on realistic operating loads.

Sometimes the service or operating loads can be readily determined, as are those on some engines, compressors, and electric generators that operate at known torques and speeds. Often the loads are difficult to determine, as are those on automotive chassis components (which depend on road surfaces and driving practices) or on the structure of an airplane (which depends on air turbulence and pilot decisions). Sometimes experimental methods are used to obtain a statistical definition of applied loads. In other instances engineers use records of service failures together with analyses of strength in order to infer reasonable estimates of loads encountered in service. The determination of appropriate loads is often a difficult and challenging initial step in the design of a machine or structural component.

2.2   *Equilibrium Equations and Free-Body Diagrams*

After certain initial applied loads have been determined or estimated, the basic equations of equilibrium enable loads at other points to be determined. For a nonaccelerating body, these equations can be simply expressed as

$$\Sigma F = 0 \quad \text{and} \quad \Sigma M = 0 \tag{2.1}$$

For an accelerating body they are

$$\Sigma F = ma \quad \text{and} \quad \Sigma M = I\alpha \tag{2.2}$$

These equations apply with respect to each of any three mutually perpendicular axes (commonly designated *X*, *Y*, and *Z*), although in many problems forces and moments are present with respect to only one or two of these axes.

The importance of equilibrium analysis as a means of load determination can hardly be overemphasized. The student is urged to study each of the following examples carefully.

SAMPLE PROBLEM 2.1   Automobile Traveling Straight Ahead at Constant Speed on Smooth, Level Road

The 3000-lb (loaded weight) car shown in Figure 2.1 is going 60 mph and at this speed the aerodynamic drag is 16 hp. The center of gravity (CG) and the center of aerodynamic pressure (CP), are located as shown. Determine the ground reaction forces on the front and rear wheels.

SOLUTION

Known: A car of specified weight travels at a given speed with known drag force.

Find: Determine the pavement forces on the tires.

Schematic and Given Data:

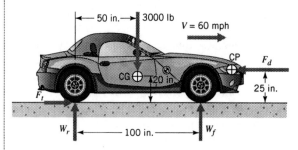

FIGURE 2.1
Free-body diagram of auto traveling at constant speed.

Assumptions:

1. The speed is constant.
2. The car has rear-wheel drive.
3. Vertical aerodynamic forces are negligible.
4. The rolling resistance of the tires is negligible.

Analysis:

1. Power is force times velocity; 1 hp = 33,000 ft·lb/min, and 60 mph = 5280 ft/min; hence,

$$hp = \frac{\text{drag force (lb)} \cdot \text{velocity (ft/min)}}{33,000}$$

$$16 = \frac{(F_d)(5280)}{33,000}$$

$$F_d = 100 \text{ lb}$$

2. Summation of forces in the direction of motion is zero (no acceleration forces exist at constant velocity); hence, thrust force F_t is 100 lb in the forward direction. This is the force applied *by* the road surface *to* the tires. (The force applied by the tires to the road is equal but opposite in direction.) This force is divided equally between the rear wheels for the rear-wheel-drive car shown; it could be applied to the front tires for a front-wheel-drive car without altering any other forces.

3. Applying the moment equilibrium equation with respect to moments about an axis passing through the rear tire road contacts, we have

$$\Sigma M = (3000 \text{ lb})(50 \text{ in.}) - (100 \text{ lb})(25 \text{ in.}) - (W_f)(100 \text{ in.}) = 0$$

from which $W_f = 1475$ lb.

4. Finally, from the summation of vertical forces equals zero, we have

$$W_r = 3000 \text{ lb} - 1475 \text{ lb}$$
$$= 1525 \text{ lb}$$

Comments: Before leaving this problem, we note two further points of interest.

1. The weight of the vehicle *when parked* is carried equally by the front and rear wheels—that is, $W_f = W_r = 1500$ lb. When traveling at 60 mph, forces F_d and F_t introduce a front-lifting couple about the lateral axis (any axis perpendicular to the paper in Figure 2.1) of 100 lb times 25 in. This is balanced by an opposing couple created by the added force of 25 lb carried by the rear wheels and the reduced force of 25 lb carried by the front wheels. (Note: This simplified analysis neglects *vertical* aerodynamic forces, which can be important at high speeds; hence, the use of "spoilers" and "wings" on race cars.)

2. The thrust force is not, in general, equal to the weight on the driving wheels times the coefficient of friction, but it *cannot exceed* this value. In this problem the wheels will maintain traction as long as the coefficient of friction is equal to or above the extremely small value of 100 lb/1525 lb, or 0.066.

SAMPLE PROBLEM 2.2   Automobile Undergoing Acceleration

The car in Figure 2.1, traveling 60 mph, is suddenly given full throttle. A curve similar to Figure 1.11 shows the corresponding engine power to be 96 hp. Estimate the ground reaction forces on the front and rear wheels, and the acceleration of the vehicle.

SOLUTION

Known: A car of specified weight, with known drag force and speed, is given full throttle.

Find: Determine the ground forces on the tires and the vehicle acceleration.

Schematic and Given Data:

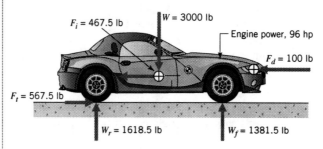

FIGURE 2.2
Free-body diagram of auto undergoing forward acceleration.

Assumptions:

1. The rotational inertia effect is equivalent to a car weighing 7 percent more.
2. The rear wheels develop the required traction.

Analysis:

1. The influence of the *rotating* inertia of the car wheels, engine flywheel, and other rotating members should be considered. When the car accelerates, power is consumed in *angularly* accelerating these members. Detailed calculations typically indicate that in "high" gear the effect of the rotational inertia is to increase the weight of the car by about 7 percent. This means that only 100/107 of the power available for acceleration goes to *linearly* accelerating the car mass.

2. In this problem, 16 hp gives the forward wheel thrust of 100 lb needed to maintain constant speed. With total horsepower increased to 96, 80 hp produces acceleration, of which 80(100/107) or 74.8 hp causes linear acceleration. If 16 hp produces a 100-lb thrust, then, by proportion, 74.8 hp will increase the thrust by 467.5 lb.

3. From Eq. 2.2,

$$a = \frac{F}{m} = \frac{Fg}{W} = \frac{(467.5 \text{ lb})(32.2 \text{ ft/s}^2)}{3000 \text{ lb}} = 5.0 \text{ ft/s}^2$$

4. Figure 2.2 shows the car in equilibrium. The 467.5-lb inertia force acts toward the rear and causes an additional shift of 93.5 lb from the front to the rear wheels (calculation details are left to the reader).

Comment: In this problem the wheels will maintain traction as long as the coefficient of friction is equal to or above the value of 567.5/1617, or 0.351.

**SAMPLE PROBLEM 2.3   Automotive Power
                        Train Components**

Figure 2.3 shows an exploded drawing of the engine, transmission, and propeller shaft of the car in Figures 2.1 and 2.2. The engine delivers torque T to the transmission, and the transmission speed ratio (ω_{in}/ω_{out}) is R. Determine the loads, exclusive of gravity, acting on these three members.

SOLUTION

Known: An engine of known general configuration delivers power to a transmission and drive shaft of an automobile.

Find: Determine the loads on the engine, transmission, and drive shaft.

Schematic and Given Data:

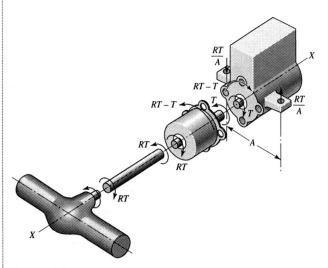

FIGURE 2.3
Equilibrium of moments about the X axis for engine, transmission, and propeller shaft of a front-engine, rear-wheel-drive automobile (T = engine torque, R = transmission torque ratio; engine rotates counterclockwise viewed from transmission).

Assumptions:

1. The engine is supported at two points as shown.
2. The weight of the components are neglected.
3. Transmission friction losses are neglected.

Analysis:

1. Consider first the transmission. This member receives torque T from the engine and delivers torque RT to the propeller shaft[1] (through a universal joint, not shown). The propeller shaft applies equal and opposite reaction torque RT to the transmission, as shown. For equilibrium, torque $RT - T$ *must* be applied *to* the transmission housing *by* the engine structure to which it is attached.

2. The engine receives torques T and $RT - T$ from the transmission (action–reaction principle). Moment RT must be applied by the frame (through the engine mounts), as shown.

---

[1] Neglecting transmission friction losses.

3. The propeller shaft is in equilibrium under the action of equal and opposite torques applied at its two ends.

Comment: This simplified power train analysis gives an estimate of the component forces and moments.

SAMPLE PROBLEM 2.4   Automotive Transmission Components

Figure 2.4*a* shows a simplified version of the transmission represented in Figure 2.3. The engine is delivering a torque $T = 3000$ lb · in. to the transmission, and the transmission is in low gear with a ratio $R = 2.778$. (For this problem consider R to be a torque ratio, T_{out}/T_{in}. To the degree that friction losses are present, the speed ratio, ω_{in}/ω_{out}, would have to be slightly greater.) The other three portions of the figure show the major parts of the transmission. Gear diameters are given in the figure.

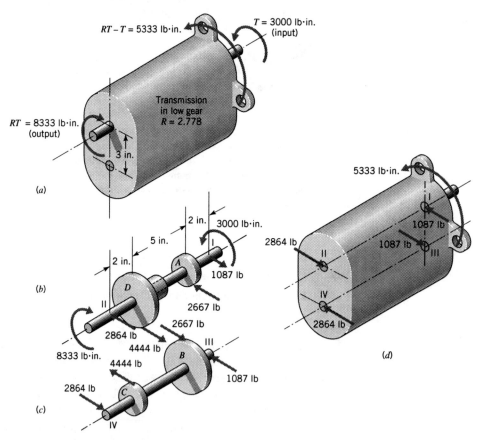

FIGURE 2.4

Free-body diagram of transmission and major components: (*a*) Complete transmission assembly. (*b*) Main shaft (front and rear halves rotate freely with respect to each other). (*c*) Countershaft. (*d*) Housing. Note: Diameters of gears *A* and *C* are $2\frac{1}{4}$ in. Diameters of gears *B* and *D* are $3\frac{3}{4}$ in.

Input gear *A* rotates at engine speed and drives countershaft gear *B*. Countershaft gear *C* meshes with main shaft output gear *D*. (The construction of the main shaft is such that the input and output ends rotate about a common axis, but the two halves are free to rotate at different speeds.) The main shaft is supported in the housing by bearings I and II. Similarly, the countershaft is supported by bearings III and IV. Determine all loads acting on the components shown in Figures 2.4*b*, *c*, and *d*, thus representing them as free bodies in equilibrium. Suppose that the forces acting between mating gear teeth are tangential. (This amounts to neglecting the radial and axial components of load. These load components are discussed in Chapters 15 and 16, dealing with gears.)

SOLUTION

Known: A transmission of known general configuration and given ratio, $R = T_{out}/T_{in}$, receives a specified torque *T* from an engine. The arrangement and locations of the gears, shafts, and bearings inside the transmission are also known, as are the diameters of all gears.

Find: Determine all loads acting on the components.

Assumptions:

1. The forces acting between mating gear teeth are tangential.

2. The transmission input and output torques are steady (no acceleration or deceleration).

Analysis:

1. A very important initial observation is that equilibrium of the *total* transmission (Figure 2.4*a*) is *independent* of anything inside the housing. This free-body diagram would pertain equally well to transmissions of $R = 2.778$ having *no* gears inside—such as hydraulic or electric transmissions. In order for the transmission to work, whatever parts are inside *must* provide for the *torque of 5333 lb · in. to be reacted by the housing*. (A striking example of this concept came to the first author's attention when many persons sent the major automobile companies voluminous material pertaining to automatic transmission designs they wished to sell. To study all the drawings, analyses, descriptions, and so on would have required numerous hours. For many of the proposals, however, it could be quickly determined that there was no provision for a torque reaction to be transmitted to the housing, and that therefore the transmission could not possibly work.)

2. The input portion of the mainshaft (Figure 2.4*b*) requires the tangential force of 2667 lb to balance the input torque of 3000 lb · in., thus satisfying $\Sigma M = 0$ about the axis of rotation. This force is applied *to* gear *A by* gear *B*. Gear *A* applies an equal and opposite force to gear *B*, as shown in Figure 2.4*c*. Since there are no torques applied to the countershaft except by the two gears, it follows that gear *C* must receive a 4444-lb force from gear *D*. An opposite 4444-lb force is applied by gear *C* to gear *D*. Equilibrium of moments about the axis of the output half of the main shaft requires that a torque of 8333 lb · in. be applied to the output shaft by the propeller shaft as shown. (Note that the output torque can

also be obtained by multiplying the input torque by the gear diameter ratios, B/A and D/C. Thus

$$3000 \text{ lb} \cdot \text{in.} \times \frac{3\frac{3}{4}\text{in.}}{2\frac{1}{4}\text{in.}} \times \frac{3\frac{3}{4}\text{in.}}{2\frac{1}{4}\text{in.}} = 8333 \text{ lb} \cdot \text{in.})$$

3. The force applied to the main shaft by bearing II is found by taking moments about bearing I. Thus

$$\Sigma M = 0: \quad (2667 \text{ lb})(2 \text{ in.}) - (4444 \text{ lb})(7 \text{ in.}) + (F_{II})(9 \text{ in.}) = 0$$

or

$$F_{II} = 2864 \text{ lb}$$

The force at bearing I is found by $\Sigma F = 0$ (or by $\Sigma M_{II} = 0$). Countershaft bearing reactions are found in the same way.

4. Figures 2.4*b* and *c* show bearing forces applied *to* the shafts, through the bearings, and *by* the housing. Figure 2.4*d* shows the corresponding forces applied *to* the housing, through the bearings, and *by* the shafts. The *only* members in contact with the housing are the four bearings and the bolts that connect it to the engine structure. Figure 2.4*d* shows that the housing is indeed a free body in equilibrium, as both forces and moments are in balance.

Comments:

1. The foregoing examples have illustrated how the powerful free-body-diagram method can be used to determine loads at various levels—that is, loads acting on a complex total device (as on an automobile), loads acting on a complex unit within the total device (as on the automotive transmission), and loads acting on one part of a complex unit (transmission countershaft).

2. Free-body-equilibrium concepts are equally effective and valuable in determining *internal* loads, as illustrated below in Sample Problem 2.5. This is also true of internal loads in components like the transmission countershaft in Figure 2.4*c*, as will be seen in the next section.

SAMPLE PROBLEM 2.5   Determination of Internal Loads

Two examples of load-carrying members are shown in Figures 2.5*a* and 2.6*a*. Using free-body diagrams, determine and show the loads existing at cross section *AA* of each member.

SOLUTION

Known: The configuration and load orientation of two members is given.

Find: Determine and show the loads at cross section *AA* of each member.

Schematic and Given Data:

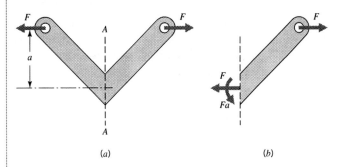

FIGURE 2.5
Loads acting on an internal section as determined from a
free-body diagram.

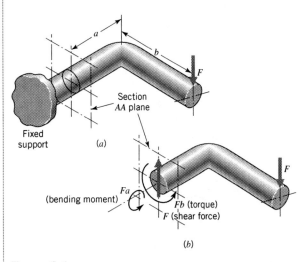

FIGURE 2.6
Loads acting on an internal section as determined from a
free-body diagram.

Assumption: Deflections of the members do not cause a significant change
in geometry.

Analysis: Figures 2.5*b* and 2.6*b* show segments on one side of section *AA* as free
bodies in equilibrium. The forces and moments acting at the section are determined
from the equations of equilibrium.

Comment: Deflection of the member shown in Figure 2.5*a* would cause the
moment *aF* to decrease. For most loads this change would be insignificant.

The next two examples illustrate the determination of loads acting on three-
force members where only one of the three forces is completely known and a second
is known in direction only.

SAMPLE PROBLEM 2.6   Three-Force Member

Figure 2.7 shows a bell crank (link 2) that pivots freely with respect to the fixed frame (link 1). A horizontal rod (link 3, not shown) attaches at the top, exerting a force of 40 lb, as shown. (Note the subscript notation: F_{32} is a force applied *by* link 3 *to* link 2.) A rod 30° from horizontal (link 4, not shown) attaches to the bottom, exerting force F_{42} of unknown magnitude. Determine the magnitude of F_{42}, and also the direction and magnitude of force F_{12} (the force applied by fixed frame 1 to link 2 through the pinned connection near the center of the link).

SOLUTION

Known: A bell crank of specified geometry is loaded as shown in Figure 2.7.

Find: Determine F_{12} and the magnitude of F_{42}.

Schematic and Given Data:

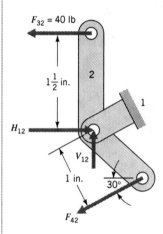

FIGURE 2.7
Bell crank forces—analytical solution.

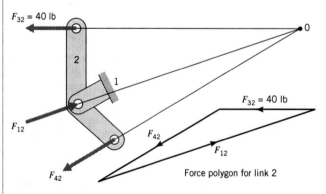

Force polygon for link 2

FIGURE 2.8
Bell crank forces—graphical solution.

Assumptions:

1. The pin joints are frictionless.

2. The bell crank is not accelerating.

Analysis A (Analytical):

1. Summation of moments about the pivot pin requires that $F_{42} = 60$ lb (note that 40 lb $\times$ $1\frac{1}{2}$ in. = 60 lb $\times$ 1 in.).

2. Dividing F_{12} into horizontal and vertical components, and setting the summation of vertical and horizontal forces acting on link 2 equal to zero yields $V_{12} = (60$ lb$)$ $(\sin 30°) = 30$ lb; $H_{12} = 40$ lb $+ (60$ lb$) \cos 30° = 92$ lb. The magnitude of F_{12} is $\sqrt{30^2 + 92^2} = 97$ lb; its direction is upward and to the right at an angle of $\tan^{-1} 30/92 = 18°$ from horizontal.

Analysis B (Graphical):

1. For equilibrium, the summation of moments of all forces acting on link 2 must be equal to zero when these moments are taken about *any* point, including point 0, which is the intersection of the two known force lines of action. Since two of the three forces have no moment about point 0, equilibrium requires that the third force also have no moment about 0. This can only be satisfied if the line of action of F_{12} also passes through 0.

2. We know one force completely, and the other two in direction only. A graphical solution for summation of forces equals zero is provided by the force polygon shown in Figure 2.8. This is constructed by first drawing known force F_{32} in proper direction and with length representing its 40-lb magnitude to any convenient scale. A line with the direction of F_{12} is drawn through either end of the vector representing F_{32}, and a line with the direction of F_{42} is drawn through the other end of this vector. Magnitudes of the two unknown forces can now be scaled from the polygon. (Note that the same result is obtained if a line of the direction of F_{42} is drawn through the *tail* of vector F_{32}, with the direction of F_{12} being drawn through the *tip* of F_{32}.)

Comment: The analytical solution solved the three equations for equilibrium in a plane for three unknowns. This same solution of simultaneous equations was accomplished graphically in Figure 2.8. An understanding of the graphical procedure adds to our insight into the nature of the force directions and magnitudes necessary for equilibrium of the link.

SAMPLE PROBLEM 2.7   Human Finger as Three-Force Member

The principles of mechanical engineering design that are traditionally applied to components of inanimate machines and structures are being increasingly applied in the relatively new field of *bioengineering*. A case in point is the application of free-body load analysis procedures to the internal load-carrying components of the human finger in studies of arthritic deformity [2,4]. Figure 2.9 illustrates one simplified portion of this study wherein a 10-lb pinch force at the tip of a finger is created by muscle contraction causing tendon force F_t. Determine the force in the tendon and in the finger bone.

SOLUTION

Known: The thumb and finger exert a known pinching force on a round object. The geometry is given.

Find: Estimate the tensile force in the tendon and the compressive force in the finger bone.

Schematic and Given Data:

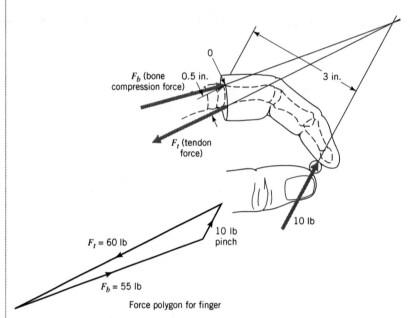

F_b (bone compression force)   0.5 in.   0

F_t (tendon force)

3 in.

10 lb

F_t = 60 lb   10 lb pinch

F_b = 55 lb

Force polygon for finger

FIGURE 2.9
Force study of human finger.

Assumptions:

1. The load in the finger is carried solely by the tendon and the bone.
2. The finger is not accelerating.
3. The weight of the finger can be neglected.

Analysis: Since the tendon force has a moment arm about pivot point 0 of only one-sixth that of the pinch force, the tensile force in the tendon must be 60 lb. The force polygon shows that the compressive force between the finger bone (proximal phalanx) and mating bone in the hand (metacarpal) is about 55 lb—a value that may cause crushing of deteriorated arthritic bone tissue.

Other examples of free-body-diagram analysis are given in Section 20.3 and in [1], [3] and [5].

2.3 *Beam Loading*

"Beam loading" refers to the lateral loading of members that are relatively long in comparison with their cross-sectional dimensions. Torsional or axial loading or both may or may not be involved as well. By way of review, two cases are shown in Figure 2.10. Note that each incorporates three basic diagrams: external loads, internal transverse shear forces (V), and internal bending moments (M). All expressions for magnitudes are the result of calculations the reader is advised to verify as a review exercise. (Reactions R_1 and R_2 are calculated first, on the basis of $\Sigma F = 0$ and $\Sigma M = 0$, with distributed load w treated as a concentrated load wb acting in the middle of span b.)

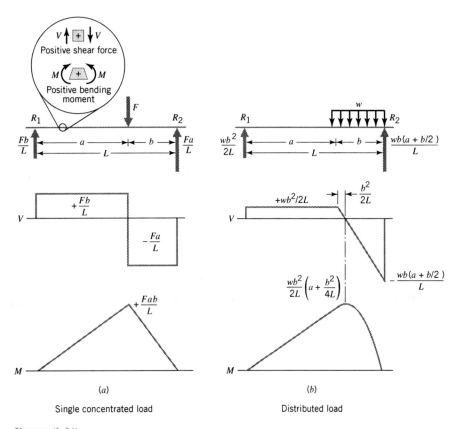

FIGURE 2.10
Examples of beam load, shear force, and bending moment diagrams.

The sign convention of the shear diagram is arbitrary, but the one used here is recommended: proceed from left to right, following the direction of the applied loads. In this case there are no loads to the left of reaction R_1 and hence no shear forces. At R_1 an upward force of Fb/L is encountered. Proceeding to the right, there are no loads—hence no *change* in the shear force—until the downward load of F is reached. At this point the shear diagram drops an amount F, and so forth. The diagram must come to zero at R_2, as no loads exist to the right of this reaction.

The internal transverse shear forces *V* and the internal bending moments *M* at a section of the beam are positive when they act as shown in Figure 2.10*a*. The shear at a section is positive when the portion of the beam to the left of the section tends to move upward with respect to the portion to the right of the section. The bending moment in a horizontal beam is positive at sections for which the top of the beam is in compression and the bottom is in tension. Generally, a positive moment will make the beam "smile."

The sign conventions presented are summarized as follows: The internal transverse shear forces *V* and the internal bending moments *M* at a section of beam are positive when they act in the directions shown in Figure 2.10*a*.

The (arbitrary) sign convention recommended here for bending follows from the relationship that

1. *The value of the shear force (V) at any point along the beam is equal to the slope of the bending moment diagram (M) at that point.*

Thus, a constant positive value of shear in the left portion of the beam results in a constant positive slope of the bending moment diagram over the same portion.

The student is reminded of three other important rules or relationships relative to load, shear, and moment diagrams.

2. *The value of local load intensity at any point along the beam is equal to the slope of the shear force diagram (V) at that point. (For example, the end supports, acting as "points," produce a theoretically infinite upward force intensity. Hence, the slope of the shear diagram at these points is infinite.)*

3. *The difference in the values of the shear load, at any two points along the beam, is equal to the area under the load diagram between these same two points.*

4. *The difference in the values of the bending moment, at any two points along the beam, is equal to the area under the shear diagram between these two points.*

SAMPLE PROBLEM 2.8   Internal Loads in a Transmission Countershaft

Locate the cross section of the shaft in Figure 2.11 (Figure 2.4*c*) that is subjected to the greatest loading, and determine the loading at this location.

SOLUTION

Known: A shaft of uniform diameter and given length supports gears located at known positions *B* and *C* on the shaft.

Find: Determine the shaft cross section of greatest loading and the loads at this section.

Schematic and Given Data:

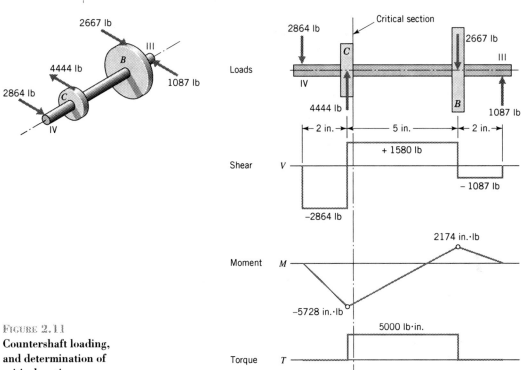

FIGURE 2.11
Countershaft loading, and determination of critical section.

Assumptions:

1. The shaft and gears rotate at uniform velocity.

2. Transverse shear stresses are negligible in comparison to bending and torsional shear stresses.

Analysis:

1. Figure 2.11 shows loading, shear, moment, and torque diagrams for this shaft. Note in particular the following.

   a. The load diagram is in equilibrium—the forces and moments acting in the plane of the paper are balanced.

   b. The recommended sign convention and the four basic relationships just given in italics are illustrated.

   c. The sign convention used in the *torque diagram* is arbitrary. Zero torque exists outboard of the gears, for bearing friction would normally be neglected. Torques of (4444 lb)(2.25 in./2) and (2667 lb)(3.75 in./2) are applied to the shaft at *C* and *B*.

2. The critical location of the shaft is just to the right of gear *C*. Here we have maximum torque together with essentially maximum bending. (The transverse shear force is less than maximum, but except for highly unusual cases involving extremely short shafts, shear loads are unimportant in comparison with bending loads.)

61

Comment: Figure 2.12 shows the portion of the countershaft to the left of the critical section as a free body. Note that this *partial* member constitutes a *free body in equilibrium* under the action of all loads external to it. These include the external loads shown, and also the *internal* loads applied *to* the free body *by* the right-hand portion of the countershaft.

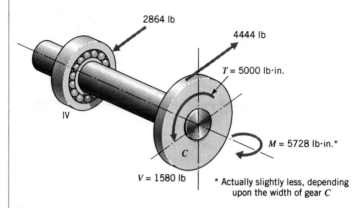

FIGURE 2.12
Loading at countershaft critical section.

2.4   *Locating Critical Sections—Force Flow Concept*

The sections chosen for load determination in the previous examples (i.e., in Figures 2.5, 2.6, and 2.12) were, by simple inspection, clearly those subjected to the most critical loading. In more complicated cases, however, several sections may be critical, and their locations less obvious. In such instances it is often helpful to employ an orderly procedure of following the "lines of force" (approximate paths taken by the force, determined by simple inspection) through the various parts, and noting along the way any sections suspected of being critical. Such a procedure is illustrated in the following example.

SAMPLE PROBLEM 2.9   Yoke Connection

Using the force flow concept, locate the critical sections and surfaces in the members shown in Figure 2.13.

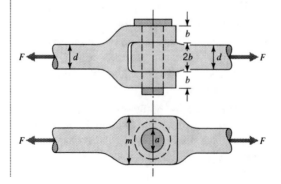

FIGURE 2.13
Yoke connection.

SOLUTION

Known: A yoke connection is loaded in tension.

Find: Locate the critical sections and surfaces in the yoke fork, pin, and blade.

Schematic and Given Data:

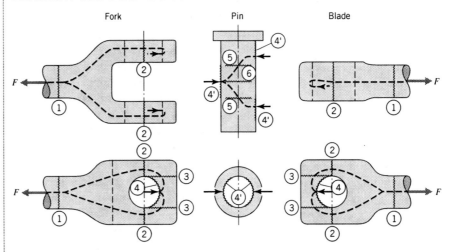

FIGURE 2.14
Force flow lines and critical sections in yoke connection.

Assumptions:

1. The weight of the yoke connection can be ignored.
2. The load is divided equally between the two prongs of the fork (the loads and yoke connection are perfectly symmetrical).
3. The load in each prong is divided equally between the portions on each side of the hole.
4. Distributed loads are represented as concentrated loads.
5. The effects of pin, blade, and fork deflections on load distribution are negligible.
6. The pin fits snugly in the fork and blade.

Analysis: A force flow path through each member is indicated by the dashed lines in Figure 2.14. Along this path from left to right, the major critical areas are indicated by the jagged lines and identified by the circled numbers.

a. Tensile loading exists at section ① of the fork. If the transition sections have ample material and generous radii, the next critical location is ②, where the force flow encounters a bottleneck because the area is reduced by the holes. Note that with this symmetrical design, force F is divided into four identical paths, each having an area at location ② of $\frac{1}{2}(m - a)b$.

b. The force flow proceeds on to the next questionable section, which is at ③. Here, the turning of the flow path is associated with shearing stresses tending to "push out" the end segments bounded by jagged lines ③.

c. The next critical area is interface ④ and ④, where bearing loading exists between the fork-hole and pin surfaces, respectively. In like manner, equal bearing loads are developed at the interface between the pin and the blade-hole surfaces.

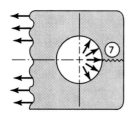

FIGURE 2.15
Distributed bearing loading may cause hoop tension failure at 7.

d. The forces at ④ load the pin as a beam, causing direct shear loading of sections ⑤ (note that the pin is in "double shear" as the two surfaces ⑤ are loaded in parallel, each carrying a shear load of *F*/2). Moreover, the bearing loads produce a maximum bending moment at area ⑥, in the center of the pin.

e. After the forces emerge from the pin and enter the blade, they flow across critical areas ④, ③, ②, and ①, which correspond directly to the like-numbered sections of the fork.

f. Although not brought out in the simplified force-flow pattern of Figure 2.14, it should be noted that the bearing loads applied to the surfaces of the holes are not concentrated on the load axis but are, as assumed, *distributed* over these surfaces as shown in Figure 2.15. This gives rise to *hoop tension* (or circumferential tensile loading), tending to cause tensile failure in the section identified as ⑦.

Comments: Although the determination of stresses at the various critical sections is beyond the scope of this chapter, this is a good time to give a word of caution regarding the simplifying assumptions that we might make when these stresses are calculated.

a. The section at ② might be assumed to be in uniform tension. Actually, bending is also present, which *adds* to the tension at the inner, or hole surface, and subtracts at the outer surface. This can be visualized by imagining the distortion of fork and blade members made of rubber and loaded through a metal connecting pin. The *quantitative* evaluation of this effect involves details of the geometry and is not a simple matter.

b. The distribution of compressive loading on surfaces ④ and ④ might be assumed uniform, but this could be far from the actual case. The major factors involved are the fit of the pin in the hole and the rigidity of the members. For example, bending of the pin tends to cause highest bearing loading near the fork–blade interfaces. Moreover, the extent of pin bending depends not only on its own flexibility but also on the tightness of fit. The degree to which the pin is restrained from bending by a close fit has a major influence on the pin-bending stresses.

Like many engineering problems, this one illustrates three needs: (1) to be able to make reasonable simplifying assumptions and get usable answers quickly, (2) to be *aware* that such assumptions were made and interpret the results accordingly, and (3) to make a good engineering judgment whether a simplified solution is adequate in the particular situation, or whether a more sophisticated analysis, requiring more advanced analytical procedures and experimental studies, is justified.

2.5 *Load Division Between Redundant Supports*

A *redundant* support is one that could be removed and still leave the supported member in equilibrium. For example, in Figure 2.16, if the center support (which is redundant) were removed, the beam would be held in equilibrium by the end supports. When redundant supports (reactions) are present, the simple equations of equilibrium no longer suffice to determine the magnitude of load carried by *any* of the supports. This is true because there are more unknowns than equilibrium equations.

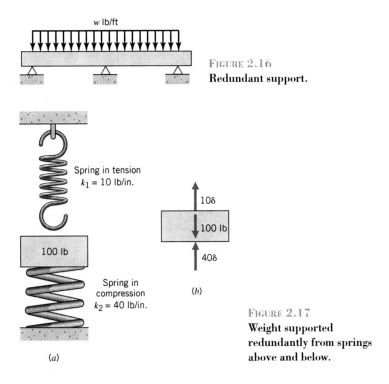

FIGURE 2.16
Redundant support.

FIGURE 2.17
Weight supported redundantly from springs above and below.

A redundant support *adds stiffness* to the structure and carries a portion of the load proportional to its stiffness. For example, the 100-lb weight in Figure 2.17a is supported from below by a coil spring in compression and above by a coil spring in tension. (Assume that except for the 100-lb load, the springs would be stress-free). The top spring has a *rate* or *stiffness constant* of 10 lb/in., the lower spring a constant of 40 lb/in. Under the pull of gravity the weight moves downward, stretching the top spring by an amount δ and compressing the lower spring by the same amount. Thus, the weight is in equilibrium under the action of a gravity force of 100 lb and spring forces of 10δ and 40δ (Figure 2.17b). From $\Sigma F = 0$, we have $\delta = 2$ in. Hence, the top and bottom spring forces are 20 and 80 lb, respectively, illustrating that the *load is divided in proportion to the stiffness of the redundant supports.*

Suppose now that in order to reduce the deflection a third support is added—this in the form of a 10-in. length of steel wire, 0.020 in. in diameter inside the top spring, with the top end of the wire attached to the upper support and the lower end attached to the weight. The spring rate (*AE/L*) of the wire would be about 942 lb/in., and the *total* stiffness supporting the weight would then be 992 lb/in. Hence the wire would carry 942/992 of the 100-lb load, or 95 lb. Its stress would be

$$\frac{P}{A} = \frac{95 \text{ lb}}{0.000314 \text{ in.}^2}, \quad \text{or} \quad 303{,}000 \text{ psi}$$

which is a value in excess of its probable tensile strength; hence it would fail (break or yield). Thus, *the strengths of redundant load-carrying members should be made approximately proportional to their stiffnesses.*

To illustrate this point further, consider the angle iron shown in Figure 2.18. Suppose that when installed as part of a machine or structure, the angle iron has inadequate

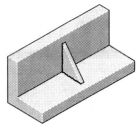

FIGURE 2.18
Web reinforcement added to an angle iron.

rigidity in that the 90° angle deflects more than desired, although this does not cause breakage. The angular deflection is reduced by welding the small triangular web in place as shown. It becomes a redundant support that limits angular deflection. But it may well add stiffness far out of proportion to its strength. Cracks may appear in or near the welded joint, thereby eliminating the added stiffness. Furthermore, the cracks so formed may propagate through the main angle iron. If so, the addition of the triangular "reinforcement" would actually *weaken* the part. Sometimes failures in a complicated structural member (as a casting) can be corrected by *removing* stiff but weak portions (such as thin webs), *provided* the remaining portions of the part are sufficiently strong to carry the increased load imposed upon them by the increased deflection, and provided, of course, the increased deflection is itself acceptable.

A useful procedure (Castigliano's method) for calculating redundant load reactions for a completely *elastic* system is given in Section 5.9. At the other extreme, the loading pattern associated with *ductile* failure of a set of redundant supports is discussed in the next section.

2.6   *Force Flow Concept Applied to Redundant Ductile Structures*

As noted in Section 2.5, loads shared among parallel redundant paths are divided in proportion to path stiffnesses. If the paths are brittle and the load is increased to failure, one path will fracture first, thereby transferring its share of the load to the other paths, and so on, to failure of all paths. For the usual case involving materials of some ductility, one path will *yield* first, thereby reducing its stiffness (stiffness then being proportional to the *tangent modulus*),[2] which allows some of its load to be transferred to other paths. For the ductile case, general yielding of the total structure occurs only after the load has been increased sufficiently to bring all the parallel paths to their yield strengths.

The force flow concept, introduced in Section 2.4, is helpful in dealing with ductile redundant structures. This is illustrated in the following example.

SAMPLE PROBLEM 2.10   Riveted Joint [1]

Figure 2.19*a* shows a triple-riveted butt joint, wherein two plates are butted together and loads are transmitted across the joint by top and bottom straps. Each strap has a thickness of two-thirds the plate thickness and is made of the same material as the plates. Three rows of rivets attach each plate to the straps, as shown. The rivet pattern that is drawn for a width of one pitch is repeated over the full width of the joint. Determine the critical sections, and discuss the strength of the joint, using the force flow concept.

SOLUTION

Known: A triple-riveted butt joint of specified geometry is loaded in tension.

Find: Determine the critical sections.

---

[2] The tangent modulus is defined as the slope of the stress–strain diagram at a particular stress level.

Schematic and Given Data:

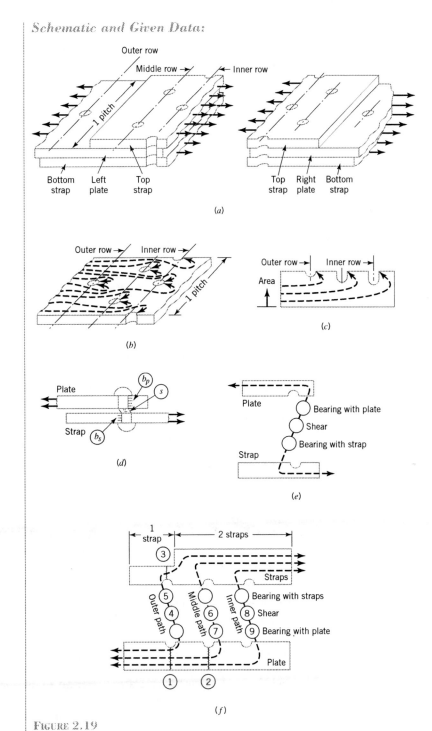

FIGURE 2.19

Force flow concept applied to triple-riveted butt joint. (*a*) Complete joint, broken at center, showing total load carried by straps. (*b*) Force flow through plate to rivets. (*c*) Diagram of force flow versus plate cross-sectional area. (*d*) Force flow through rivet. (*e*) Diagrammatic representation of force flow through rivet. (*f*) Complete diagrammatic representation of force flow.

Assumptions:

1. The weight of the riveted joint can be ignored.

2. The load is distributed evenly across the width of the joint (there is no misalignment).

3. The rivets fit snuggly in the plate and straps.

Analysis:

1. Figure 2.19*b* shows a diagrammatic sketch of the force flow pattern in the plate. A portion of the load is transferred to each of the three rows of rivets. (Since static equilibrium could be satisfied by using any one row, the structure is redundant.) Note that at the outer row the entire force flows across a section containing one rivet hole. At the middle row, a section containing two rivet holes is subjected to all the force not going to the outer row of rivets. The section of plate at the inner row transmits only the force going to the inner row of rivets. This relation between force and area at each section of plate is represented diagrammatically in Figure 2.19*c*. Note the representation of the reduction in area owing to rivet holes at the middle and inner rows being twice those at the outer row.

2. Figure 2.19*d* shows how each rivet is associated with three important loadings: bearing with the plate, shear, and bearing with the strap. A diagrammatic force flow representation of this is given in Figure 2.19*e*, which shows the force path encountering five critical sections in series: the reduced tensile area containing the holes in the plate, the sections corresponding to the three loadings involving the rivet, and the reduced tensile area of the strap.

3. Figure 2.19*f* shows a similar representation of the entire joint. Critical sections are identified and numbered ① to ⑨. Basically, three parallel force paths are involved, one going through each row of rivets. Starting at the lower left, all three paths flow across the reduced plate section at the outer row. This is critical area ①. Failure at this point severs all force flow paths, causing total fracture of the joint. Only two paths flow across the plate at ②, but since the area here is less than at ①, failure is possible. Failure is not possible in the plate at the inner path, for only one force path flows across an area identical with that at ②.

4. Turning to the possibilities of tensile failure in the straps, note that the relative thickness of plate and straps is such that strap tensile failure is possible only at the outer row at critical point ③.

5. With respect to possibilities of failure involving the rivets themselves, each rivet is vulnerable in shear and at *one* bearing area (whichever is smaller). In the outer row, the vulnerable bearing area involves the strap, because the strap is thinner than the plate. In the other rows, the vulnerable bearing area involves the plate, for the strap-bearing load is shared by two straps, the combined thickness of which exceeds that of the plate. Note also that the middle- and inner-row rivets divide their shear load between *two* areas (i.e., they are loaded in *double shear*), whereas the outer-row rivets have but a single shear area. The possibilities of rivet failure are numbered ④ to ⑨.

6. The distribution of load among the three redundant paths depends on relative stiffnesses; but since riveted joints are invariably made of ductile materials, slight local yielding permits a redistribution of the load. Thus, final failure of

the joint will occur only when the external load exceeds the combined load-carrying capacity of all three paths. This involves simultaneous failure of all paths and can occur in three possible ways:

a. Tensile failure at ①.

b. Simultaneous failure of the weakest link in each of the three paths.

c. Simultaneous failure at ② and at the weakest link in the outer path (③, ④, or ⑤).

References

1. Juvinall, Robert C., *Engineering Consideration of Stress, Strain and Strength,* McGraw-Hill, New York, 1967.

2. Juvinall, Robert C., "An Engineering View of Musculoskeletal Deformities," Proceedings of the IVth International Congress of Physical Medicine, Paris, 1964.

3. Riley, William F., L. D. Sturges, and D. H. Morris, *Statics and Mechanics of Materials: An Integrated Approach,* 2nd ed., Wiley, New York, 2001.

4. Smith, Edwin M., R. C. Juvinall, L. F. Bender, and J. R. Pearson, "Flexor Forces and Rheumatoid Metacarpophalangeal Deformity," *J. Amer. Med. Assoc.,* **198** (Oct. 10, 1966).

5. Craig, R. R., Jr., *Mechanics of Materials,* 2nd ed., Wiley, New York, 2000.

Problems

Section 2.2

2.1D   Write definitions for the terms *free-body diagram, equilibrium analysis, internal loads, external loads,* and *three-force members.*

2.2D   Draw a free-body diagram for the motorcycle of weight W shown in Figure P2.2D for (a) rear wheel braking only, (b) front wheel braking only, and (c) front and rear wheel braking. Also, determine the magnitudes of the forces exerted by the roadway on the two tires during braking for the above cases. The motorcycle has a wheel base of length L. The center of gravity is a distance c forward of the rear axle and a distance of h above the road. The coefficient of friction between the pavement and the tires is μ.

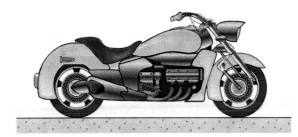

FIGURE P2.2D

2.3   Draw a free-body diagram of an automobile of weight W that has a wheel base of length L during four-wheel braking. The center of gravity is a distance c forward of the rear axle and a distance of h above the ground. The coefficient of friction between the pavement and the tires is μ. Also show that the load carried by the two front tires during braking with the motor disconnected is equal to $W(c + \mu h)/L$.

2.4   Repeat Problem 2.3, except assume that the automobile is towing a one-axle trailer of weight W_t. Determine the minimum stopping distance for the automobile and trailer assuming (a) no braking on the trailer and (b) full braking on the trailer. What is the minimum stopping distance for the automobile if it is not towing a trailer?

2.5   Repeat Problem 2.3, except assume that the automobile is traveling downhill at a grade of 10:1.

2.6D   Select a metal with known density for solid rods *A* and *B*. Rod *A* and rod *B* are positioned inside a vertical wall channel *C*. Sketch free-body diagrams for rod *A*, rod *B*, and channel *C*, shown in Figure P2.6D. Also determine the magnitude of the forces acting on rod *A*, rod *B*, and channel *C*.

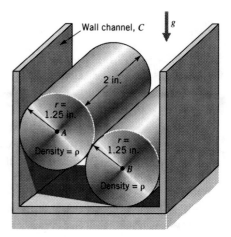

FIGURE P2.6D

2.7D   Sketch free-body diagrams for sphere *A*, sphere *B*, and the container, shown in Figure P2.7D. Also determine the magnitude of the forces acting on sphere *A*, sphere *B*, and the container.

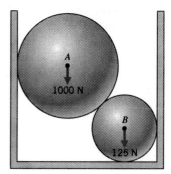

FIGURE P2.7D

2.8   Draw the free-body diagram for the pinned assembly shown in Figure P2.8. Find the magnitude of the forces acting on each member of the assembly.

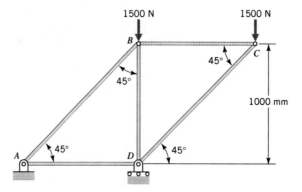

FIGURE P2.8

2.9 The drawing (Figure P2.9) shows an exploded view of an 1800-rpm motor, a gear box, and a 6000-rpm blower. The gear box weighs 20 lb, with center of gravity midway between the two mountings. All shafts rotate counterclockwise, viewed from the blower. Neglecting friction losses, determine all loads acting on the gear box when the motor output is 1 hp. Sketch the gear box as a free body in equilibrium.

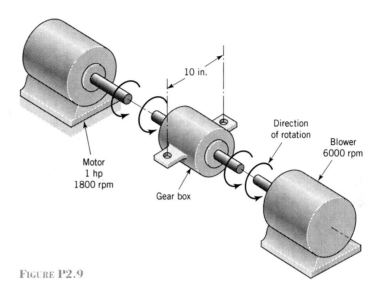

FIGURE P2.9

2.10 The motor shown operates at constant speed and develops a torque of 100 lb-in. during normal operation. Attached to the motor shaft is a gear reducer of ratio 5:1, i.e., the reducer output shaft rotates in the same direction as the motor but at one-fifth motor speed. Rotation of the reducer housing is prevented by the "torque arm," pin-connected at each end as shown in Figure P2.10. The reducer output shaft drives the load through a flexible coupling. Neglecting gravity and friction, what loads are applied to (a) the torque arm, (b) the motor output shaft, (c) the reducer output shaft?

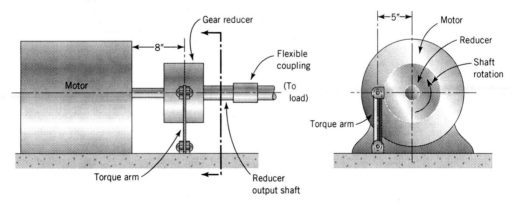

FIGURE P2.10

2.11   The drawing (Figure P2.11) shows the engine, transmission, and propeller shaft of a prototype automobile. The transmission and engine are not bolted together but are attached separately to the frame. The transmission weighs 100 lb, receives an engine torque of 100 lb-ft at *A* through a flexible coupling, and attaches to the propeller shaft at *B* through a universal joint. The transmission is bolted to the frame at *C* and *D*. If the transmission ratio is −3, i.e., reverse gear with propeller shaft speed $= -\frac{1}{3}$ engine speed, show the transmission as a free body in equilibrium.

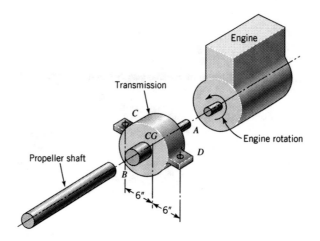

FIGURE P2.11

2.12   The drawing (Figure P2.12) shows an electric fan supported by mountings at *A* and *B*. The motor delivers a torque of 2 N · m to the fan blades. They, in turn, push the air forward with a force of 20 N. Neglecting gravity forces, determine all loads acting on the fan (complete assembly). Sketch it as a free body in equilibrium.

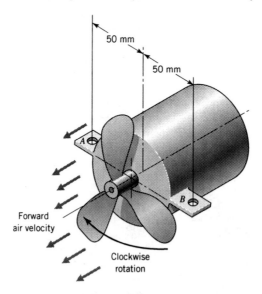

FIGURE P2.12

2.13   Figure P2.13 shows an exploded drawing of a pump driven by a 1.5-kW, 1800-rpm motor integrally attached to a 4 : 1 ratio gear reducer. Reducer shaft *C* is connected directly to pump shaft *C′* through a flexible coupling (not shown). Face *A* of the reducer housing is bolted to flange *A′* of the connecting tube (a one-piece solid unit).

Pump face B is similarly attached to flange B'. Sketch the connecting tube and show all loads acting on it. (Neglect gravity.)

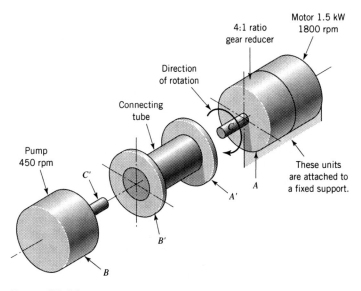

FIGURE P2.13

2.14 Figure P2.14 shows an exploded view of an airplane engine, reduction gear, and propeller. The engine and propeller rotate clockwise, viewed from the propeller end. The reduction gear housing is bolted to the engine housing through the bolt holes shown. Neglect friction losses in the reduction gear. When the engine develops 150 hp at 3600 rpm,

(a) What is the direction and magnitude of the torque applied *to* the engine housing *by* the reduction gear housing?

(b) What is the magnitude and direction of the torque reaction tending to rotate (roll) the aircraft?

(c) What is an advantage of using opposite-rotating engines with twin-engine propeller-driven aircraft?

[Ans.: (a) 109 lb · ft ccw, (b) 328 lb · ft ccw]

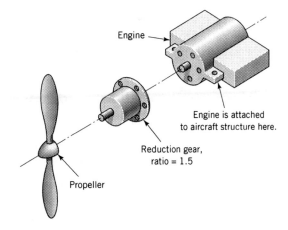

FIGURE P2.14

2.15   A marine engine delivers a torque of 200 lb-ft to a gearbox which provides a reverse ratio of −4 : 1. What torque is required to hold the gearbox in place?

2.16   A motor delivers 50 lb-ft torque at 2000 rpm to an attached gear reducer. The reducer and motor housings are connected together by six bolts located on a 12-in.-dia. circle, centered about the shaft. The reducer has a 4 : 1 ratio. Neglecting friction and weight, what average shearing force is carried by each bolt?

2.17D   Select a single-cylinder reciprocating compressor. Sketch the crankshaft, connecting rod, piston, and frame as free bodies when the piston is 60° before head-end dead center on the compression stroke. Sketch the entire compressor as a single free body for this condition.

2.18   Figure P2.18 shows the gear reduction unit and propeller of an outboard motor boat. It is attached to the boat structure at the mounting flange at the top. The motor is mounted above this unit, and turns the vertical shaft with a torque of 20 N · m. By means of bevel gearing, this shaft turns the propeller at half the vertical shaft speed. The propeller provides a thrust of 400 N to drive the boat forward. Neglecting gravity and friction, show all external loads acting on the assembly shown. (Make a sketch, and show moments applied to the mounting flange using the notation suggested in the drawing.)

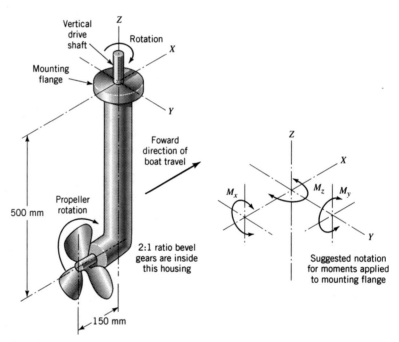

FIGURE P2.18

2.19   The drawing (Figure P2.19) represents a bicycle with an 800-N rider applying full weight to one pedal. Treat this as a two-dimensional problem, with all components in the plane of the paper. Draw as free bodies in equilibrium

(a)   The pedal, crank, and pedal sprocket assembly.

(b)   The rear wheel and sprocket assembly.

(c)   The front wheel.

(d)   The entire bicycle and rider assembly.

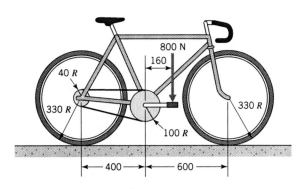

2.20 The solid, continuous round bar shown in Figure P2.20 can be viewed as comprised of a straight segment and a curved segment. Draw free-body diagrams for the segments 1 and 2. Also, determine the forces and moments acting on the ends of both segments. Neglect the weight of the member.

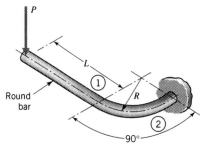

FIGURE P2.20

2.21 For the spring clip (Figure P2.21) having a force P acting on the free end, draw free-body diagrams for segments 1 and 2. Also, determine the force and moments acting on the ends of both segments. Neglect the weight of the member.

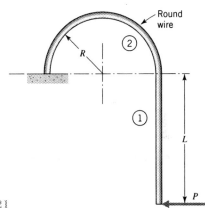

FIGURE P2.21

2.22 A semicircular bar of rectangular cross section has one pinned end (Figure P2.22). The free end is loaded as shown. Draw a free-body diagram for the entire semicircular bar and for a left portion of the bar. Discuss what influence the weight of the semicircular bar has on this problem.

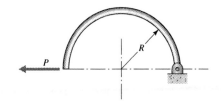

FIGURE P2.22

2.23 The drawing (Figure P2.23) shows a bevel gear reducer driven by an 1800-rpm motor delivering a torque of 12 N·m. The output drives a 600-rpm load. The reducer is held in place by vertical forces applied at mountings A, B, C, and D. Torque reaction about the motor shaft is reacted at A and B; torque reaction about the output shaft is reacted at C and D. Determine the forces applied to the reducer at each of the mountings,

(a) Assuming 100% reducer efficiency.

(b) Assuming 95% reducer efficiency.

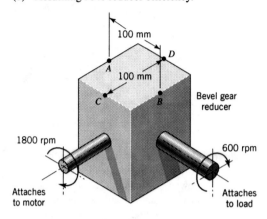

2.24   The drawings (Figure P2.24) pertain to a spur gear reducer. A motor applies a torque of 200 lb · ft to the pinion shaft, as shown. The gear shaft drives the output load. Both

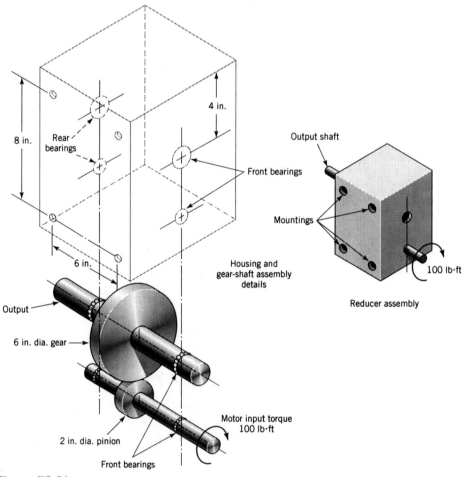

FIGURE P2.24

shafts are connected with flexible couplings (which transmit only torque). The gears are mounted on their shafts midway between the bearings. The reducer is supported by four identical mountings on the side of the housing, symmetrically spaced on 6-in. and 8 in. centers, as shown. For simplicity, neglect gravity and assume that forces between the gears (i.e., between gear and pinion) act tangentially. Sketch, as free bodies in equilibrium,

(a) The pinion and shaft assembly.

(b) The gear and shaft assembly.

(c) The housing.

(d) The entire reducer assembly.

2.25 The drawing (Figure P2.25) is a highly simplified diagrammatic representation of the engine, transmission, drive shafts, and front axle of a four-wheel-drive car. All members shown may be treated as a single free body supported by mountings at A, B, C, and D. The engine rotates 2400 rpm and delivers a torque of 100 lb · ft. The transmission ratio is 2.0 (drive shafts rotate 1200 rpm); the front and rear axle ratios are both 3.0 (wheels rotate 400 rpm). Neglect friction and gravity, and assume that the mountings exert only vertical forces. Determine the forces applied to the free body at A, B, C, and D.

[Ans.: 150 lb down, 150 lb up, 100 lb down, and 100 lb up, respectively]

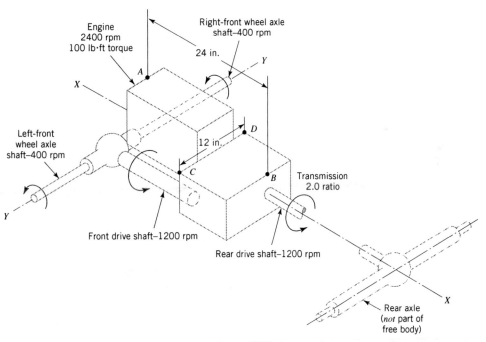

Figure P2.25

2.26D The drawing in Figure P2.26D shows a mixer supported by symmetric mountings at A and B. Select a motor torque between 20 N · m and 50 N · m for driving the mixing paddles and then determine all loads acting on the mixer. Sketch the free body in equilibrium.

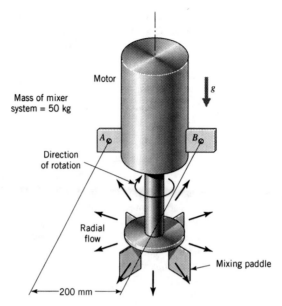

Motor

Mass of mixer
system = 50 kg

g

A

B

Direction
of rotation

Radial
flow

Mixing paddle

200 mm

FIGURE P2.26D

2.27D   The drawing in Figure P2.27D shows a electric squirrel cage blower supported by
symmetric mountings at *A* and *B*. The motor delivers a torque of 1 N · m to the fan.
Select a mounting width between 75 mm and 150 mm and then determine all loads
acting on the blower. Sketch the free body in equilibrium.

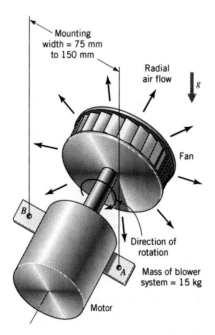

Mounting
width = 75 mm
to 150 mm

Radial
air flow

g

Fan

B

Direction of
rotation

A

Mass of blower
system = 15 kg

Motor

FIGURE P2.27D

2.28 Draw a free-body diagram for the gear and shaft assembly shown in Figure P2.28. Also sketch free-body diagrams for gear 1, gear 2, and the shaft.

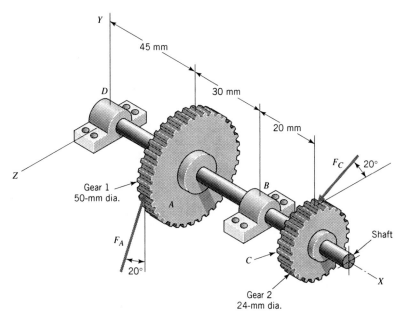

FIGURE P2.28

Section 2.3

2.29 The solid continuous member shown in Figure P2.29 can be viewed as comprised of several straight segments. Draw free-body diagrams for the straight segments 1, 2, and 3 of Figure P2.29. Also, determine the magnitudes (symbolically) of the force and moments acting on the straight segments. Neglect the weight of the member.

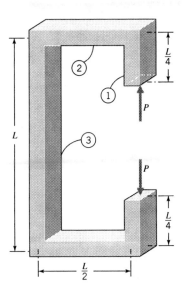

FIGURE P2.29

2.30 The drawings (Figure P2.30) show steel shafts supported by self-aligning bearings (which can provide radial but not bending loads to the shaft) at *A* and *B*. A gear (or a pulley or sprocket) causes each force to be applied as shown. Draw shear and bending moment diagrams neatly and to scale for each case. (Given dimensions are in millimeters.)

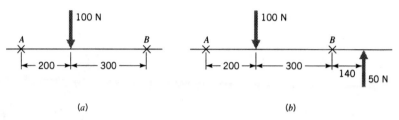

(a)   (b)

FIGURE P2.30

2.31 For each of the six cases shown in Figure P2.31, determine bearing reactions and draw appropriate shear and bending-moment diagrams for the 2-in.-dia. steel shaft supported by self-aligning ball bearings at *A* and *B*. A special 6-in.-pitch-diameter gear mounted on the shaft causes forces to be applied as shown.

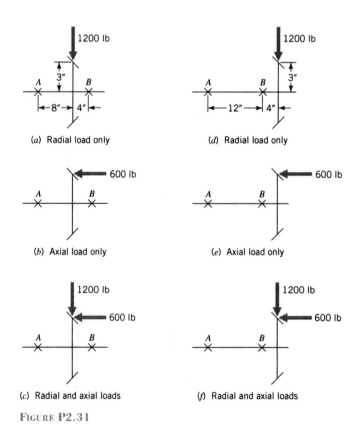

(a) Radial load only   (d) Radial load only

(b) Axial load only   (e) Axial load only

(c) Radial and axial loads   (f) Radial and axial loads

FIGURE P2.31

2.32 With reference to Figure P2.32

(a) Draw a free-body diagram of the structure supporting the pulley.

(b) Draw shear and bending moment diagrams for both the vertical and horizontal portions of the structure.

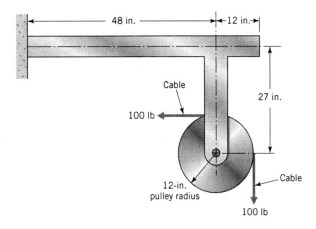

FIGURE P2.32

2.33 The drawing (Figure P2.33) shows a bevel gear attached to a shaft supported by self-aligning bearings at *A* and *B* and driven by a motor. Axial and radial components of the gear force are shown. The tangential or torque-producing component is perpendicular to the plane of the paper and has a magnitude of 2000 N. Bearing *A* takes thrust; *B* does not. Dimensions are in millimeters.

(a) Draw (to scale) axial load, shear, bending moment, and shaft torque diagrams.

(b) To what values of axial load and torque is the shaft subjected, and what portion(s) of the shaft experience these loads?

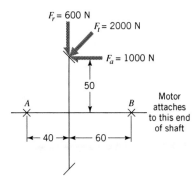

FIGURE P2.33

2.34 The shaft with bevel gear shown in Figure P2.34 is supported by self-aligning bearings *A* and *B*. (Given dimensions are in millimeters.) Only bearing *A* takes thrust. Gear loads in the plane of the paper are shown (the tangential or torque-producing force component is perpendicular to he paper). Draw axial load, shear, bending moment, and torque diagrams for the shaft.

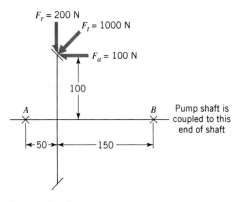

FIGURE P2.34

2.35   Same as Problem 2.34, except that the shaft in this drawing (Figure P2.35) has one bevel and one spur gear, and neither end of the shaft is connected to a motor or load.

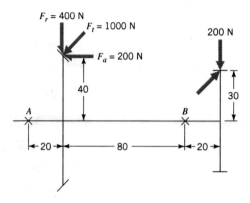

FIGURE P2.35

2.36   Same as Problem 2.34, except that the shaft in this drawing (Figure P2.36) has two bevel gears, and neither end of the shaft is connected to a motor or load.

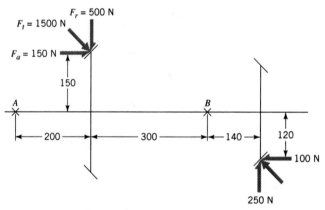

FIGURE P2.36

Section 2.4

2.37   Figure P2.37 shows a static force, *F*, applied to the tooth of a gear that is keyed to a shaft. Making appropriate simplifying assumptions, identify the stresses in the key, and write an equation for each.* State the assumptions made, and discuss briefly their effect.

———————————————

*The first five sections of Chapter 4 review simple stress equations.

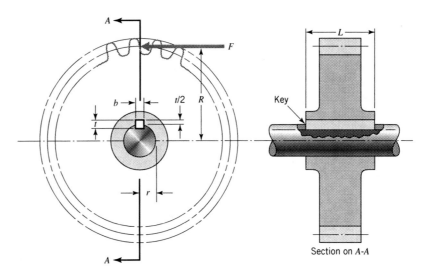

FIGURE P2.37

2.38 Figure P2.38 shows a screw with a square thread transmitting axial force F through a nut with n threads engaged (the drawing illustrates $n = 2$). Making appropriate simplifying assumptions, identify the stresses in the threaded portion of the screw and write an equation for each.* State the assumptions made, and discuss briefly their effect.

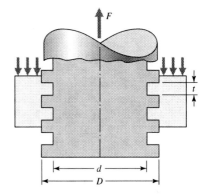

FIGURE P2.38

2.39 Figure P2.39 shows a total gas force F applied to the top of a piston.

(a) Copy the drawing and sketch the force paths through the piston, through the piston pin, and into the connecting rod.

(b) Making appropriate simplifying assumptions, identify the stresses in the piston pin and write an equation for each.* State the assumptions made, and discuss briefly their effect.

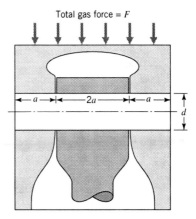

FIGURE P2.39

---

*The first five sections of Chapter 4 review simple stress equations.

2.40   Figure P2.40 shows force P applied to an engine crankshaft by a connecting rod. The shaft is supported by main bearings A and B. Torque is transmitted to an external load through flange F.

(a) Draw the shaft, and show all loads necessary to place it in equilibrium as a free body.

(b) Starting with P and following the force paths through the shaft to the flange, identify the locations of potentially critical stresses.

(c) Making appropriate simplifying assumptions, write an equation for each.* State the assumptions made.

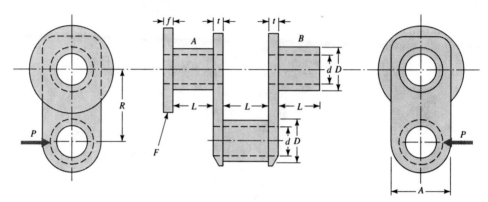

FIGURE P2.40

Section 2.5

2.41   In Figure P2.41, all the joints are pinned and all links have the same length L and the same cross-sectional area A. The central joint (pin) is loaded with a force P. Determine the forces in the bars.

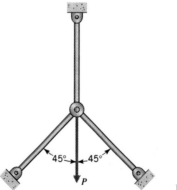

FIGURE P2.41

2.42   Repeat Problem 2.41, except where the top link has a cross-sectional area of A, and the two lower links have a cross-sectional area of A'. Determine (a) the force in the bars, and (b) the ratio A/A' that will make the force in all the links numerically equal.

---

*The first five sections of Chapter 4 review simple stress equations.

2.43   A "T" bracket, attached to a fixed surface by four bolts, is loaded at point E as shown in Figure P2.43.

(a)   Copy the drawing and sketch paths of force flow going to each bolt.

(b)   If the stiffness between point E and the plate through bolts B and C is twice the stiffness between point E and the plate through bolts A and D, how is the load divided between the four bolts?

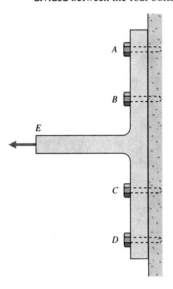

FIGURE P2.43

2.44   A very stiff horizontal bar, supported by four identical springs, as shown in Figure P2.44, is subjected to a center load of 100 N. What load is applied to each spring?

[Ans.: lower springs, 40 N; upper springs, 20 N]

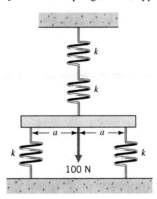

FIGURE P2.44

2.45   Repeat Problem 2.44, except assume that the horizontal bar as configured is not rigid and also has a spring constant of k.

Section 2.6

2.46   With reference to the bolts in Problem 2.43,

(a)   If they are brittle and each one fractures at a load of 6000 N, what maximum force F can be applied to the bracket?

(b)   What load can be applied if they are ductile, and each bolt has a yield strength of 6000 N?

2.47   Figure P2.47 shows two plates joined with straps and a single row of rivets (or bolts). Plates, straps, and rivets are all made of ductile steel having yield strengths in tension, compression, and shear of 300, 300, and 170 MPa, respectively. Neglect frictional forces between the plates and straps.

(a)   What force F can be transmitted across the joint per pitch, P, of joint width, based on rivet shear strength?

(b)   Determine minimum values of t, t', and P that will permit the total joint to transmit this same force (thus giving a "balanced" design).

(c)   Using these values, what is the "efficiency" of the joint (ratio of joint strength to strength of a continuous plate)?

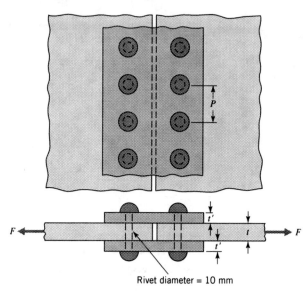

Rivet diameter = 10 mm

FIGURE P2.47

2.48   Repeat Problem 2.47, except use ductile steel having yield strengths in tension, compression and shear of 284, 284, and 160 MPa, respectively.

2.49   Plates 20 mm thick are butted together and spliced using straps 10 mm thick and rivets (or bolts) of 40-mm diameter. A double-riveted joint is used, and this is exactly as shown in Figure 2.19 except that the inner row of rivets is eliminated on both sides. All materials have tensile, compression, and shear yield strengths of 200, 200, and 120 MPa, respectively. Neglect friction between plates and straps. Determine the pitch, P, giving the greatest joint strength. How does this compare with the strength of a continuous plate?

CHAPTER 3

Materials

3.1 Introduction

The selection of materials and the processes used in fabrication are integral parts of the design of any machine component. Strength and rigidity are traditionally key factors considered in the selection of a material. Equally important are the relative reliability and durability of the part when made from alternative materials. When the component is expected to operate at extreme temperatures, this must be considered carefully when selecting the material. In recent years, choices of materials have been increasingly influenced by recyclability, energy requirements, and environmental pollution. Cost and availability are also vitally important. The cost to be considered is the *total cost of the fabricated part*, including labor and overhead as well as the material itself. The relative cost and availability of various materials vary with time, with the result that the engineer is frequently called upon to evaluate alternative materials in the light of changing market conditions. In summary, the best material for a particular application is the one that provides the best value, defined as the ratio between *overall* performance and *total* cost.

It is assumed that the reader has a previous background in the fundamentals of engineering materials. Moreover, it is acknowledged that the practicing engineer is faced with a career-long challenge to remain abreast of new materials developments as they apply to the products with which he or she is concerned. Fitting in between these two phases of engineering materials study, this chapter attempts to summarize some of the relevant basic information, and to emphasize the increasing importance of a rational approach to the use of empirical material properties test data.

The useful life of most machine and structural components ends with *fatigue failure* or *surface deterioration*. Further information on the resistance of various materials to these modes of failure is included in Chapters 8 and 9, respectively.

Information concerning properties of materials is given in Appendix C. Appendix C-1 gives physical constants for a variety of engineering materials. Mechanical properties are given in subsequent tables and graphs.

A materials property database is online at http://www.matweb.com. The database includes information on steel, aluminum, titanium, and zinc alloys, superalloys, ceramics, thermoplastics, and thermoset polymers. The database is comprised of data sheets and specification sheets supplied by the manufacturers and distributors. The web site allows for several approaches to search the database to (1) obtain property data for specific materials, or (2) search for materials that meet select property requirements. The site http://www.machinedesign.com presents general information on plastics, composites, elastomers, nonferrous metals, ferrous metals, and ceramics.

Finally, the reader is reminded that the scope and complexity of the subject is such that consultation with professional metallurgists and materials specialists is often desirable.

3.2   *The Static Tensile Test—"Engineering" Stress–Strain Relationships*

The basic engineering test of material strength and rigidity is the standard tensile test, from which stress–strain curves as shown in Figure 3.1 are obtained. The stresses and strains plotted are the nominal or so-called *engineering* values, defined as

- $\sigma = P/A_0$, where P is the load and A_0 the original *unloaded* cross-sectional area, and

- $\epsilon = \Delta L/L_0$, where ΔL is the change in length caused by the load and L_0 is the original unloaded length.

An important notation convention will be observed throughout this book: the Greek letter σ denotes normal *stress*, which is a function of the applied loads; S (with appropriate subscripts) designates *strength properties of the material*. For example, Figure 3.1 shows that when $\sigma = 39$ ksi,[1] the material begins to yield. Hence, $S_y = 39$ ksi. Similarly, the greatest (ultimate) load that the test specimen can withstand corresponds to an engineering stress of 66 ksi. Hence, $S_u = 66$ ksi.

Whereas S (with suitable subscripts) is used for all strength values including those for torsion or shear, the letter σ is used for normal stresses only, that is, stresses caused

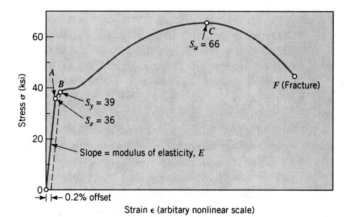

FIGURE 3.1

Engineering stress–strain curve—hot-rolled 1020 steel.

---

[1] Kilopounds (thousands of pounds) per square inch.

by tensile, compressive, or bending loads. Shear stresses, caused by torsional or transverse shear loads, are designated by the Greek letter τ.

Returning to Figure 3.1, several other mechanical properties are indicated on the stress–strain curve. Point *A* represents the *elastic limit*, S_e. It is the highest stress the material can withstand and still return exactly to its original length when unloaded. When loaded beyond point *A*, the material exhibits a partially plastic response. For most engineering materials, point *A* also approximates the *proportional limit*, defined as the stress at which the stress–strain curve first deviates (ever so slightly) from a straight line. Below the proportional limit, Hooke's law applies. The constant of proportionality between stress and strain (which is the slope of the curve between the origin and the proportional limit) is the *modulus of elasticity*, or *Young's modulus, E*. For some materials, a slight deviation from linearity occurs between the origin and a point such as *A*, at which the deviation begins to become more apparent. Such a material has no true proportional limit, nor is its modulus of elasticity definitely defined. The computed value depends on the portion of the curve used for measuring the slope.

Point *B* in Figure 3.1 represents the *yield strength*, S_y. It is the value of stress at which significant plastic yielding first occurs. In some ductile materials, notably soft steel, marked yielding occurs suddenly at a clearly defined value of stress. In other materials the onset of appreciable yielding occurs gradually, and the yield strength for these materials is determined by using the "offset method." This is illustrated in Figure 3.1; it shows a line, offset an arbitrary amount of 0.2 percent of strain, drawn parallel to the straight-line portion of the original stress–strain diagram. Point *B* is the *yield point* of the material at 0.2 percent offset. If the load is removed after yielding to point *B*, the specimen exhibits a 0.2 percent permanent elongation. Yield strength corresponding to a specified (very small) offset is a standard laboratory determination, whereas elastic limit and proportional limit are not.

3.3 Implications of the "Engineering" Stress–Strain Curve

Figures 3.1 and 3.2 represent identical stress–strain relationships, but differ in two respects: (a) Figure 3.1 uses an arbitrary nonlinear strain scale in order to illustrate more clearly the points previously discussed, whereas the strain scale in Figure 3.2 is linear; and (b) Figure 3.2 contains two additional strain scales that are described in point 3 below. Several important concepts are related to these two figures.

1. At the 36-ksi elastic limit of this particular steel, strain (ϵ) has a value of $\sigma/E = 0.0012$. Figure 3.2 shows the strain at ultimate strength and at fracture to be about 250 and 1350 times this amount. Obviously, to the scale plotted, the elastic portion of the curve in Figure 3.2 is virtually coincident with the vertical axis.

2. Suppose that a tensile member made from this steel has a notch (or hole, groove, slot, etc.) such that the strain at the notch surface is three times the nominal P/AE value. A tensile load causing a nominal stress (P/A) of 30 ksi and nominal strain (P/AE) of 0.001 produces a strain three times this large (0.003) at the notch surface. Since even this strain is almost imperceptible in Figure 3.2, the

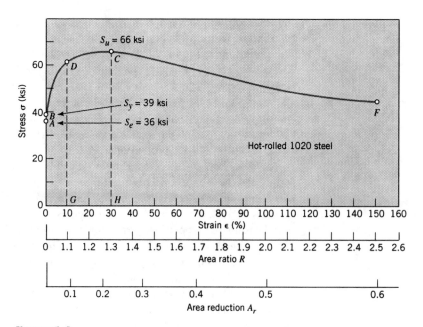

Figure 3.1 replotted to linear strain scale.

member would not be altered in any normally detectable way despite the fact that the *calculated elastic* (but totally fictitious) stress at the notch would be 90 ksi, a value well above the ultimate strength.

3. It is difficult to measure accurately the large strains that occur after "necking" of a tensile specimen. This is because the *local* elongation is immensely greater in the necking zone than elsewhere, and the calculated value of elongation depends on the gage length used. A more accurate determination of elongation at fracture in the *immediate region of failure* can be obtained indirectly by measuring the cross-sectional area at the fracture location. Elongation is then computed by assuming that there has been a negligible change in material volume. For example, let both the original cross-sectional area and extremely short gage length be unity. Suppose the area after fracture is 0.4. This gives a *ratio R of initial area to final area of 1/0.4 = 2.5.* Similarly, the *reduction in area A_r would be 60 percent of the original area, or 0.6.* If volume remains constant, the gage length must have increased to 2.5, thereby giving a strain (ϵ) owing to elongation of 1.5. The three abscissa scales in Figure 3.2 all represent quantities commonly used in the literature. Relations between them will now be derived. For constant volume, and using subscripts 0 and f to denote initial and final values, respectively, we have

$$A_0 L_0 = A_f(L_0 + \Delta L) = A_f L_0(1 + \epsilon)$$

or

$$A_f = \frac{A_0}{1 + \epsilon} \tag{3.1}$$

$$\text{Area ratio } R = \frac{A_0}{A_f} = 1 + \epsilon \qquad \text{(3.2a)}$$

$$\Delta A = A_0 - A_f = A_0\left(1 - \frac{1}{1 + \epsilon}\right) \qquad \text{(3.2b)}$$

$$\text{Area reduction } A_r = \frac{\Delta A}{A_0} = 1 - \frac{1}{1 + \epsilon} = 1 - \frac{1}{R} \qquad \text{(3.3)}$$

For practice, it is suggested that the reader verify the agreement of the three abscissa scales in Figure 3.2 at one or two points.

4. When we experimentally determine the σ–ϵ curve for most engineering materials, the load can be removed at any point and then restored without significantly altering the subsequent test points. Thus, if the load is removed at point D of Figure 3.2, the stress reduces to zero along line DG, which has a slope of $E = 30 \times 10^6$ psi. Reapplication of the load brings the material back essentially to point D, and additional load increases produce the same result as though the load removal had not taken place. Suppose that we regard the test specimen at G as a *new* specimen and determine *its* yield strength, ultimate strength, and reduction in area when fractured. The "new" specimen will have a yield strength higher than the original—in fact, its yield strength will be higher than the 62 ksi shown at point D because the area of the new specimen is less than that of the original. At point G the specimen has been permanently stretched to 11/10 of its initial length; hence, its area is only 10/11 of the original. On the basis of the new area, the yield strength of the "new" specimen is 62 ksi divided by 10/11, or $S_y = 68$ ksi. Similarly, the ultimate strength of the "new" specimen is 66 divided by 10/11, or $S_u = 73$ ksi. The reduction in area at fracture for the "new" specimen is from 10/11 (area at G) to 10/25 (area at F), or 56 percent. This compares with $A_r = 60$ percent based on the original area.

SAMPLE PROBLEM 3.1   Estimate Steel Strength and Ductility

The critical location of a specimen made from hot-rolled AISI 1020 steel is cold-worked during its fabrication to an extent coresponding to point C of Figure 3.2. What values of S_u, S_y, and ductility (in terms of ϵ, R, and A_r at fracture) are applicable to this location?

SOLUTION

Known: The critical location of a specimen made from a known steel is cold-worked during fabrication.

Find: Estimate S_u, S_y, and the ductility.

Schematic and Given Data: Refer to Figure 3.2.

Assumption: After cold working, the stress–strain curve for the critical location starts at point *H*.

Analysis:

1. At point *H* in Figure 3.2, the specimen has been permanently stretched to 1.3 times its initial length. Hence, its area is 1/1.3 times its original area A_0.

2. On the basis of the new area, the yield strength of the specimen is $S_y = 66$ ksi(1.3) = 85.8 ksi and the ultimate strength is $S_u = 66(1.3) = 85.8$ ksi.

3. The area A_H at point *H* is 1/1.3 times the initial area A_0. Similarly A_f at point *F* is 1/2.5 times the initial area A_0. Hence, the area ratio $R = A_H/A_F = 2.5/1.3 = 1.92$.

4. Using Eq. 3.3, we find that the reduction in area, A_r, from an initial area at point *H* to a final area at point *F* is

$$A_r = 1 - 1/R = 1 - 1/1.92 = 0.480 \quad \text{or 48 percent.}$$

5. Using Eq. 3.2, we find the strain to be $\epsilon = R - 1 = 1.92 - 1 = 0.92$ or 92 percent.

Comment: Severe cold work, as occurs in loading to point *C* or beyond, exhausts the material's ductility, causing S_y and S_u to be equal.

An important implication of the preceding is that the strength and ductility characterstsics of metals change substantially during fabrication processes involving cold working.

3.4 The Static Tensile Test—"True" Stress–Strain Relationships

A study of Figure 3.2 revealed that whenever a material is elongated to many times its maximum elastic strain (perhaps 20 or 30 times), the calculated "engineering" stress becomes somewhat fictitious because it is based on an area significantly different than that which actually exists. In such cases this limitation can be avoided by computing the "*true*" stress (in this text designated as σ_T), defined as load divided by the cross-sectional area that exists when the load is acting. Thus, $\sigma = P/A_0$, and $\sigma_T = P/A_f$.

Substituting the equivalent of A_f from Eq. 3.1 gives

$$\sigma_T = (P/A_0)(1 + \epsilon) = \sigma(1 + \epsilon) = \sigma R \tag{3.4}$$

If one were to replot Figure 3.2 using true stress, the values at points *B*, *C*, and *F* would be 39(1) = 39, 66(1.3) = 86, and 45(2.5) = 113 ksi, respectively. Note that true stress increases continuously to the point of fracture.

In like manner, engineering strain is not a realistic measure where large strains are involved. In such cases it is appropriate to use true strain values, ϵ_T. Consider, for example, a very ductile specimen of unit length that is stretched to a length of 5 units, and then stretched further to 5.1 units. The engineering strain added by the final 0.1

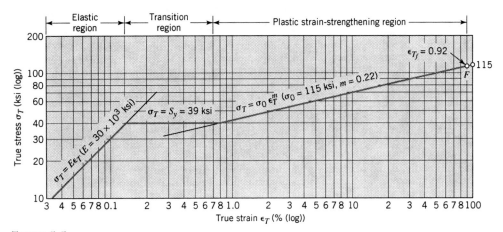

True-stress–true-strain curve—hot-rolled 1020 steel (corresponds to Figs. 3.1 and 3.2).

unit of stretch is 0.1/1 or 0.1. The corresponding true strain, however, is only 0.1/5 or 0.02 (change in length divided by the length existing *immediately prior to* the last small strain increment). Mathematically, true strain is defined as

$$\epsilon_T = \sum_{L_0}^{L_f} \frac{\Delta L}{L} = \int_{L_0}^{L_f} \frac{dL}{L} = \ln R = \ln(1 + \epsilon) \tag{3.5}$$

where L_0 and L_f represent the initial and final lengths, respectively, and ln denotes the natural logarithm. For metals, engineering and true strains are essentially the same when they are less than several times the maximum *elastic* strain.

Figure 3.3 is a true-stress–true-strain plot of the data represented in Figure 3.2. Such plots illustrate general relationships that are helpful in predicting the effect of cold working on the strength properties of many metals. A study of the three regions identified in Figure 3.3 reveals several important relationships and concepts.

1. *Elastic region.* Strictly speaking, Young's modulus is the ratio of *engineering* stress and strain, but with negligible error it is also the ratio of *true* stress and strain; hence

$$\sigma_T = E\epsilon_T \tag{3.6}$$

On the log-log coordinates of Figure 3.3, this equation plots as a straight line of unit slope, positioned so that the line (extended) passes through the point $(\epsilon_T = 1, \sigma_T = E)$. Note that E can be thought of as the value of stress required to produce an elastic strain of unity.

2. *Plastic strain-strengthening region.* This region corresponds to the strain-strengthening equation

$$\sigma_T = \sigma_0 \epsilon_T^m \tag{3.7}$$

Note that this equation has the same form as Eq. 3.6 except for the strain-hardening exponent m, is the slope of the line when plotted on log-log coordinates.

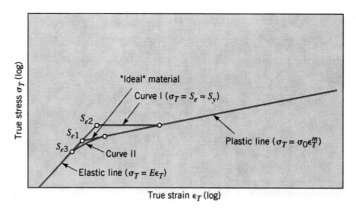

FIGURE 3.4
True-stress–true-strain curves showing transition region variations.

The strain-strengthening prportionality constant σ_0 is analogous to the elastic proportionality constant E, in that σ_0 can be regarded as the value of true stress associated with a true strain of unity.[2]

3. *Transition region.* For an "ideal" material, the value of the elastic limit (approximated as the yield point) corresponds to the intersection of the elastic and plastic lines, as shown in Figure 3.4. Actual materials may have values of S_e, which are either higher or lower, requiring the addition of an empirical transition curve, as I or II of Figure 3.4.

Unfortunately, numerical values of the strain-hardening characteristics of many engineering materials are not yet available. Much of the available information has been obtained by Datsko [2]. Values for several materials are given in Appendix C-2. These values are typical, but vary somewhat owing to small differences in chemical composition and processing history. This is particularly true of the true strain at fracture (ϵ_{Tf}).

3.5   *Energy-Absorbing Capacity*

Some parts must be designed more on the basis of absorbing energy than of withstanding loads. Since energy involves both loads and deflections, stress–strain curves are particularly relevant. Figure 3.5 will be used for illustration. It is essentially the same as Figure 3.1 except that the strain scale has been further expanded near the origin in the interest of clarity.

The capacity of a material to absorb energy within the elastic range is called *resilience.* Its standard measure is *modulus of resilience R_m*, defined as the energy absorbed by a unit cube of material when loaded in tension to its elastic limit.[3] This is equal to the triangular area under the elastic portion of the curve (Figure 3.5); thus

---

[2] Since σ_0 is a material property, the symbol S_0 might be more appropriate; however, σ_0 is used because of its general acceptance in the engineering literature on materials.

[3] In practice, S_y is usually substituted for S_e since S_y is easier to estimate and is so near S_e.

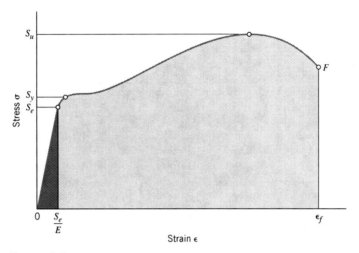

FIGURE 3.5
Resilience and toughness as represented by the stress–strain curve.

$$R_m = \tfrac{1}{2}(S_e)(S_e/E) = S_e^2/2E \quad \text{(see footnote 3)} \tag{3.8}$$

The total capacity of a material to absorb energy without fracture is called *toughness*. The *modulus of toughness* T_m is the energy absorbed per unit volume of material when loaded in tension to fracture. This is equal to the total shaded area under the curve in Figure 3.5:

$$T_m = \int_0^{\epsilon_f} \sigma \, d\epsilon \tag{3.9}$$

It is often convenient to perform this integration graphically. A rough approximation sometimes used is

$$T_m \approx \frac{S_y + S_u}{2}\epsilon_f \tag{3.10}$$

It should be noted that members designed for energy absorption are commonly subjected to impact loading, and that special tests (traditionally, the Charpy and Izod test) are used to estimate more accurately the impact energy-absorbing capacity of various materials at various temperatures.

3.6 *Estimating Strength Properties from Penetration Hardness Tests*

Penetration hardness tests (usually Brinell or Rockwell) provide a convenient and nondestructive means of estimating the strength properties of metals. Basically, penetration hardness testers measure the resistance to permanent deformation of a material when subjected to a particular combination of triaxial compressive stress and steep stress gradient.

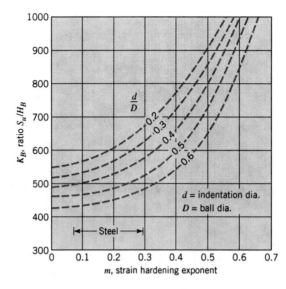

FIGURE 3.6

Approximate relationships between K_B and m [2].

Results of the Brinell hardness test have been found to correlate well with ultimate tensile strength, the relationship being

$$S_u = K_B H_B \tag{3.11}$$

where H_B is the Brinell hardness number, K_B is a constant of proportionality, and S_u is the tensile strength in psi. For most steels, $K_B \approx 500$. Datsko [1,2] has shown a rational basis for K_B being a function of the strain-hardening exponent, m. Figure 3.6 gives empirical curves representing this relationship.

Figure 3.7 gives approximate relationships between Brinell, Rockwell, and other hardness numbers.

After analyzing extensive data, Datsko [2] concluded that reasonably good estimates of the tensile yield strength of stress-relieved (*not* cold-worked) steels can be made from the equation

$$S_y = 1.05S_u - 30,000 \text{ psi} \tag{3.12}$$

or, by substituting Eq. 3.11 with $K_B = 500$, we have

$$S_y = 525H_B - 30,000 \text{ psi} \tag{3.13}$$

SAMPLE PROBLEM 3.2   Estimating the Strength of Steel from Hardness

---

An AISI 4340 steel part is heat-treated to 300 Bhn (Brinell hardness number). Estimate the corresponding values of S_u and S_y.

SOLUTION

Known: An AISI 4340 steel part is heat-treated to 300 Bhn.

Find: Estimate S_u and S_y.

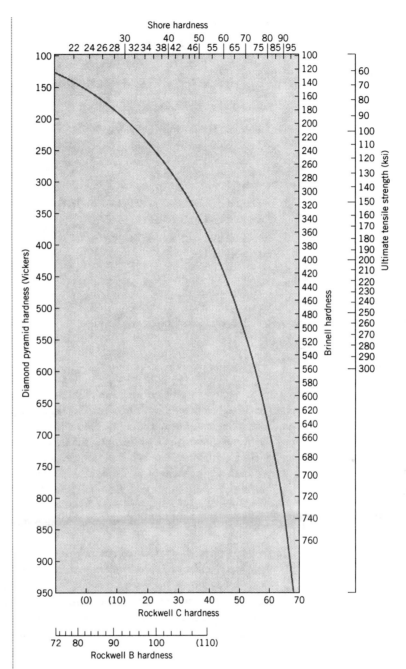

FIGURE 3.7

Approximate relationships between hardness scales and ultimate tensile strength of steel. (Courtesy International Nickel Company, Inc.)

Assumptions:

1. The experimentally determined relationship of ultimate strength to hardness is sufficiently accurate.

2. The experimentally developed relationship of yield strength to ultimate strength is sufficiently accurate for our purposes.

Analysis:

1. S_u can be estimated using Eq. 3.11.

$$S_u = K_B H_B$$
$$S_u = 500(300) = 150,000 \text{ psi}$$

where $K_B \approx 500$ for most steels.

2. S_y can be estimated by using Eq. 3.12.

$$S_y = 1.05 S_u - 30,000 \text{ psi} = 1.05(150,000) - 30,000 = 127,500 \text{ psi}$$

Comments:

1. Equation 3.12 is a good estimate of the tensile yield strength of stress-relieved (not cold-worked) steels.

2. Experimental data would be helpful in refining the preceding equations for this material.

3.7   Use of "Handbook" Data for Material Strength Properties

Ideally, an engineer would always base strength calculations on actual test data for the exact material used in the part involved. This would require the use of test specimens that correspond to the material in the fabricated part not only in chemical composition but also in all details of mechanical and thermal history. Because data from such specimens are seldom available, standard test data reported in handbooks and other sources, such as Appendix C of this book, are frequently used.

There are pitfalls in using "handbook" data, as evidenced by the fact that one frequently finds contradictory information in different references. In using this data, the engineer must be concerned with questions such as the following.

1. Do the published values represent the results of a single test, or are they average, median, typical, or minimum values from several tests? Depending on the precision with which the variables associated with composition, thermal history, and mechanical history are controlled, there will be a statistical scatter in the material strength. In many situations it is good to consider strength properties in terms of mean values and standard deviations (see Section 6.14).

2. Do the composition, size, previous heat treatment, and previous mechanical working of the specimens tested correspond *closely enough* to those of the actual part in its final as-fabricated condition?

3. Are the published data consistent within themselves, and consistent with the general pattern of accepted test results for similar materials? In other words, are the data reasonable?

Many tables of materials properties give values of the tensile elastic modulus and Poisson's ratio (ν). From elastic theory, the torsional or shear modulus can then be calculated as

$$G = \frac{E}{2(1 + \nu)} \tag{3.14}$$

3.8 Machinability

The cost of producing a machined part is obviously influenced both by the cost of the material and by the ease with which it can be machined. Empirically determined ratings of machinability (defined as relative cutting speed for a fixed tool life under prescribed standard cutting conditions) are published for various materials. Although often useful, these data are sometimes unreliable and even contradictory. In an effort to relate machinability to material parameters on a rational basis, Datsko [1] showed that machinability is a secondary material property that is a function of three primary material physical properties,

$$V_{60} = \frac{1150k}{H_B}(1 - A_r)^{1/2} \tag{3.15}$$

where

V_{60} = cutting speed in ft/min for 60-min tool life under standard cutting conditions

$\quad k$ = thermal conductivity in Btu/($h \cdot$ ft $\cdot$ °F)

H_B = Brinell hardness number

$\quad A_r$ = area reduction at fracture

Since the value of k is about the same for all metals, the machinability of metal is essentially a function of *hardness* and *ductility*.

3.9 Cast Iron

Cast iron is a four-element alloy containing iron, carbon (between 2 and 4 percent), silicon, and manganese. Additional alloying elements are sometimes added. The physical properties of an iron casting are strongly influenced by its cooling rate during solidification. This, in turn, depends on the size and shape of the casting and on details of foundry practice. Because of this (and unlike other engineering materials), cast iron is usually specified by its *mechanical properties* rather than by chemical analysis.

The distinctive properties of cast iron result largely from its carbon content. (1) The high carbon content makes molten iron very fluid, so that it can be poured into intricate shapes. (2) The precipitation of carbon during solidification counteracts normal shrinkage to give sound sections. (3) The presence of graphite in the metal provides excellent machinability (even at wear-resisting hardness levels), damps vibration, and aids boundary lubrication at wearing surfaces. When "chilled," that is, when heat is removed rapidly from the surface during solidification, virtually all the carbon near the surface remains combined as iron carbides, giving an extremely hard, wear-resistant surface.

Mechanical properties of several cast irons are given in Appendix C-3.

Gray Iron   The appearance of gray iron comes from the carbon that is precipitated in the form of graphite flakes. Even the softer grades have good wear resistance. Increased hardnesses (giving even better wear resistance) are obtainable by using special foundry techniques, heat treatment, or additional alloying elements. Because the graphite flakes markedly weaken cast iron in tension, the compressive strength is three to five times as high. Advantage is often taken of this strength differential, such as incorporating ribs on the compression side of a member loaded in bending.

Typical applications of gray iron include gasoline and diesel engine blocks, machine bases and frames, gears, flywheels, and brake disks and drums.

Ductile (Nodular) Iron   Ductile iron is alloyed with magnesium, which causes the excess carbon to precipitate in the form of small spheres or nodules. These nodules disrupt the structure less than do the graphite flakes of gray iron, thereby giving substantial ductility along with improved tensile strength, stiffness, and impact resistance. Ductile iron is specified by three numbers, as 60-40-18, which denote tensile strength (60 ksi), yield strength (40 ksi), and elongation (18 percent).

Typical applications include engine crankshafts, heavy-duty gears, and hardware items such as automobile door hinges.

White Iron   White iron (so-called because of the white appearance of fracture surfaces) is produced in outer portions of gray and ductile iron castings by *chilling* selected surfaces of the mold, thereby denying time for carbon precipitation. The resulting structure is extremely hard, wear-resistant, and brittle.

Typical applications are found in ball mills, extrusion dies, cement mixer liners, railroad brake shoes, rolling mill rolls, crushers, and pulverizers.

Malleable Iron

Typical uses are for heavy-duty parts having bearing surfaces, which are needed in trucks, railroad equipment, construction machinery, and farm equipment.

3.10   *Steel*

Steel is the most extensively used material for machine components. By suitably varying the composition, thermal treatment, and mechanical treatment, manufacturers can obtain a tremendous range of mechanical properties. Three basic relationships are fundamental to the appropriate selection of steel composition.

1. All steels have essentially the same moduli of elasticity. Thus, if *rigidity* is the critical requirement of the part, *all steels perform equally* and the least costly (including fabricating costs) should be selected.

2. Carbon content, almost alone, determines the maximum hardness that can be developed in steel. Maximum potential hardness increases with carbon content up to about 0.7 percent. This means that relatively small, regularly shaped parts can be heat-treated to give essentially the same hardness and strength with plain carbon steel as with more costly alloy steels.

3. Alloying elements (manganese, molybdenum, chromium, nickel, and others) improve the ease with which steel can be hardened. Thus, the potential hardness

and strength (which is controlled by carbon content) can be realized with less drastic heat treatments when these alloying elements are used. This means that with an alloy steel (a) parts with large sections can achieve higher hardnesses in the center or core of the section, and (b) irregularly shaped parts, subject to warpage during a drastic quench, can achieve the desired hardness from a more moderate heat treatment.

Mechanical properties of a few of the more commonly used steels are given in Appendixes C-4 through C-8.

Plain Carbon Steels   Plain carbon steels contain only carbon as a significant alloying element. Low-carbon steels have less than 0.3 percent C, medium-carbon steels have 0.3 to 0.5 percent, and high-carbon steels above 0.5 percent. Appendix C-4b gives typical uses for steels having various levels of carbon content.

Alloy Steels   As already indicated, the basic purpose of adding alloying elements to steel is to increase hardenability. Hardenability is commonly measured by the Jominy end-quench test (ASTM A-255 and SAE J406b), originated by the late Walter Jominy of the Chrysler Corporation. In this test a 1-in.-diameter by 4-in.-long bar is suspended, heated above its critical temperature, and then the bottom end is quenched with water while the top end air-cools (Figure 3.8a). Hardness is then measured at 1/16-in. increments from the quenched end (Figure 3.8b). The distance to which the hardening action extends is a measure of the hardenability imparted by the alloying elements.

Table 3.1 represents the results of a study by Datsko [2] of the relative effectiveness of various alloying elements in imparting hardenability to steel. The elements are listed in order of decreasing effectiveness. The equations give a relative hardenability factor *f* as a function of the concentration of the element used. For example,

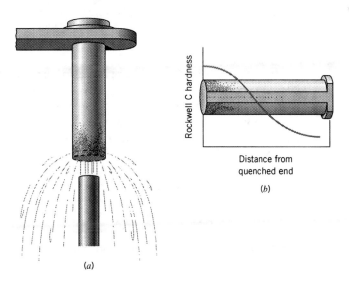

FIGURE 3.8
End quenching and method of hardness testing and end-quench hardenability specimen: (*a*) specimen being water-quenched; (*b*) finished quenched specimen after grinding and checking Rockwell C hardness [3].

TABLE 3.1   Relative Effectiveness of Steel Alloying Elements [2]

Element	Concentration (percent)	Relative Hardenability Effectiveness
Boron	$B < 0.002$	$f_B = 17.23B^{0.0268}$
Manganese	$Mn < 1.2$	$f_{Mn} = 3.46Mn + 1$
Manganese	$1.2 < Mn < 2.0$	$f_{Mn} = 5.125Mn - 1$
Molybdenum	$Mo < 1.0$	$f_{Mo} = 3.0\,Mo + 1$
Chromium	$Cr < 2.0$	$f_{Cr} = 2.18Cr + 1$
Silicon	$Si < 2.0$	$f_{Si} = 0.7Si + 1$
Nickel	$Ni < 2.0$	$f_{Ni} = 0.4Ni + 1$

manganese is the second most effective element, and the equation is valid for concentrations of up to 1.2 percent. If 1 percent Mn is used, the hardenability factor is 4.46. Similarly, a 2 percent concentration of chromium is only a little more effective, giving a factor of 5.36. Table 3.1 is not complete (a notable omission being vanadium), and alloying elements may also have significant secondary influences. Nevertheless, the equations of Table 3.1 provide a useful guide to the selection of the most economical means for obtaining a required level of hardenability.

Most alloy steels can be classed as either "through-hardening" or "carburizing," the latter being used where a tough core and relatively shallow, hard surface layer are desired. Nitriding and other surface-hardening processes are also used.

HSLA Steels   High-strength low-alloy (HSLA) steels were first developed around 1940 as a class of relatively low-cost steels providing much of the advantage of more costly regular alloy steels. In many applications, their greater strength compared to plain carbon steel permits a weight reduction with little if any increase in the total cost of the part. In recent years, the use of HSLA steels in automobiles has been substantial.

Case-Hardening Steels   Case hardening is a hardening of only the surface material (called the case). It is usually accomplished by carburizing, cyaniding, nitriding, induction hardening, or flame hardening. *Carburizing* introduces additional carbon into the surface of an otherwise low-carbon steel and then heat-treats it to give a high surface hardness. Some specific materials and hardnesses are listed in Appendix C-7.

Cyaniding is a similar process that adds nitrogen as well as carbon to the surfaces of low- and medium-carbon steels.

Nitriding adds nitrogen to an already machined and heat-treated part. The temperature of the process is 1000°F (538°C) or less, and no quenching is involved. This feature eliminates possible distortion problems. For maximum case hardness, special "nitralloy" steels (containing aluminum as an alloy) are often used. Medium-carbon alloy steels (notably 4340) are also nitrided.

Induction hardening and *flame hardening* heat only the surfaces of parts made of medium-carbon and alloy steels, then quenching and tempering.

Stainless Steels   Stainless steels contain, by definition, a minimum of 10.5 percent chromium. Wrought stainless steels are austenitic, ferritic, martensitic, or precipitation hardening. Mechanical properties of some wrought stainless steels are given in Appendix C-8. Cast stainless steels are usually classed as heat-resistant or corrosion-resistant.

Iron-Based Superalloys Iron-based superalloys are used primarily for elevated-temperature applications, as in turbines. Properties of typical iron-based superalloys are listed in Appendix C-9. Some authorities consider only the austenitic materials to be true superalloys. In general, they are used at temperatures above 1000°F (538°C), and the martensitic materials are used at lower temperatures. Significant properties of superalloys include at high temperatures strength and resistance to creep, oxidation, corrosion, and wear. Typical uses are for parts (including bolts) of gas turbines, jet engines, heat exchangers, and furnaces.

3.11   *Nonferrous Alloys*

Aluminum Alloys Literally hundreds of aluminum alloys are available, in both wrought and cast forms. Properties of a few of the more common ones are listed in Appendixes C-10 and C-11. The chemical composition of aluminum alloys is designated by four digits for wrought forms and by three digits for cast alloys. Thermal treatment, mechanical treatment, or both are indicated by a temper designation that follows the alloy identification number. Temper designations are given in Appendix C-12.

The heat treatment of aluminum alloys to increase hardness and strength is quite different from the heat treatment of steel. Aluminum alloys are first held at an elevated temperature long enough to bring the hardening constituents (as Cu, Mg, Mn, Si, Ni) into solution, then quenched, and finally age-hardened. The latter causes some of the hardening elements to precipitate throughout the structure. Some alloys precipitate at room temperature; others require an elevated temperature (artificial aging).

Although aluminum is a readily castable metal serving a host of useful applications, casting problems do exist. Shrinkage during casting is relatively large (3.5 to 8.5 percent by volume), and there is no mechanism analogous to the beneficial carbon precipitation in cast iron to counteract shrinkage. Hot shortness and gas absorption can be problems unless details of appropriate foundry practice are specified and controlled.

Copper Alloys Copper alloys include a variety of *brasses*, alloys made principally of copper and zinc, and *bronzes*, alloys made principally of copper and tin. As a class, copper alloys have good electrical conductivity, thermal conductivity, and resistance to corrosion, but relatively low ratios of strength to weight. They can be hot- or cold-worked, but they strain-harden in the process. Ductility can be restored by annealing or by heat associated with welding or brazing. Specific desired properties, such as greater strength, resistance to heat softening, and machinability, can often be markedly improved by adding small amounts of additional alloying agents.

Properties of several common copper alloys are given in Appendix C-13.

Magnesium Alloys Magnesium alloys are the lightest engineering metals. They are designated by a system established by the American Society for Testing and Materials (ASTM), which covers both chemical composition and tempers. The designation begins with two letters representing alloying elements of the greatest and second greatest concentration. The letter designations are

A—Aluminum	K—Zirconium	Q—Silver
E—Rare earths	L—Lithium	S—Silicon
H—Thorium	M—Manganese	Z—Zinc

Next are two digits that represent the respective percentages of these two elements, rounded off to whole numbers. Following these digits is a serial letter that indicates some variation in composition or minor alloying constituents or impurities. The temper designations at the end are identical with those used with aluminum (Appendix C-12). For example, alloy AZ31B-H24 contains 3 percent aluminum, 1 percent zinc, and is strain-hardened.

Mechanical properties of a few common magnesium alloys are given in Appendix C-14.

Nickel Alloys, Including Nickel-Based Superalloys   Nickel alloys are used in a variety of structural applications that usually require specific corrosion resistance, and strength and toughness at temperature extremes as great as 2000°F (1093°C) and as low as −400°F (−240°C).

Typical physical properties are given in Appendix C-15. The nickel and Duranickel alloys contain over 94 percent nickel. Monel represents a series of nickel–copper alloys, based on the mutual solubility of these two elements in all proportions. They are strong and tough at subzero temperatures, and especially resistant to stress corrosion cracking (Section 9.5). Hastelloy designates a series of Ni–Mo and Ni–Mo–Cr superalloys. Several Hastelloys resist oxidation and maintain useful strength and creep properties in the range of 2000°F (1093°C). The Inconel, Incoloy, Rene, and Udimet alloys listed in Appendix C-15 are Ni–Cr and Ni–Cr–Fe alloys.

Titanium Alloys   Titanium alloys are nonmagnetic and extremely corrosion-resistant, have low thermal conductivity, and have outstanding strength–weight ratios. On the negative side, they are very expensive and difficult to machine. Mechanical properties of some of the more common alloys are given in Appendix C-16.

Zinc Alloys   Zinc is a relatively inexpensive metal with moderate strength. It has a low melting temperature and so is readily and economically die-cast. Typical zinc die castings include automotive parts, building hardware, office machine components, and toys. Limited use is made of the metal in other forms. Mechanical properties of common zinc die-cast alloys are listed in Appendix C-17. Also included is a relatively new alloy (ZA-12) that can be cast using various methods.

3.12   *Plastics*

The information contained in this section is a brief overview of an extensive and complex field. Plastics constitute a large and varied group of synthetic organic materials. The basic chemical units of plastic materials are *monomers*. Under appropriate conditions, usually involving heat, pressure, or both, *polymerization* takes place, combining monomers into *polymers*. Typical monomers and their corresponding repeating polymer units are shown in Figure 3.9.

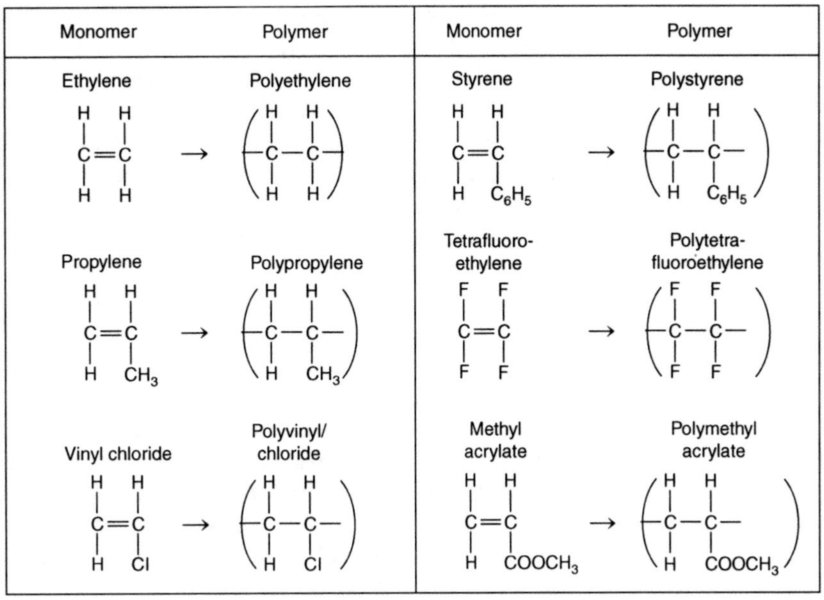

Typical monomers and their repeating polymer units.

The addition of more and more monomers to form longer and longer polymer chains increases molecular weight and vastly alters physical properties. For example, Figure 3.10 shows CH_4, which is methane gas. Adding one CH_2 unit gives heavier ethane gas (C_2H_6). Continued addition of CH_2 units gives pentane, a liquid (C_5H_{12}), and paraffin wax ($C_{18}H_{38}$). At approximately $C_{100}H_{202}$, the material is tough enough to be a useful plastic, known as *low-molecular-weight polyethylene*. The toughest

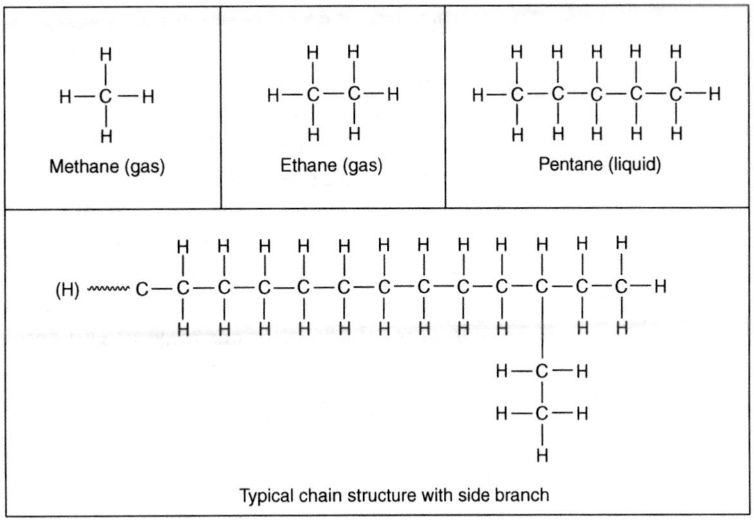

FIGURE 3.10
Molecular chains.

polyethylene, called *high-molecular-weight polyethylene*, contains nearly a half-million CH_2 units in a single polymer chain.

Polymer chain structures can incorporate side branching, also shown in Figure 3.10. The degree of branching influences the closeness with which the chains fit together. This, in turn, influences physical properties. Minimal branching promotes tight packing of the polymer chains (hence, strong intermolecular attractive forces), giving relatively high density, rigid crystalline structures, and also relatively extensive mold shrinkage. Extensive branching produces a more flexible, amorphous material with less mold shrinkage and distortion. Physical properties of the finished plastic can also be altered by *copolymerization*, the building of polymer chains with two monomers, and by *alloying*, a strictly mechanical mixing or blending of constituents which does not involve chemical bonds.

Plastics have traditionally been designated as *thermoplastic*, softening with heat, and *thermosetting*, not softening with heat. A preferred designation is *linear* and *cross-linked*. The polymer chains in linear plastics remain linear and separate after molding. The chains in cross-linked plastics are initially linear but become joined *irreversibly* during molding into an interconnected molecular network.

Cross-linking can be initiated by heat, chemical agents, irradiation, or a combination of these. Some plastics can be either cross-linked or linear. The cross-linked form is more resistant to heat, chemical attack, and creep (better dimensional stability). On the other hand, the linear form is less brittle (more impact-resistant), more easily processed, and better adapted to complex shapes.

Glass fiber reinforcement improves the strength of plastics by a factor of two or more. At substantially increased cost, a further improvement is obtainable by carbon fiber reinforcement. These relatively new materials (with 10 to 40 percent carbon) have tensile strengths as high as 40 ksi. Compared to glass-reinforced resins, they have less mold shrinkage, lower coefficients of expansion, and improved creep resistance, wear resistance, and toughness. The new fiber-reinforced plastics are being increasingly used for machine and structural components requiring light weight and high strength-to-weight ratios.

Technical information related to engineering polymers is available at http://plastics.dupont.com/ and at http://www.geplastics.com/.

Properties of a few common plastics are given in Appendix C-18a. A comparison of properties of thermoplastics with and without glass reinforcement is given in Appendix C-18b. Thermosetting plastics benefit similarly from glass reinforcement, the most commercially important being polyester and epoxy resins. In using tables giving properties of plastics, the reader should recall Section 3.7, which gives pitfalls in the use of such handbook data on the properties of materials. The pitfalls given in this section are particularly true for the data on plastics. Published values reflect values obtained from *standardized* molding conditions that are simple, economical, and readily reproduced. Strength values corresponding to *actual* molding conditions may differ significantly. Furthermore, temperature and rate of loading influence the strength of plastics to a greater extent than they do the strength of metals, thus requiring additional effort for the proper selection of a plastic.

Appendix C-18c gives a listing of typical applications of the more common plastics. Comments relating to each of these follow. Recall that *thermoplastics* are generally impact resistant; *thermosets* are generally heat resistant.

Common Plastics [4]

Thermoplastics

ABS (acrylonitrile–butadiene–styrene): Very tough, yet hard and rigid; fair chemical resistance; little water absorption, hence good dimensional stability; high abrasion resistance; easily electroplated.

ACETAL: Very strong, stiff engineering plastic with exceptional dimensional stability and resistance to creep and vibration fatigue; low coefficient of friction; high resistance to abrasion and chemicals; retains most properties when immersed in hot water; little tendency to stress-crack.

ACRYLIC: High optical clarity; excellent resistance to outdoor weathering; hard, glossy surface; excellent electrical properties, fair chemical resistance; available in brilliant, transparent colors.

CELLULOSICS: Family of tough, hard materials; cellulose acetate, propionate, butyrate, and ethyl cellulose. Property ranges are broad because of compounding; available with various degrees of weather, moisture, and chemical resistance; fair to poor dimensional stability; brilliant colors.

FLUOROPLASTICS: Large family (PTFE, FEP, PFA, CTFE, ECTFE, ETFE, and PVDF) of materials characterized by excellent electrical and chemical resistance, low friction, and outstanding stability at high temperatures; strength is low to moderate; cost is high.

NYLON (polyamide): Family of engineering resins having outstanding toughness and wear resistance; low coefficient of friction, and excellent electrical properties and chemical resistance. Resins are hygroscopic; dimensional stability is poorer than that of most other engineering plastics.

PHENYLENE OXIDE: Excellent dimensional stability (very little moisture absorption); superior mechanical and electrical properties over a wide temperature range. Resists most chemicals but is attacked by some hydrocarbons.

POLYCARBONATE: Highest impact resistance of any rigid, transparent plastic; excellent outdoor stability and resistance to creep under load; fair chemical resistance; some aromatic solvents cause stress cracking.

POLYESTER: Excellent dimensional stability, electrical properties, toughness, and chemical resistance, except to strong acids or bases; notch-sensitive; not suitable for outdoor use or for service in hot water; also available in thermosetting formulations.

POLYETHYLENE: Wide variety of grades: low-, medium-, and high-density formulations. LD types are flexible and tough. MD and HD types are stronger, harder, and more rigid; all are lightweight, easy-to-process, low-cost materials; poor dimensional stability and heat resistance; excellent chemical resistance and electrical properties. Also available in ultrahigh-molecular-weight grades.

POLYIMIDE: Outstanding resistance to heat (500°F continuous, 900°F intermittent) and to heat aging. High impact strength and wear resistance; low coefficient of thermal expansion; excellent electrical properties; difficult to process by conventional methods; high cost.

POLYPHENYLENE SULFIDE: Outstanding chemical and heat resistance (450°F continuous); excellent low-temperature strength; inert to most chemicals over a wide temperature range; inherently flame-retardant; requires high processing temperature.

POLYPROPYLENE: Outstanding resistance to flex and stress cracking; excellent chemical resistance and electrical properties; good impact strength above 15°F; good thermal stability; light weight, low cost, can be electroplated.

POLYSTYRENE: Low-cost, easy-to-process, rigid, crystal-clear, brittle material; little moisture absorption, low heat resistance, poor outdoor stability; often modified to improve heat or impact resistance.

POLYSULFONE: Highest heat deflection temperature of melt-processible thermoplastics; requires high processing temperature; tough (but notch-sensitive), strong, and stiff; excellent electrical properties and dimensional stability, even at high temperature; can be electroplated; high cost.

POLYURETHANE: Tough, extremely abrasion-resistant and impact-resistant material; good electrical properties and chemical resistance; can be made into films, solid moldings, or flexible foams; ultraviolet exposure produces brittleness, lower properties, and yellowing; also made in thermoset formulations.

POLYVINYL CHLORIDE (PVC): Many formulations available; rigid grades are hard, tough, and have excellent electrical properties, outdoor stability, and resistance to moisture and chemicals; flexible grades are easier to process but have lower properties; heat resistance is low to moderate for most types of PVC; low cost.

Thermosets

ALKYD: Excellent electrical properties and heat resistance; easier and faster to mold than most thermosets; no volatile by-products.

ALLYL (diallyl phthalate): Outstanding dimensional stability and electrical properties; easy to mold; excellent resistance to moisture and chemicals at high temperatures.

AMINO (urea, melamine): Abrasion-resistant and chip-resistant; good solvent resistance; urea molds faster and costs less than melamine; melamine has harder surface and higher heat and chemical resistance.

EPOXY: Exceptional mechanical strength, electrical properties, and adhesion to most materials; little mold shrinkage; some formulations can be cured without heat or pressure.

PHENOLIC: Low-cost material with good balance of mechanical, electrical, and thermal properties; limited in color to black and brown.

POLYESTER: Excellent balance of properties; unlimited colors, transparent or opaque; gives off no volatiles during curing, but mold shrinkage is considerable; can use low-cost molds without heat or pressure; widely used with glass reinforcement to produce "fiber-glass" components; also available in thermoplastic formulations.

POLYURETHANE: Can be flexible or rigid, depending on formulation; outstanding toughness and resistance to abrasion and impact; particularly suitable for large foamed parts, in either rigid or flexible types; also produced in thermoplastic formulations.

SILICONE: Outstanding heat resistance (from $-100°$ to $+500°$F), electrical properties, and compatibility with body tissue; cures by a variety of mechanisms; high cost; available in many forms; laminating resins, molding resins, coatings, casting or potting resins, and sealants.

3.13 *Materials Selection Charts*[4]

The information contained in this section is a brief overview of Ashby's materials selection charts that graphically present information concisely to assist in selecting types of materials based on properties such as stiffness, strength, and density. The information contained in the charts are for rough calculations and not for final design analysis. Actual properties of a material selected should be used in final design followed by experimental verification and testing. Appendix C-19 gives the classes and abbreviations for the materials selection charts.

3.13.1 Strength-Stiffness Chart

Various materials are plotted in Figure 3.11 for strength versus Young's modulus. The plotted values for strength are: (a) yield strength for metals and polymers, (b) compressive strength for ceramics and glasses, (c) tensile strength for composites, and (d) tear strength for elastomers. Design requirements for values of strength or Young's modulus suggest materials to select. For design requirements that are bounded by elastic design or a ratio of strength versus Young's modulus, the proper materials can be selected or compared by (1) energy storage per volume as in springs, $S^2/E = C$; (2) radius of bending as in elastic hinges, $S/E = C$; or (3) deflection under load as in diaphragm design, $S^{3/2}/E = C$. For example, if we want to maximize energy storage per volume before failure, we want to maximize the value of $S^2/E = C$. Without other design limitations, inspection of the chart shows that engineering ceramics have the highest allowable S^2/E, followed by elastomers, engineering alloys (steels), engineering composites, engineering polymers, woods, and polymer foams having decreased values.

3.13.2 Strength-Density Chart

For a wide variety of materials, strength ranges from 0.1 MPa to 10,000 MPa while density ranges from 0.1 to 20 Mg/m^3. Figure 3.12 illustrates strength-to-density

---

[4] This section is adapted from Ashby, M. F., *Materials Selection in Mechanical Design*, Pergamon Press, Oxford, England, 1992.

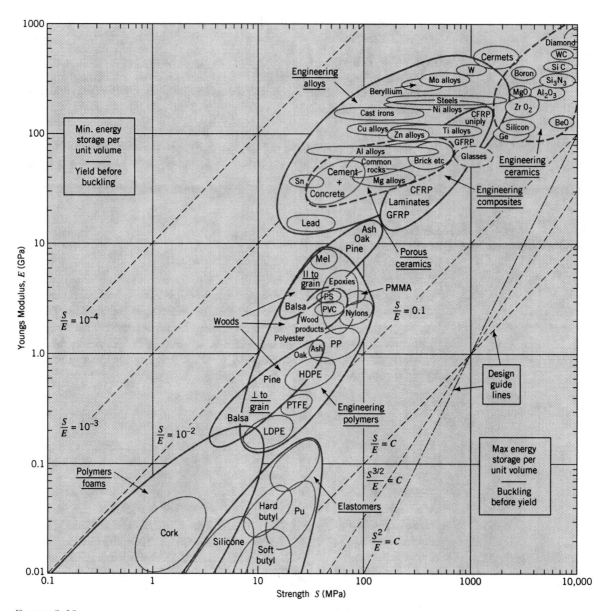

FIGURE 3.11

Strength, S, versus modulus, E. Strength, S, is yield strength for metals and polymers, compressive strength for ceramics, tear strength of elastomers, and tensile strength for composites. From Ashby, M. F., *Materials Selection in Mechanical Design*, Pergamon Press, 1992.

relationships for various materials. The guide lines of constants $S/\rho = C$, $S^{2/3}/\rho = C$, and $S^{1/2}/\rho = C$ are used respectively in minimum weight design of (i) rotating disks, (ii) beams (shafts), and (iii) plates. The value of the constants increase as the guide lines are displaced upward and to the left. Materials with the greatest strength-to-weight ratios are located in the upper left corner.

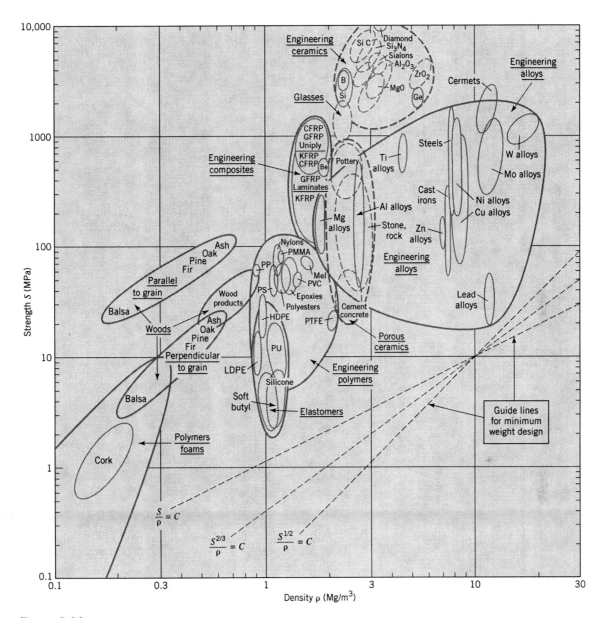

FIGURE 3.12
Strength, S, versus density, ρ. Strength, S, is yield strength for metals and polymers, compressive strength for ceramics, tear strength for elastomers, and tensile strength for composites. From Ashby, M. F., *Materials Selection in Mechanical Design*, Pergamon Press, 1992.

3.13.3 Strength-Temperature Chart

Only ceramics have strength above 1000°C, metals become soft at 800°C, and polymers have little strength above 200°C. Figure 3.13 presents an overview of high-temperature strength for various materials. The insert figure explains the shape of the lozenges. Strength at temperature, $S(T)$, is yield strength at temperature for metals and polymers, compressive strength at temperature for ceramics, tear strength at

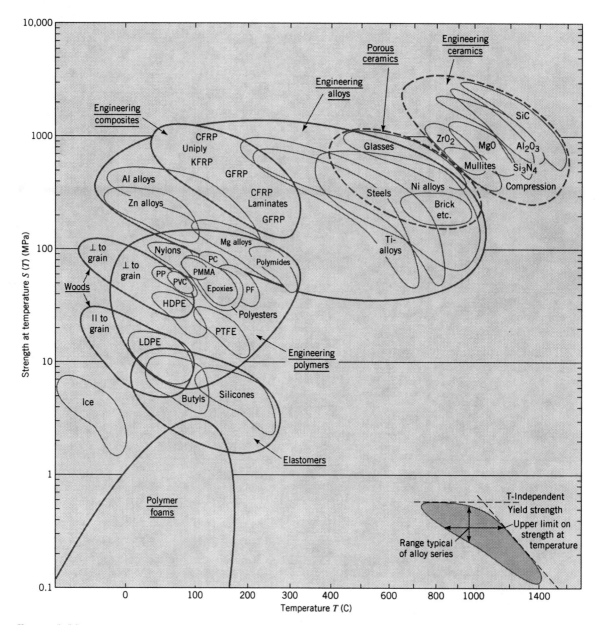

FIGURE 3.13

Strength at temperature, $T(S)$, versus temperature, T. Strength at temperature, $S(T)$, is yield strength at temperature for metals and polymers, compressive strength at temperature for ceramics, tear strength at temperature of elastomers, and tensile strength at temperature for composites. The insert figure explains the shape of the lozenges. From Ashby, M. F., *Materials Selection in Mechanical Design*, Pergamon Press, 1992.

temperature for elastomers, and tensile strength at temperature for composites. For engineering alloys, the "strength" is a short-term yield strength, for one hour loading. The strengths are lower for long loading times (e.g., 10,000 h) and would involve design for creep and/or creep rupture—see Juvinall, R. C., *Engineering Considerations of Stress, Strain, and Strength*, McGraw-Hill, New York, 1967.

3.14   *Engineering Material Selection Process*

3.14.1   Introduction

As stated in the introduction to this chapter, the selection of materials and the processes used in fabrication are integral parts of the design of a machine component. The goal of this section is to give the engineering student an introduction to the process of making an intelligent choice when selecting materials for machine components. Although material selection is based on experience and know-how, this section presents a rational method for selection of materials.

Table 3.2 presents a list of general performance characteristics for a machine component application. Once the characteristics of the application and the function of the component are understood, the material selection is based on (1) availability of the material in the form and shape desired, (2) total cost of the material including initial and future cost, (3) material properties as they relate to service performance requirements, and (4) the processing of the material into a finished part. Section 3.14.2 gives material information sources that can be used to identify materials.

Other factors to be considered in the selection of a material include: (1) the limits of the materials properties, (2) pressures to reduce cost, (3) increased product/machine energy efficiency through weight reduction, (4) material shortages, (5) ease of recovery and recycling, (6) disposal, and (7) legal and health issues.

In the *design process*, machine performance specifications are established, then components are identified and specifications for their performance are developed from the overall design concept of the machine. The specification of selection of materials typically takes place when the detailed drawings of the components are prepared, Figure 3.14 illustrates a material selection and evaluation process for a component.

The material selection process typically involves satisfying more than one service performance requirement, i.e., more than one specific characteristic of the application.

TABLE 3.2   **General Characteristics of the Application**

Capacity (power, load, thermal)
Motion (kinematics, vibration, dynamics, controllability)
Interfaces (appearance, space limits, load type(s), environmental compatibility)
Cost (initial, operating)
Life
Reliability
Safety and Health
Noise
Producibility
Maintainability
Geometry (size, shape)
Rigidity
Elastic stability (buckling)
Weight
Uncertainties (load, environment, cost)

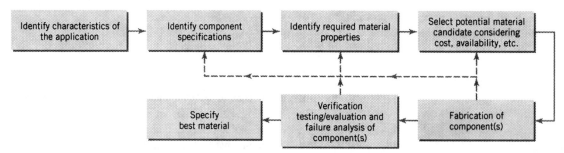

FIGURE 3.14
Material selection for a machine component.

This can be accomplished by weighing the various performance requirements with respect to the significant material properties that control performance. The specifications are then transformed into material properties, and materials that have the desired properties and can meet the performance specifications are identified. Performance, cost, and availability are considered to arrive at a single or small set of materials for the component. The smaller group of materials become the candidate materials for further evaluation and possible testing in the detail design phase. Tests may be conducted to eliminate or rank the materials. Extensive testing may be required to establish the integrity and variability of the materials, the effect of manufacturing processes, and the effect of mating parts, etc. Indeed the entire machine, subassembly, product, or component may be evaluated in simulated or actual service conditions tests. Also, it is not uncommon that components placed into service are monitored as operational experience begins to accumulate, and if service failures occur, material selection and/or design corrections are implemented and replacement parts are readied for scheduled maintenance and replacement.

Material selection (like design itself) is an iterative decision-making process of synthesis requiring experience, training, and engineering know-how combined with art to select a material that will be suitable for the task. Past experience with material selection yields an understanding of material systems, familiarity with specific engineering materials, an understanding of the properties of a small repertoire of materials—a few metals, plastics, ceramics, tool steels, etc. This experience is helpful when the prior learning is applicable to a new selection problem. Experience allows the designer to rely less on the materials engineer and metallurgist.

3.14.2   Sources of Information on Material Properties

Published technical literature in the form of technical articles, company reports, trade literature, handbooks, and Internet documents provides a wealth of available material property data. Compendiums of data on material properties are also found at large corporations and at government agencies such as NASA.

Properties of materials are given in Appendix C. Typical uses of common materials are given in Appendix C-3a, C-3b, C-3c, C-4b, C-8, C-10, C-11, C-18c, and C-23. References listed at the end of this chapter list properties of materials, and these references are available in most technical libraries. Appendix C-20 presents a small subset of engineering materials used in component design.

Material property data are usually presented in a statistical format with a mean value and a standard deviation. Property data listed in handbooks and published technical literature give a single value for a property. This single value should be viewed as a typical value. When there is variation, a range of values (largest and smallest) may be listed or shown graphically by scatter bands. For critical applications it may be required to determine the frequency distribution for the material property and for the corresponding parameter that describes the service performance.

Computerized material selection processes are available; for example, see http://www.grantadesign.com. Commercially available computer engineering systems can provide (1) comparison of materials, (2) characterization and specifications of metals and nonmetals, (3) material selection systems, (4) examples of material selection, (5) fabrication methods and processes, and (6) frequently updated cost data on materials and processes.

3.14.3 Material Selection Factors

The principal selection factors that have a bearing on the selection of a material and fulfill a design requirement are:

1. Availability
2. Cost
3. Material properties—mechanical, physical, chemical, dimensional
4. Manufacturing processes—machining, formability, joinability, finishing and coatings

Table 3.3 lists subfactors related to these important selection parameters. Not using the proper material selection factors and choosing an inappropriate material can compromise function of the material, service life, and cost of the component and product.

Service Performance (Specifications) Once the general characteristics of the application are known, they can be reduced to service performance requirements. Examples of service performance conditions would be fluctuating loads, high temperatures, and a highly oxidizing atmosphere. The service performance, also called performance specifications or functional requirements, for a machine component

TABLE 3.3   Characteristics of the Material

Properties, mechanical (strength, elasticity, hardness, Poisson's ratio, damping, tensile, compression, impact, toughness, fatigue, creep, wear, stiffness, shear)

Properties, physical (density, electrical, magnetic, optical, conduction, expansion, flammability, melting point, specific heat, emissivity, absorptivity)

Properties, chemical (corrosion resistance, degradation, composition, bonding, structure, oxidation, stability, embrittlement, environmental factors)

Properties, dimensional (size, shape, flatness, profile, surface finish, stability, tolerances)

Manufacturing Processes (castability, coatability, heat treatability, hardenability, formability, machinability, joinability, weldability)

Availability (in stock, order elsewhere, order requirements, suppliers, special manufacturing processing required)

Cost (raw material, quantity required, predicted service life, additional fabrication required)

Legal (code compliance, environmental, health, recyclability, disposability, product liability)

needs to be related to the properties of the material. This is because the properties of materials are indicators of service performance; i.e., wear is related to hardness, stiffness is related to modulus of elasticity, weight is related to density. The designer must be able to translate the service performance requirements into select material properties.

Another view of this is that the general service performance characteristics (operating conditions), described generally in Table 3.2 and described specifically by stresses, motions, and applied forces, etc., need to be translated into mechanical properties of the material. That is, the material must have the characteristics—properties, cost, and availability—suited for the service conditions, loads, and stresses.

Availability   Even though the potential material candidates have the required material properties, they must also be "available." Answering the following questions can assist the designer in whether the material candidates meet availability criteria:

1. What is the total time to obtain the material?
2. Is there more than one supplier that can provide the material?
3. Is the material available in the geometry configuration required?
4. What is the limit on the amount of material available?
5. What is the probability of the material being available in the future?
6. Is special processing required?
7. Will special processing limit the availability of the material?

It is the designer's responsibility to establish a timeline for procurement of materials. The time to obtain a material needs to coincide with the time dictated by the schedule.

Economics (Total Cost)   Cost should be used as an initial factor in screening materials, yet true prices of materials for a component can only be obtained through quotes from vendors as the pricing structure of many engineering materials is complex. Relative costs of some engineering materials are presented in Figure 3.15 which pictures costs of various materials in dollars per pound and dollars per cubic inch.

The most appropriate cost to consider is the total life-cycle cost. Total cost includes (1) initial material cost, (2) cost of processing and manufacturing, (3) cost of installation, and (4) cost of operation and maintenance. Other factors to consider include: (1) anticipated service life, (2) shipping and handling expense, (3) recyclability, and (4) disposal.

Material Properties   A knowledge and understanding of the properties of metals, plastics, ceramics, etc., their designations and numbering systems, and their favorable and unfavorable qualities are fundamental in the selection of a material. Material properties to consider include (1) physical; (2) mechanical; (3) chemical—environmental resistance, corrosion, rust; and (4) dimensional—tolerances, surface finish, etc.—see Table 3.3. Table 3.3 is a checklist of material properties important to evaluate in satisfying service performance conditions.

Manufacturing Processes   It is important to recognize the links between material properties and uses of the materials. Although related to material properties, the

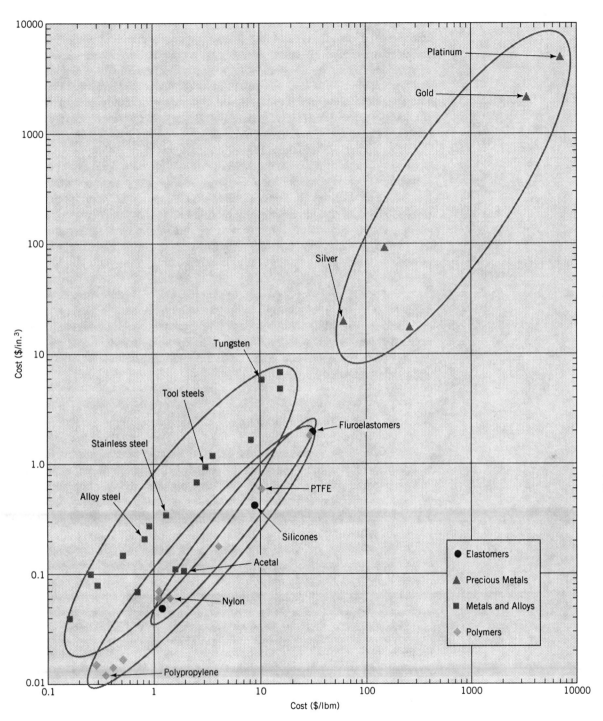

Fɪɢᴜʀᴇ 3.15
Cost of materials in bulk quantities in December 2000. For details see [10].

manufacturing process will influence the type of material that can be used and the material will dictate the type of manufacturing process that can be employed. Also, the material (because of its properties) may impose limitations on the design and manufacturability of the component. In other words, the methods of manufacturing, forming, joining, and fastening are dictated by the material choice, and likewise if a certain manufacturing process will be used to fabricate a component then the material choice may be limited (see Appendix C-21, which shows processing methods used most frequently with different materials).

Formability and Joinability   Although formability and joinability are related to material properties, the ability of forming, joining, and fastening materials is an important consideration in material selection. The material must be able to be formed, joined, or fastened into the desired shape by shearing, blanking, piercing, bending, spinning, drawing, peening, welding, brazing, soldering, threading, riveting, stapling, or adhesive bonding. Appendix C-22 shows how materials affect joinability.

Finishing and Coatings   Although related to material properties, the finishing and/or coating ability of a design material has an influence (is another factor) in the selection of a component material. For example, low carbon steel trencher teeth when hard faced (with overlays applied by welding operations) results in a wear-resistant and lower-cost part. Table 3.4 lists heat treatments, surface treatments, and coatings.

3.14.4   Selection Procedure

Introduction   Problems in material selection for machine design usually involve the selection of a material for a new or redesigned component, and although the goals generally involve performance, reliability, and cost, the selection process usually involves making a decision with insufficient or inaccurate property data subject to multiple constraints, sometimes competing, and usually without a clear-cut (known) objective.

A methodology of materials selection is based on (1) the engineering performance considerations for a given application, (2) the relative importance of the

TABLE 3.4   **Material Treatments and Coatings [10]**

Heat Treatments	**Surface Treatments**	**Coatings**
Age hardening	Anodizing	Hard surfacing
Annealing	Boronize	Metallize
Flame hardening	Carbonitride	Organosols
Induction hardening	Carburize	Paints
Normalizing	Chromating	Plasma
Quench hardening	Cyanide	Plastisols
Solution treating	Nitride	Plating
Stress relieving	Oxides	
Tempering	Phosphating	

required material properties, and (3) the availability and final cost of the component. The goal is to select an appropriate material to best meet the demands of the design requirement. For a given application, the approach is to identify the connection between the functional requirements and the material requirements and thus reduce the number of candidate materials from which to select. When selecting among candidates the choice in some cases can be unambiguous or the reason for difficulties of choosing may be revealed.

Although material selection involves iterative decision making, when we have a description or definition of the part or component, we recognize that the steps in selecting a material for a component follows a typical path:

(a) Determine the "purpose" of the component. Establish the service performance requirements for the part. The service performance or operational conditions for the component need to be well understood as these conditions influence the material selection. For example, a gear operating under heavy load and high speed at an elevated temperature would probably require a different material than a low-speed, low-torque gear operating at room temperature.

This first step may require an analysis of the material requirements; i.e., a determination of the conditions of operation and the environment that the product must withstand, so that the service performance conditions can be translated into corresponding critical material properties. Table 3.3 provides a list of important material characteristics that can be reviewed to recall general areas to examine.

(b) Select a material that appears suitable for the "purpose." This second step may initially involve screening and ranking candidate materials before a candidate material is selected. The Material Selection Charts of Section 3.13 can be used to make initial choices of materials that will meet performance requirements. Appendix C-23 lists candidate materials for common machine components.

Knowledge of the material groups—plastics, metals, ceramics, and composites—and the type of component in which the material has previously been used, allows the designer to compare materials knowing what heat treatment and other processes to use when specifying the material. Also, use experience, review Appendix C for typical uses of common materials, and do not reinvent the wheel unless it is important to do so. For example, Appendix C-10 might suggest considering 6063-T6 aluminum for terracruiser lightweight fuel tanks. Availability, cost, and fabrication should be considered at the onset of the material selection process even though a detailed cost is not possible to attain.

Besides experience, a rational method of selecting materials is to utilize failure analysis of similar parts (to a new design) that have failed in service. Materials are selected that are unlikely to fail based on the knowledge gained from a failure analysis for the component. Appendix Table C-24 identifies material properties that are related to common failure modes. Since service performance conditions are complex, usually more than one material property is required to identify the properties important in a mode of failure. When selecting materials, it should be kept in mind that the useful life of most machines and components ends with fatigue failure or surface deterioration—pitting, spalling, or excessive wear.

After listing material considerations, select a few candidate materials that best match the critical material properties, cost, and availability constraints. Reconsider formability, fabrication, fastening and joining, availability, and cost of the material as well as the cost due to the production process. When screening candidate materials, ask this question: "Should this material be evaluated further for this application?". Decision making needs to be done carefully but quickly. There is no perfect knowledge.

(c) Make a final evaluation of the candidate materials including manufacturing processes and finishing methods if necessary and make a final recommendation. Select the best material for the application. The best material for a particular application is the one that provides the best value, defined as the ratio of *overall* performance over *total* cost, and defined by the material selection index where

$$SI = \text{Selection Index} = \frac{(\text{availability})(\text{performance})}{(\text{total cost})}$$

The higher the value of SI, the better the choice. The selection index can be used to rank order materials. Unfortunately, for available material and processes, in many cases, the best engineering solution and the best economic solution for a given design do not usually match, and the final material will be a compromise that yields an optimal selection that combines sets of requirements.

(d) Test, test, test. Once a material candidate has met the material properties, availability, and cost criteria, it is recommended that the candidate selected be tested. The test(s) should simulate the product operating conditions. If the selected materials satisfy all the requirements, then there is no need to select an alternate candidate(s). As a final step, the product itself may need to be tested and the material selections reevaluated. Whether or not an extensive testing program is required depends on total cost, service conditions, and experience (with the material and the application).

The degree of uncertainty in the material selection with respect to performance and risk needs to be weighed; i.e., the consequences of failure require that an analysis of the risk be considered in the material selection process.

3.14.5 Summary

The material selection process can be as challenging as other aspects of the design process because it follows the same decision-making approach. The steps in the material selection process, although iterative, are: (1) analysis of the requirements, (2) identification of materials, (3) selection and evaluation of candidate materials, and (4) testing and verification. The key is to establish the properties/service performance requirements needed for a design. Once needed properties are identified, the designer selects one or two candidate materials and treatments. It is appropriate to compare specific candidate materials for availability and economics. Finally, serviceability and risk should be considered. Final selection involves a compromise of availability, properties, processes, and economics.

In short, material selection should include consideration of availability, total cost, material properties, and manufacturing processes by using experience, engineering know-how, selection index, and knowledge of possible failure modes to choose the best material.

SAMPLE PROBLEM 3.3   Selecting a Material

For a bolt, select a machinable wrought stainless steel material that has a yield strength to avoid plastic deformation of at least 88 ksi.

SOLUTION

Known: A bolt needs to be machined from wrought stainless steel material with a yield strength of 88 ksi or greater.

Find: Select a machinable wrought stainless steel material with a yield strength of at least 88 ksi.

Schematic and Given Data:

FIGURE 3.16
Sample Problem 3.3—a stainless steel bolt.

Assumptions:

1. The data provided in Appendix C-8 are accurate.
2. The material can be selected based on machinability and material properties.
3. Cost and availability are assumed to be relatively unimportant.

Analysis:

1. According to the "typical uses" column in Appendix C-8, the following stainless steel materials are used for bolts: Class 303, 414, 410, and 431.
2. Class 303 and class 410 stainless steel are eliminated because their yield strength is less than 88 ksi. When body stresses are above the yield strength, the material enters the plastic zone and permanent deformation occurs. The bolt must not plastically deform at 88 ksi.
3. Class 414 and class 431 have yield strengths above 88 ksi. These materials will not permanently deform at 88 ksi.
4. Class 431 is eliminated because it has poor machinability.
5. The material selected is Class 414 because it has fair machinability and a yield strength above 88 ksi.

Comments:

1. The stainless steel material selected must satisfy the material property requirements.
2. Cost and availability normally must also be factored into the material selection process.

References

1. Datsko, J., *Material Properties and Manufacturing Processes*, Wiley, New York, 1966.

2. Datsko, J., *Materials in Design and Manufacturing*, Malloy, Ann Arbor, Mich., 1977.

3. Lindberg, R. A., *Materials and Manufacturing Technology*, Allyn and Bacon, Boston, 1977.

4. *Machine Design 1981 Materials Reference Issue*, Penton/IPC, Cleveland, Ohio, Vol. 53, No. 6, March 19, 1981.

5. *SAE Handbook, Part 1: Materials, Parts and Components*, Society of Automotive Engineers, Warrendale, Pa., 1993.

6. *ASM Handbook, Vol 1: Properties and Selection: Irons, Steels, and High Performance Alloys*, 10th ed., ASM International, Metals Park, Ohio, 1990.

7. *ASM Handbook, Vol 2: Properties and Selection: Nonferrous Alloys and Special-Purpose Materials*, 10th ed., ASM International, Metals Park, Ohio, 1990.

8. Ashby, M. F., *Materials Selection in Mechanical Design*, Butterworth Heinemann Publications, Oxford, 1999.

9. Hill, Percy H., *The Science of Engineering Design*, Holt, Rinehart and Winston, New York, 1970.

10. Budinski, K. G., and M. K. Budinski, *Engineering Materials: Properties and Selection*, 7th ed., Prentice Hall, Upper Saddle River, New Jersey, 2002.

11. Budinski, K. G., and M. K. Budinski, *Engineering Materials: Properties and Selection*, 8th ed., Prentice Hall, Upper Saddle River, New Jersey, 2005.

12. Dieter, G. E., *Engineering Design: A Materials and Processing Approach*, McGraw-Hill, New York, 2000.

13. Harper, C. A. (ed.), *Modern Plastics Handbook*, McGraw-Hill, New York, 2000.

14. *SAE Handbook, Vol 1: Metals, Materials, Fuels, Emissions, Threads, Fasteners, and Common Parts*, SAE International, Warrendale, Pa., 2004.

Problems

Sections 3.1–3.3

3.1   Discuss the purpose in this textbook of using (1) the Greek letter σ to denote *normal stress* caused by tensile, compressive, or bending loads; (2) the Greek letter τ to denote *shear stress* caused by torsional or transverse shear loads; and (3) the letter S to designate *strength properties of the material*.

3.2D   Search the materials property database at http://www.matweb.com and list values for the (1) modulus of elasticity, E, (2) ultimate tensile strength, S_u, (3) elongation at break in %, and (4) density in g/cc, for the following:

(a)   AISI carbon steels: 1010 cold drawn, 1020 cold rolled, 1040 as rolled, 1050 as rolled, 1080 as rolled, and 1116 cold drawn;

(b)   Alloy steels: 4140 annealed, 4340 annealed, and 4620 annealed.

3.3D   Repeat Problem 3.2D except for the following:

(a)   Cast iron: ASTM class 20 and class 35

(b)   Aluminum alloys: 3003-H12, 3003-H18, 5052-H32, 5052-H38, 5052-O, 6061-T4, 6061-T91, and 7075-O.

3.4D   Write definitions for the terms *stress, strength, yield strength, ultimate strength, elastic limits, proportional limit, modulus of elasticity*, and *yield point*.

3.5D   (a) Search the materials property database at http://www.matweb.com and identify five materials that have a modulus of elasticity, E, greater than that of steel where $E = 30 \times 10^6$ psi (207 GPa). (b) Also, identify five materials with ultimate strength, S_u, greater than 200 ksi (1378 MPa).

3.6   What materials listed in Appendix C-1 have a lower density and a higher thermal conductivity than steel?

3.7   The critical location of a part made from hot-rolled AISI 1020 steel is cold-worked during its fabrication to an extent corresponding to point D of Figure 3.2. What values of S_u, S_y, and ductility (in terms of ϵ, R, and A_r at fracture) are applicable to this location?

3.8   The critical location of a part made from AISI 1020 steel is cold-worked during its fabrication to an extent corresponding to point I (which lies between D and C of Figure 3.2 and corresponds to a strain (ϵ) of 20 percent). What values of S_u, S_y, and ductility (in terms of ϵ, R, and A_r at fracture) are applicable to this location?

3.9   A tensile specimen made of hot-rolled AISI 1020 steel is loaded to point C of Figure 3.2. What are the values of σ, ϵ, σ_T, and ϵ_T involved? Next, the specimen is unloaded. Treating it then as a *new* specimen, it is reloaded to point C. What are the values of these same quantities for the new specimen?

3.10   A tensile specimen made of hot-rolled AISI 1020 steel is loaded to point D of Figure 3.2. What are the values of σ, ϵ, σ_T, and ϵ_T involved? Next, the specimen is unloaded. Treating it as a *new* specimen, it is reloaded to point D. What are the values of these same quantities for the new specimen?

3.11   A tensile specimen made of hot-rolled AISI 1020 steel is loaded to point I (which lies between D and C of Figure 3.2 and corresponds to a strain (ϵ) of 20 percent). What are the values of σ, ϵ, σ_T, and ϵ_T involved? Next, the specimen is unloaded. Treating it as a *new* specimen, it is reloaded to point I. What are the values of these same quantities for the new specimen?

Sections 3.4–3.14

3.12   An AISI 4340 steel part is annealed to 217 Bhn. Estimate the values of S_u and S_y. Compare these values with those corresponding to another AISI 4340 steel part that is normalized to 363 Bhn.

3.13D   Select a steel from Appendix C-4a, and estimate S_u and S_y from the given value of Brinell hardness.

3.14D   Select an annealed steel from Appendix C-4a, and estimate S_u and S_y from the given value of Brinell hardness. Compare the results to the given tensile and yield strengths.

3.15D   Select a steel from Appendix C-4a that has properties listed for as-rolled, normalized, and annealed conditions. Estimate S_u and S_y for the three conditions from the given Brinell hardness value. Compare the results to the given tensile and yield strengths.

3.16   An AISI 1020 steel part is annealed to 111 Bhn. Estimate the values of S_u and S_y for this part.

3.17   An AISI 3140 steel component is heat-treated to 210 Bhn. Estimate the values of S_u and S_y for this component.

3.18   If the curve in Figure P3.18 represents the results of a Jominy end-quench test of AISI 4340 steel, draw corresponding curves (roughly) for low-alloy steel and for

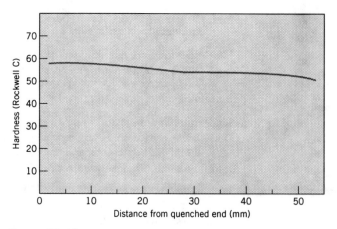

FIGURE P3.18

plain carbon steel, each having 0.40 percent carbon and heat-treated to the same surface hardness as the 4340 steel.

3.19D For each of the following applications calling for steel, choose between (1) 0.1 percent carbon and 0.4 percent carbon, and between (2) plain carbon and alloy steel.

(a) A machine frame requiring extreme rigidity (when massive enough to satisfy this requirement, stresses will be very low).

(b) A small, round rod subjected to high bending and torsional stresses.

(c) A large, irregularly shaped part subjected to high stresses.

(d) A rail car wheel (interior stresses low but surface must be carburized to resist wear).

3.20D Copy the material properties of aluminum 7075-0 from www.matweb.com. Highlight the UNS number for 7075-0 aluminum. Compare the values from your copy with those listed in Appendix C-10 for 7075-0 aluminum alloy.

3.21D Repeat Problem 3.20D, except for 2024-T4 aluminum.

3.22D Repeat Problem 3.20D, except for 6061-T6 aluminum.

3.23D An experienced design engineer who has worked in the telephone manufacturing industry provides a list of his favorite materials:

(a) 1020 steel, 1040 steel, 4340 steel

(b) 2024-T4 aluminum

(c) Nylon (6/6), acetal

Compare the specific material properties for each material.

3.24 Search the materials property database at http://www.matweb.com and list the properties of nylon 6 with 30% glass fibers. Compare the 30% glass-filled nylon properties with those of unreinforced nylon 6.

3.25D Select a material for the shaft of a gear train. The shaft carries high loads and stops abruptly.

CHAPTER 4

Static Body Stresses

4.1 *Introduction*

Once the external *loads* applied to a member have been determined (see Chapter 2), the next item of interest is often the resulting *stresses*. This chapter is concerned with *body* stresses, existing within the member as a whole, as distinguished from *surface* or *contact* stresses in localized regions where external loads are applied. This chapter is also concerned with stresses resulting from essentially *static* loading, as opposed to stresses caused by impact or fatigue loading. (Impact, fatigue, and surface stresses are considered in Chapters 7, 8, and 9, respectively.)

As noted in Section 3.2, this book follows the convention of reserving the capital letter S for *material strength* (i.e., S_u for ultimate strength, S_y for yield strength, etc.) and using Greek letters σ and τ for normal and shear stress, respectively.

4.2 *Axial Loading*

Figure 4.1 illustrates a case of simple *tension*. If external loads P are reversed in direction (i.e., have negative values), the bar is loaded in simple *compression*. In either case, the loading is *axial*. Small block E represents an arbitrarily located infinitesimally small element of material that is shown by itself in Figures 4.1*b* and *c*. Just as equilibrium of the bar as a whole requires the two external forces P to be equal, equilibrium of the element requires the tensile stresses acting on the opposite pair of elemental faces to be equal. Such elements are commonly shown as in Figure 4.1*c*, where it is important to remember that the stresses are acting on faces *perpendicular to the paper*. This is made clear by the isometric view in Figure 4.1*b*.

Figure 4.1*d* illustrates equilibrium of the left portion of the link under the action of the external force at the left and the tensile stresses acting on the cutting plane. From this equilibrium we have perhaps the simplest formula in all of engineering:

$$\sigma = P/A \qquad (4.1)$$

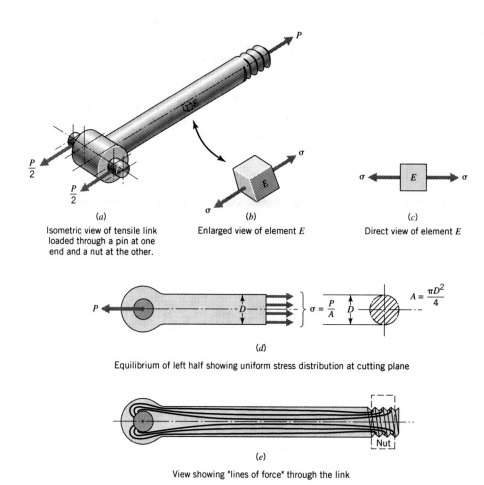

(a)
Isometric view of tensile link
loaded through a pin at one
end and a nut at the other.

(b)
Enlarged view of element E

(c)
Direct view of element E

$$\sigma = \frac{P}{A} \qquad A = \frac{\pi D^2}{4}$$

(d)
Equilibrium of left half showing uniform stress distribution at cutting plane

(e)
View showing "lines of force" through the link

FIGURE 4.1
Axial loading.

It is important to remember that although this formula is always correct as an expression for the *average* stress in any cross section, disastrous errors can be made by naively assuming that it also gives the correct value of *maximum* stress in the section. Unless several important requirements are fulfilled, the maximum stress will be greater than *P/A*, perhaps by several hundred percent. The maximum stress is equal to *P/A* only if the load is *uniformly distributed* over the cross section. This requires the following.

1. The section being considered is well removed from the loaded ends. Figure 4.1*e* shows "lines of force flow" to illustrate the general nature of the stress distribution in cross sections at various distances from the ends. A substantially uniform distribution is reached at points about three diameters from the end fittings in most cases.

2. The load is applied *exactly* along the centroidal axis of the bar. If, for example, the loads are applied a little closer to the top, the stresses will be highest at the top of the bar and lowest at the bottom. (Looking at it another way, if the load is eccentric by amount *e*, a bending moment of intensity *Pe* is superimposed on the axial load.)

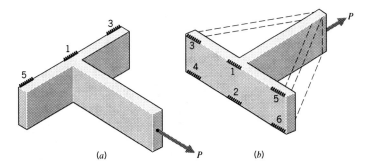

FIGURE 4.2
Tensile-loaded T bracket
attached by six welds.

3. The bar is a perfect straight cylinder, with no holes, notches, threads, internal imperfections, or even surface scratches. Any of these give rise to *stress concentration*, which will be dealt with in Section 4.12.

4. The bar is totally free of stress when the external loads are removed. This is frequently not the case. The manufacture of the part and its subsequent mechanical and thermal loading history may have created *residual stresses*, as described in Sections 4.14, 4.15, and 4.16.

5. The bar comes to stable equilibrium when loaded. This requirement is violated if the bar is relatively long and loaded in compression. Then it becomes elastically unstable, and *buckling* occurs. (See Sections 5.10 through 5.15.)

6. The bar is homogeneous. A common example of *non* homogeneity is a composite material, such as glass or carbon fibers in a plastic matrix. Here the matrix and the fibers carry the load *redundantly* (see Section 2.5), and the stiffer material (i.e., having the higher modulus of elasticity) is the more highly stressed.

Figure 4.2 shows an example in which unexpected failure can easily result from the naive assumption that the calculation of axial stress involves no more than "*P/A*." Suppose that the load *P* is 600 N and that six identical welds are used to attach the bracket to a fixed flat surface. The *average* load per weld would be, of course, 100 N. However, the six welds represent redundant force paths of very different stiffnesses. The paths to welds 1 and 2 are *much* stiffer than the others; hence, these two welds may carry nearly all the load. A much more uniform distribution of load among the six welds could be obtained by adding the two side plates shown dotted in Figure 4.2*b*, for these would stiffen the force paths to welds 3 to 6.

At this point one might despair of *ever* using *P/A* as an acceptable value of maximum stress for relating to the strength properties of the material. Fortunately, such is not the case. The student should acquire increasing insight for making "engineering judgments" relative to these factors as his or her study progresses and experience grows.

4.3 *Direct Shear Loading*

Direct shear loading involves the application of equal and opposite forces so nearly colinear that the material between them experiences shear stress, with negligible bending. Figure 4.3 shows a bolt serving to restrain relative sliding of two plates subjected

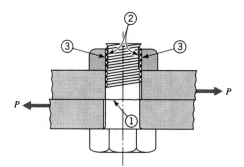

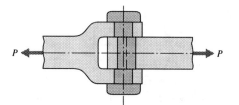

FIGURE 4.3
Bolted joint, showing three areas of
direct shear.

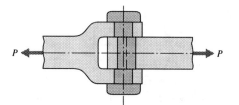

FIGURE 4.4
Direct shear loading (showing failure in
double shear).

to opposing forces P. With plate interface friction neglected, the bolt cross section of
area A (marked ①) experiences direct shear stress of *average* value

$$\tau = P/A \tag{4.2}$$

If the nut in Figure 4.3 is tightened to produce an initial bolt tension of P, the direct
shear stresses at the root of the bolt threads (area ②), and at the root of the nut threads (area
③), have *average* values in accordance with Eq. 4.2. The thread root areas involved are
cylinders of a height equal to the nut thickness.[1] If the shear stress is excessive, shearing
or "stripping" of the threads occurs in the bolt or nut, whichever is weaker.

Similar examples of direct shear occur in rivets, pins, keys, splines, and so on.
Moreover, direct shear loading is commonly used for cutting, as in ordinary household
shears or scissors, paper cutters, and industrial metal shears.

Figure 4.4 shows a hinge pin loaded in *double* shear, where the load P is carried
in shear through two areas in parallel; hence, the area A used in Eq. 4.2 is *twice* the
cross-sectional area of the pin. Examples of pins loaded in double shear are common:
cotter pins used to prevent threaded nuts from rotating (as with automobile wheel
bearing retaining nuts), shear pins used to drive boat propellers (the pin fails in double shear when the propeller strikes a major obstruction, thus protecting more expensive and difficult-to-replace members), transverse pins used to hold telescoping
tubular members in a fixed position, and many others.

Direct shear loading does not produce *pure* shear (as does torsional loading), and
the actual stress distribution is complex. It involves fits between the mating members
and relative stiffnesses. The maximum shear stress will always be somewhat in excess
of the P/A value given by Eq. 4.2. In the design of machine and structural members,
however, Eq. 4.2 is commonly used in conjunction with appropriately conservative

---

[1] Strictly true only for threads with a sharp "V" profile. Shear areas for standard threads are a little less.
See Section 10.4.5.

values of working shear stress. Furthermore, to produce total shear fracture of a ductile member, the load must simultaneously overcome the shear strength in every element of material in the shear plane. Thus, for total fracture, Eq. 4.2 would apply, with τ being set equal to the ultimate shear strength, S_{us}.

4.4   *Torsional Loading*

Figure 4.5 illustrates torsional loading of a round bar. Note that the direction of the applied torque (T) determines that the left face of element E is subjected to a *downward* shear stress, and the right face to an *upward* stress. Together, these stresses exert a *counterclockwise* couple on the element that must be balanced by a corresponding *clockwise* couple, created by shear stresses acting on the top and bottom faces. The state of stress shown on element E is *pure shear*.

The sign convention for axial loading (positive for tension, negative for compression) distinguishes between two basically different types of loading: compression can cause buckling whereas tension cannot, a chain or cable can withstand tension but not compression, concrete is strong in compression but weak in tension, and so on. The sign convention for *shear* loading serves no similar function—positive and negative shear are basically the same—and the sign convention is purely arbitrary. Any shear sign convention is satisfactory so long as the *same* convention is used throughout any one problem. This book uses the convention of *positive-clockwise*; that is, the shear stresses on the top and bottom faces of element E (in Figure 4.5) tend to rotate the element *clockwise*, hence are regarded as *positive*. The vertical faces are subjected to *counterclockwise* shear, which is *negative*.

For a round bar in torsion, the stresses vary linearly from zero at the axis to a maximum at the outer surface. Strength of materials texts contain formal proofs that the shear stress intensity at any radius r is

$$\tau = Tr/J \tag{4.3}$$

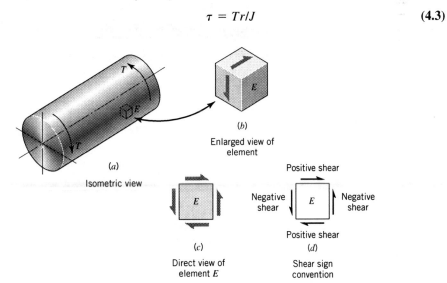

FIGURE 4.5
Torsional loading of a round bar.

Of particular interest, of course, is the stress at the surface, where r is equal to the outside radius of the bar and J is the polar moment of inertia of the cross section, which is equal to $\pi d^4/32$ for a solid round bar of diameter d (see Appendix B-1). Simple substitution of this expression in Eq. 4.3 gives the equation for surface torsional stress in a solid round bar of diameter d:

$$\tau = 16T/\pi d^3 \qquad \textbf{(4.4)}$$

The corresponding equation for torsional stress in a *hollow* round bar (i.e., round tubing or pipe) follows from substitution of the appropriate equation for polar moment of inertia (see Appendix B-1).

The important assumptions associated with Eq. 4.3 are

1. The bar must be straight and round (either solid or hollow), and the torque must be applied about the longitudinal axis.

2. The material must be homogeneous and perfectly elastic within the stress range involved.

3. The cross section considered must be sufficiently remote from points of load application and from stress raisers (i.e., holes, notches, keyways, surface gouges, etc.).

For bars of nonround cross section, the foregoing analysis gives *completely* erroneous results. This can be demonstrated for rectangular bars by marking an ordinary rubber eraser with small square elements 1, 2, and 3 as shown in Figure 4.6. When the eraser is twisted about its longitudinal axis, Eq. 4.3 implies that the highest shear stress would be at the corners (element 2) because these are farthest from the neutral axis. Similarly, the lowest surface stress should be at element 1 because it is closest to the axis. Observation of the twisted eraser shows exactly the opposite—element 2 (if it could be drawn small enough) does not distort at all, whereas element 1 experiences the *greatest* distortion of any element on the entire surface!

A review of a formal derivation of Eq. 4.3 reminds us of the basic assumption that *what are transverse planes before twisting remain planes after twisting*. If such a plane is represented by drawing line "*A*" on the eraser, obvious distortion occurs upon twisting; therefore, the assumption is not valid for a rectangular section.

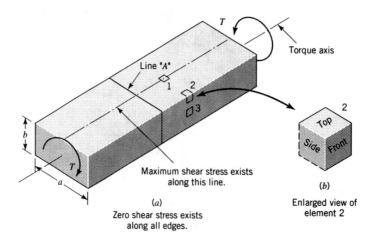

FIGURE 4.6
Rubber eraser marked to illustrate torsional deformation (hence stresses) in a rectangular bar.

The equilibrium requirement of corner element 2 makes it clear that this element *must* have zero shear stress: (1) the "free" top and front surfaces do not contact anything that could apply shear stresses; (2) this being so, equilibrium requirements prevent any of the other four surfaces from having shear. Hence, there is zero shear stress along all edges of the eraser.

Torsional stress equations for nonround sections are summarized in references such as [8]. For example, the maximum shear stress for a rectangular section, as shown in Figure 4.6, is

$$\tau_{\max} = T(3a + 1.8b)/a^2b^2 \tag{4.5}$$

4.5 Pure Bending Loading, Straight Beams

Figures 4.7 and 4.8 show beams loaded *only* in bending; hence the term, "pure bending." From studies of the strength of materials, the resulting stresses are given by the equation

$$\sigma = My/I \tag{4.6}$$

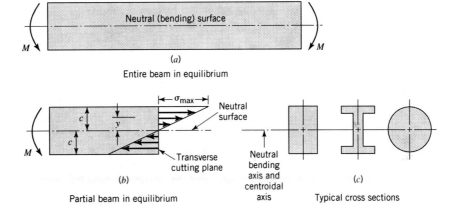

FIGURE 4.7
Pure bending of sections with two axes of symmetry.

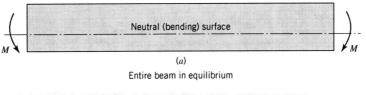

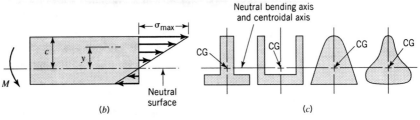

FIGURE 4.8
Pure bending of sections with one axis of symmetry.

where I is the moment of inertia of the cross section with respect to the neutral axis, and y is the distance from the neutral axis. Bending stresses are *normal* stresses, the same as axial stresses. Sometimes the two are distinguished by using appropriate subscripts, as σ_b for bending stresses and σ_a for axial stresses. For the bending shown in Figures 4.7 and 4.8, tensile stresses exist above the neutral axis of the section (or above the neutral surface of the beam), and compressive stresses below. Maximum values are at the top and bottom surfaces.

Equation 4.6 applies to any cross section (such as the several that are illustrated), with these important limitations.

1. The bar must be initially straight and loaded in a plane of symmetry.
2. The material must be homogeneous, and all stresses must be within the elastic range.
3. The section for which stresses are calculated must not be too close to significant stress raisers or to regions where external loads are applied.

Figure 4.7 shows a bending load applied to a beam of cross section having two axes of symmetry. Note that the cutting-plane stresses marked σ_{max} are obtained from Eq. 4.6 by substituting c for y, where c is the distance from the neutral axis to the extreme fiber. Often the *section modulus Z* (defined as the ratio I/c) is used, giving the equation for maximum bending stress as

$$\sigma_{max} = M/Z \tag{4.7}$$

For a solid round bar, $I = \pi d^4/64$, $c = d/2$, and $Z = \pi d^3/32$. Hence, for this case

$$\sigma_{max} = 32M/\pi d^3 \tag{4.8}$$

Properties of various cross sections are given in Appendix B-1.

Figure 4.8 shows bending of sections having a single axis of symmetry, and where the bending moment lies in the plane containing the axis of symmetry of each cross section. At this point the reader will find it profitable to spend a few moments verifying that the offset stress distribution pattern shown is necessary to establish equilibrium in Figure 4.8b (i.e., $\Sigma F = \Sigma \sigma \, dA = 0$, and $\Sigma M = M + \Sigma \sigma \, dA \, y = 0$).

4.6   *Pure Bending Loading, Curved Beams*

When initially curved beams are loaded in the plane of curvature, the bending stresses are only approximately in accordance with Eqs. 4.6 through 4.8. Since the shortest (hence stiffest) path along the length of a curved beam is at the inside surface, a consideration of the relative stiffnesses of redundant load paths suggests that the stresses at the inside surface are *greater* than indicated by the straight-beam equations. Figure 4.9 illustrates that this is indeed the case. This figure also shows that equilibrium requirements cause the neutral axis to shift inward (toward the center of curvature) an amount e, and the stress distribution to become hyperbolic. These deviations from straight-beam behavior are important in severely curved beams, such as those commonly encountered in C-clamps, punch press and drill press frames, hooks, brackets, and chain links.

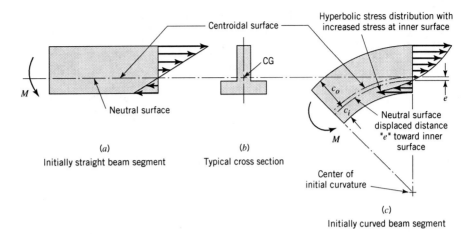

FIGURE 4.9
Effect of initial curvature, pure bending of sections with one axis of symmetry.

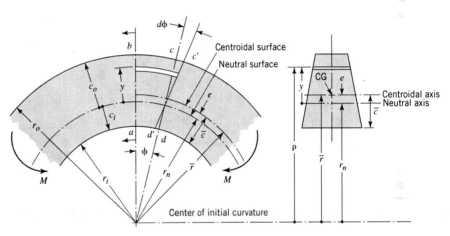

FIGURE 4.10
Curved beam in bending.

To understand more clearly the behavior pattern shown in Figure 4.9c, let us develop the basic curved-beam stress equations. With reference to Figure 4.10, let *abcd* represent an element bounded by plane of symmetry *ab* (which does not change direction when moment *M* is applied) and plane *cd*. Moment *M* causes plane *cd* to rotate through angle *dφ* to new position *c'd'*. (Note the implied assumption that plane sections remain plane after loading.) Rotation of this plane is, of course, about the neutral bending axis, displaced an as-yet-unknown distance *e* from the centroidal axis.

The strain on the fiber shown at distance *y* from the neutral axis is

$$\epsilon = \frac{y \, d\phi}{(r_n + y)\phi} \tag{a}$$

133

For an elastic material, the corresponding stress is

$$\sigma = \frac{Ey\,d\phi}{(r_n + y)\phi} \qquad \textbf{(b)}$$

Note that this equation gives a hyperbolic distribution of stress, as illustrated in Figure 4.9c.

Equilibrium of the beam segment on either side of plane cd (Figure 4.10) requires

$$\Sigma F = 0: \quad \int \sigma\,dA = \frac{E\,d\phi}{\phi} \int \frac{y\,dA}{r_n + y} = 0$$

and, since $E \neq 0$,

$$\int \frac{y\,dA}{r_n + y} = 0 \qquad \textbf{(c)}$$

$$\Sigma M = 0: \quad \int \sigma y\,dA = \frac{E\,d\phi}{\phi} \int \frac{y^2\,dA}{r_n + y} = M \qquad \textbf{(d)}$$

The quantity $y^2/(r_n + y)$ in Eq. d can be replaced by $y - r_n y/(r_n + y)$, giving

$$M = \frac{E\,d\phi}{\phi}\left(\int y\,dA - r_n \int \frac{y\,dA}{r_n + y} \right) \qquad \textbf{(e)}$$

The second integral in Eq. e is equal to zero because of Eq. c. The first integral is equal to eA. (Note that this integral would be equal to zero if y were measured from the centroidal axis. Since y is measured from an axis displaced distance e from the centroid, the integral has a value of eA.)

Substituting the preceding expressions into Eq. e gives

$$M = \frac{E\,d\phi}{\phi}eA \quad \text{or} \quad E = \frac{M\phi}{d\phi\,eA} \qquad \textbf{(f)}$$

Substituting Eq. f into Eq. b gives

$$\sigma = \frac{My}{eA(r_n + y)} \qquad \textbf{(g)}$$

Substituting $y = -c_i$ and $y = c_o$ in order to find maximum stress values at the inner and outer surfaces, we have

$$\sigma_i = \frac{-Mc_i}{eA(r_n - c_i)} = \frac{-Mc_i}{eAr_i}$$

$$\sigma_o = \frac{Mc_o}{eA(r_n + c_o)} = \frac{Mc_o}{eAr_o}$$

The signs of these equations are consistent with the compressive and tensile stresses produced in the inner and outer surfaces of the beam in Figure 4.10, where the direction of moment M was chosen in the interest of clarifying the analysis. More commonly, a positive bending moment is defined as one tending to *straighten* an initially curved beam. In terms of this convention,

$$\sigma_i = +\frac{Mc_i}{eAr_i} \quad \text{and} \quad \sigma_o = -\frac{Mc_o}{eAr_o} \tag{4.9}$$

Before we use Eq. 4.9, it is necessary to develop an equation for distance e. Beginning with the force equilibrium requirement, Eq. c, and substituting ρ for $r_n + y$, we have

$$\int \frac{y\,dA}{\rho} = 0$$

But $y = \rho - r_n$; hence,

$$\int \frac{(\rho - r_n)\,dA}{\rho} = 0$$

or

$$\int dA - \int \frac{r_n\,dA}{\rho} = 0$$

Now $\int dA = A$; hence,

$$A = r_n \int dA/\rho \quad \text{or} \quad r_n = \frac{A}{\int dA/\rho} \tag{h}$$

Distance e is equal to $\bar{r} - r_n$; hence,

$$e = \bar{r} - \frac{A}{\int dA/\rho} \tag{4.10}$$

Stress values given by Eq. 4.9 differ from the straight-beam "Mc/I" value by a curvature factor, K. Thus, using subscripts i and o to denote inside and outside fibers, respectively, we have

$$\sigma_i = K_i Mc/I = K_i M/Z \quad \text{and} \quad \sigma_0 = -K_o Mc/I = -K_o M/Z \tag{4.11}$$

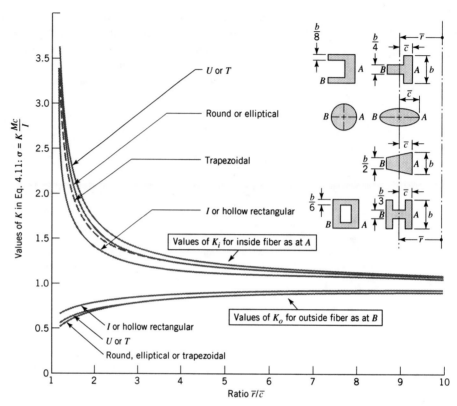

FIGURE 4.11

Effect of curvature on bending stresses, representative cross sections [8].

Values of K for beams of representative cross sections and various curvatures are plotted in Figure 4.11. This illustrates a common rule of thumb: "If $\bar{r}$ is at least ten times $\bar{c}$, inner fiber stresses are usually not more than 10 percent above the Mc/I value." Values of K_o, K_i, and e are tabulated for several cross sections in [8]. Of course, any section can be handled by using Eqs. 4.9 and 4.10. If necessary, the integral in Eq. 4.10 can be evaluated numerically or graphically. Use of these equations is illustrated by the following sample problem.

SAMPLE PROBLEM 4.1   Bending Stresses in Straight and Curved Beams

A rectangular beam has an initial curvature $\bar{r}$ equal to the section depth h, as shown in Figure 4.12. How do its extreme-fiber-bending stresses compare with those of an otherwise identical straight beam?

SOLUTION

Known: A straight beam and a curved beam of given cross section and initial curvature are loaded in bending.

Find: Compare the bending stresses between the straight beam and the curved beam.

Schematic and Given Data:

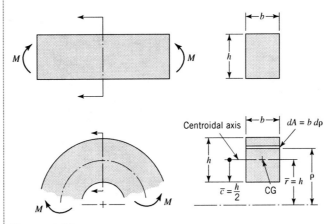

FIGURE 4.12
A curved rectangular bar with radius of curvature $\bar{r}$ equal to section depth h (giving $\bar{r}/\bar{c} = 2$) and a straight rectangular bar.

Assumptions:

1. The straight bar must initially be straight.
2. The beams are loaded in a plane of symmetry.
3. The material is homogeneous, and all stresses are within the elastic range.
4. The sections for which the stresses are calculated are not too close to significant stress raisers or to regions where external loads are applied.
5. Initial plane sections remain plane after loading.
6. The bending moment is positive; that is, it tends to straighten an initially curved beam.

Analysis:

1. For the direction of loading shown in Figure 4.12, the conventional straight-beam formula gives

$$\sigma_i = +\frac{Mc}{I} = \frac{6M}{bh^2}, \qquad \sigma_o = -\frac{6M}{bh^2}$$

2. From Eq. 4.10,

$$e = \bar{r} - \frac{A}{\int dA/\rho} = h - \frac{bh}{b\int_{r_i}^{r_o} d\rho/\rho} = h - \frac{h}{\ln(r_o/r_i)} = h\left(1 - \frac{1}{\ln 3}\right)$$

$$= 0.089761h$$

3. From Eq. 4.9,

$$\sigma_i = +\frac{M(0.5h - 0.089761h)}{(0.089761h)(bh)(0.5h)} = \frac{9.141M}{bh^2}$$

$$\sigma_o = -\frac{M(0.5h + 0.089761h)}{(0.089761h)(bh)(1.5h)} = -\frac{4.380M}{bh^2}$$

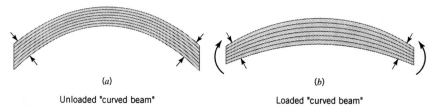

Figure 4.13
Paper pad illustrating radial tension in a curved beam loaded in bending.

4. From Eq. 4.11 with $Z = bh^2/6$,

$$K_i = \frac{9.141}{6} = 1.52 \quad \text{and} \quad K_o = \frac{4.380}{6} = 0.73$$

Comment: These values are consistent with those shown for other sections in Figure 4.11 for $\bar{r}/\bar{c} = 2$.

Note that the stresses dealt with in the bending of curved beams are *circumferential*. Additionally, *radial* stresses are present that are, in some cases, significant. To visualize these, take a paper pad and bend it in an arc, as shown in Figure 4.13a. Apply compressive forces with the thumbs and forefingers so that the sheets will not slide. Next, carefully superimpose (with the thumbs and forefingers) a small bending moment, as in 4.13b. Note the separation of the sheets in the center of the "beam," indicating the presence of *radial tension* (radial compression for opposite bending). These radial stresses are small if the center portion of the beam is reasonably heavy. But for an I beam with a thin web, for example, the radial stresses can be large enough to cause damage—particularly if the beam is made of a brittle material or is subjected to fatigue loading. Further information on curved-beam radial stresses is contained in [8] and [9].

4.7   *Transverse Shear Loading in Beams*

Although the *average* transverse shear stress in beams such as the shaft in Chapter 2, Figure 2.11 is equal to V/A (i.e., 1580 lb divided by the cross-sectional area in the critical shaft section shown in Figure 2.12), the *maximum* shear stress is substantially higher. We will now review an analysis of the distribution of this transverse shear stress, with emphasis on an understanding of the basic concepts involved.

Figure 4.14 shows a beam of an arbitrary cross section that is symmetrical about the plane of loading. It is supported at the ends and carries a concentrated load at the center. We wish to investigate the distribution of transverse shear stress in a plane located distance x from the left support, and at a distance y above the neutral axis. A small square element at this location is shown in the upper-right drawing. The right and left faces of the element are subjected to shear stresses (the magnitude of which is to be determined) with directions established by the fact that the only external force

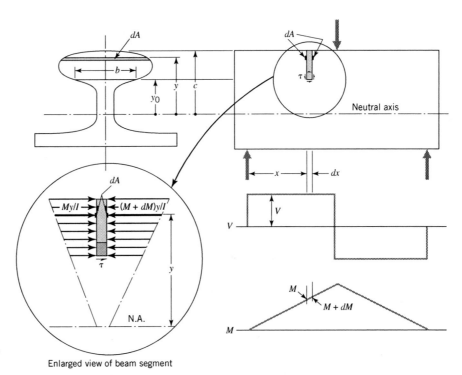

Enlarged view of beam segment

to the left of the element is directed upward, and the resultant of external forces on the right is downward. If only these two vectors acted on the element, it would tend to rotate clockwise. This is prevented by the counterclockwise shear stresses shown on the top and bottom surfaces of the element. The reality of these horizontal shear stresses is easy to visualize: if one loads a book or paper tablet with the forces in Figure 4.14, the pages slide on each other; if the plastic playing cards in a long-unused deck are stuck together, flexing the deck with this three-point beam loading breaks them loose. Coming back to the small element in the figure, we can determine the magnitude of all four shear stresses by evaluating any one of them. We now proceed to evaluate the shear stress on the *bottom* of the element.

Imagine two transverse saw cuts, distance dx apart, starting at the top of the beam and continuing down just to include the sides of the square element. This serves to isolate a segment of the beam, the bottom surface of which is the bottom surface of the element acted upon by shear stress τ. Note that the beam segment involves the full width of the beam. Its bottom surface, acted upon by the unknown shear stress, has a rectangular area of dimensions dx and b. Dimension b will, of course, be different for various values of y_0 (i.e., for various depths of "saw cut").

The enlarged view in Figure 4.14 shows the forces acting on the beam segment. A key point is that the bending stresses are *slightly greater on the right side* where the bending moment is greater than on the left side by amount dM. The unknown shear stress at the bottom must be sufficiently large to compensate for this inequality. Because the sum of horizontal forces must be zero,

$$\int_{y=y_0}^{y=c} \frac{dM\, y}{I}\, dA = \tau b\, dx$$

But $dM = V \, dx$; hence,

$$\int_{y=y_0}^{y=c} \frac{V \, dx \, y}{I} \, dA = \tau b \, dx$$

Solving for τ gives

$$\tau = \frac{V}{Ib} \int_{y=y_0}^{y=c} y \, dA \qquad \qquad \textbf{(4.12)}$$

Let us now make a few important observations concerning this equation. First, the shear stress is zero at the top (and bottom) surfaces. This is true because the saw cuts have no depth, so there is no inequality of bending forces on the two sides to be compensated for by shear stress at the bottom. (Looking at it another way, if the small element in the upper right of Figure 4.14 is moved to the very top, then the top surface of the element is part of the free surface of the beam. There is nothing in contact with this surface that could impose a shear stress. If there is no shear stress on the top of the element, the requirements of equilibrium prohibit shear stresses on any of the other three sides.) As the saw cuts acquire increasing depth, larger and larger surfaces are exposed to the inequality of bending stress; hence, the compensating shear stress must increase correspondingly. Note that at the saw cut depth shown in Figure 4.14, a great increase in shear stress would result from cutting just a little deeper (i.e., slightly reducing y_0) because the area over which the compensating shear stress acts is rapidly decreasing (i.e., b decreases rapidly as y_0 is decreased). Note further that the maximum shear stress is experienced at the neutral axis. This is a most gratifying situation! The maximum shear stress exists precisely where it can best be tolerated—at the neutral axis where the bending stress is zero. At the critical extreme fibers where the bending stress is maximum, the shear stress is zero. (A study of Eq. 4.12 indicates that for unusual sections having a width, b, *at* the neutral axis substantially greater than the width *near* the neutral axis, the maximum shear stress will not be at the neutral axis. However, this is seldom of significance.)

It often helps to establish concepts clearly in mind if we can visualize them on a physical model. Figure 4.15 shows an ordinary rubber eraser ruled with a row of elements that indicates relative shear strains (hence, stresses) when the eraser is loaded as a beam (as shown in Figure 4.15*b*). If the eraser is loaded carefully, we can see that the top and bottom elements are negligibly distorted (i.e., the initial right angles remain right angles) while the greatest distortion in the right-angle corners occurs in the center elements.

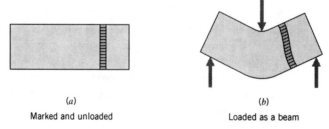

(a)

Marked and unloaded

(b)

Loaded as a beam

FIGURE 4.15

Transverse shear strain (hence stress) distribution shown by rubber eraser.

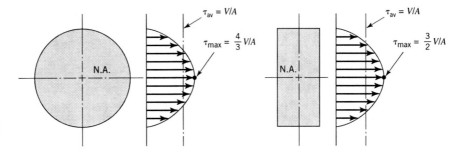

FIGURE 4.16
Transverse shear stress distribution in solid round and rectangular sections.

Applying Eq. 4.12 to solid round and rectangular sections, we find the parabolic shear stress distributions shown in Figure 4.16, with maximum values at the neutral axis for *solid round* sections of

$$\tau_{\max} = \tfrac{4}{3} V/A \qquad (4.13)$$

for *solid rectangular* sections of

$$\tau_{\max} = \tfrac{3}{2} V/A \qquad (4.14)$$

For a hollow round section, the stress distribution depends on the ratio of inside to outside diameter, but for *thin-wall tubing*, a good approximation of the maximum shear stress is

$$\tau_{\max} = 2V/A \qquad (4.15)$$

For a conventional I-beam section, width b is so much less in the web than in the flanges that the shear stresses are much higher in the web. In fact, the shear stresses throughout the web are often approximated by dividing the shear force, V, by the area of the web only, with the web considered as extending the entire depth of the beam.

In the foregoing analysis the tacit assumption was made that the shear stress is uniform across the beam width, b, at any distance, y_0, from the neutral axis (see Figure 4.14). Although not strictly correct, this assumption seldom leads to errors of engineering significance. The variation of shear stress across the width of a beam is treated in [8] and [11]. Another topic left to advanced texts in strength of materials is the loading of beams whose cross sections have no axes.

A final point to be noted is that only in very *short* beams are the transverse shear stresses likely to be of importance *in comparison with the bending stresses*. The principle behind this generalization is illustrated in Figure 4.17, where the same loads are

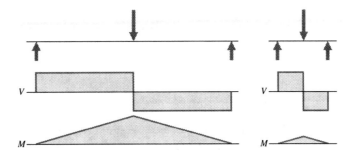

FIGURE 4.17
Effect of beam length on bending and shear loading.

141

shown applied to a long and short beam. Both beams have the same shear load and the same *slope* of the bending moment diagram. As the beam length approaches zero, the bending moment (and bending stresses) approaches zero, while the shear load and stresses remain unchanged.

SAMPLE PROBLEM 4.2   Determine Shear Stress Distribution

Determine the shear stress distribution for the beam and loading shown in Figure 4.18. Compare this with the maximum bending stress.

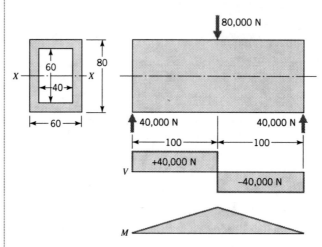

FIGURE 4.18

Sample Problem 4.2. Beam shear stress distribution. Note: all dimensions are in millimeters; section properties are $A = 2400 \text{ mm}^2$; $I_x = 1840 \times 10^6 \text{ mm}^4$.

SOLUTION

Known: A rectangular beam with given cross-sectional geometry has a specified central load.

Find: Determine the shear stress distribution and the maximum bending stress.

Assumptions:

1. The beam is initially straight.

2. The beam is loaded in a plane of symmetry.

3. The shear stress in the beam is uniform across the beam width at each location from the neutral axis.

Schematic and Given Data:

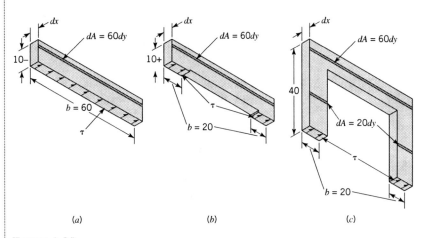

(a)   (b)   (c)

FIGURE 4.19
Sample Problem 4.2 partial solution—τ at three levels.

Analysis:

1. With reference to Figure 4.14 and Eq. 4.12, it is known at the outset that $\tau = 0$ at the top and bottom surfaces. This gives a start in plotting the shear stress distribution in Figure 4.20. As the imaginary parallel saw cuts (described in connection with Figure 4.14) proceed down from the top to increasing depth, the areas exposed to the slightly unbalanced bending stresses increase, thereby causing the compensating shear stress at the bottom of the imaginary segment to increase parabolically. This continues to a saw cut depth of 10 mm. Figure 4.19a illustrates the imaginary segment just before the saw cuts break through the interior surface of the section. The shear stress at this level (which acts on bottom area 60·dx) is calculated as

$$\tau = \frac{V}{Ib} \int_{y=y_0}^{y=c} y\,dA = \frac{40{,}000}{(1.840 \times 10^6)(60)} \int_{y=30}^{y=40} y(60\,dy)$$

$$= \frac{40{,}000}{(1.840 \times 10^6)(60)}(60)\left[\frac{y^2}{2}\right]_{y=30}^{y=40} = 7.61 \text{ N/mm}^2, \text{ or } 7.61 \text{ MPa}$$

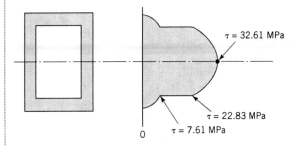

FIGURE 4.20
Plot of shear stress distribution—Sample Problem 4.2.

143

2. With a slightly deeper saw cut, the inner surface is broken through, and the area over which the shear stress acts is suddenly reduced to 20 dy, as shown in Figure 4.19b. The unbalanced bending forces acting on the segment sides are virtually unchanged. Thus, the only term that changes in Eq. 4.12 is b, which is reduced by a factor of 3, thereby giving a shear stress three times as high, or 22.83 MPa.

3. As the saw cut depth increases until it reaches the neutral axis, the area over which the shear stress acts remains the same, while greater and greater imbalances build up as additional areas dA are exposed. But, as shown in Figure 4.19c, these added areas dA are only one-third as large as those in the top portion of the section. Hence, the increased shear stress at the neutral axis is not as great as might at first be expected. When using Eq. 4.12 to find τ at the neutral axis, note that two integrals are involved, one covering the range of y from 0 to 30 mm and the other from 30 to 40 mm. (The latter integral, of course, has already been evaluated).

$$\tau = \frac{V}{Ib}\int_{y=y_0}^{y=c} y\, dA = \frac{40{,}000}{(1.840 \times 10^6)(20)}\left[\int_{y=0}^{y=30} y(20\, dy) + \int_{y=30}^{y=40} y(60\, dy)\right]$$

$$= \frac{40{,}000}{(1.840 \times 10^6)(20)}(20)\left[\frac{y^2}{2}\right]_{y=0}^{y=30} + 22.83$$

$$= 32.61 \text{ N/mm}^2, \text{ or } 32.61 \text{ MPa}$$

These calculations enable the shear stress plot in Figure 4.20 to be drawn.

4. By way of comparison, the maximum bending stresses occur in the top and bottom surfaces of the beam, halfway along its length, where the bending moment is highest. Here, the bending stress is computed as

$$\sigma = \frac{Mc}{I} = \frac{(40{,}000 \times 100)(40)}{1.84 \times 10^6} = 86.96 \text{ N/mm}^2$$

$$= 86.96 \text{ MPa}$$

Comment: Recalling that the shear stress must be zero at the exposed inner surface of the section, it is apparent that the evenly distributed shear stress assumed in Figure 4.19a is incorrect, and that the shear stresses in the outer supported portions of the section at this level will be higher than the calculated value of 7.61 MPa. This is of little importance because, to the degree that shear stresses are of concern, attention will be focused at the level just below, where the calculated value of τ is three times as high, or at the neutral axis where it is a maximum.

4.8 Induced Stresses, Mohr Circle Representation

Simple tensile or compressive loading induces shear stresses on certain planes; similarly, pure shear loading induces tension and compression. In some cases the induced stresses can be more damaging to the material than the direct stresses.

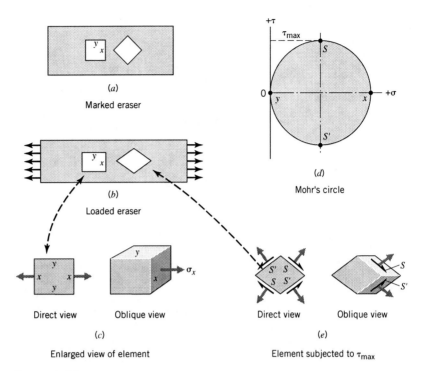

(a)
Marked eraser

(b)
Loaded eraser

(d)
Mohr's circle

Direct view   Oblique view

(c)

Enlarged view of element

Direct view   Oblique view

(e)

Element subjected to τ_{max}

FIGURE 4.21

Induced shear stress from pure tensile loading.

Figure 4.21*a* shows an ordinary rubber eraser marked with two large square elements, one oriented in the direction of the sides of the eraser, and the other at 45°. Figure 4.21*b* shows the marked surface subjected to tension (as by flexing the eraser). A *shear* distortion of the 45° square is clearly evident. If the eraser surface is loaded in compression, the shear distortion of the 45° square is reversed.

Figure 4.21*c* shows an enlarged view of a marked element with vertical and horizontal faces marked *x* and *y*, and with tensile stress σ_x acting on the *x* faces. The *x* and *y* faces of the element are, of course, perpendicular to the eraser surface, as is made clear by the oblique view, also shown in Figure 4.21*c*.

A Mohr circle plot of the stresses on the element is shown in Figure 4.21*d*. Points *x* and *y* are plotted to represent the normal and shear stresses acting on the *x* and *y* faces. The circle is then drawn with the line *xy* as a diameter.

Proof of the Mohr circle relationships is left to elementary texts on strength of materials. The emphasis here is on obtaining a clear understanding of the significance and interpretation of the Mohr plot. First, note that as an imaginary cutting plane through the element is rotated (always keeping it perpendicular to the surface), one goes from an *x* plane (vertical), to a *y* plane (horizontal), and on to an *x* plane again in *only 180°*. The normal and shear stresses acting on all these cutting planes are spread out over the full *360°* of the Mohr circle in Figure 4.21*d*. Thus, angles measured on the circle are *twice* the corresponding angles on the element itself. For example, *x* and *y* are 90° apart on the element and 180° apart on the circle.

A second important point is that if we adhere to the shear stress sign convention given in Section 4.4 (i.e., positive-clockwise), rotation of the cutting plane in either

145

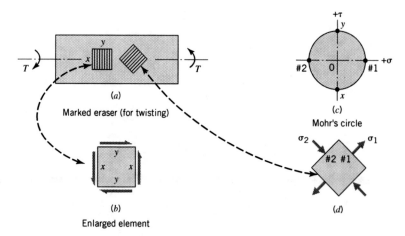

FIGURE 4.22

Induced axial stress from pure shear loading.

direction on the element corresponds to rotating *twice* as far on the circle and *in the same direction.*

Points S and S' on the circle (Figure 4.21*d*) represent planes of maximum positive and negative shear. On the circle, point S is 90° *counterclockwise* of *x*. Hence, on the element plane S is 45° *counterclockwise* of vertical plane *x*. The element drawn in Figure 4.21*e* shows the correctly oriented planes S, which are infinitesimally close together; hence, they really represent a single plane. The Mohr circle shows that S planes are acted upon by a positive axial stress and a *positive* shear stress, both of magnitude $\sigma_x/2$. These stresses are shown in Figure 4.21*e*. The S' plane orientation and stresses are correspondingly determined. (Note that the 45° square in Figures 4.21*a* and 4.21*b* represents an element subjected to *maximum* shear.)

Figure 4.22*a* shows a marked rubber eraser prior to being loaded in torsion. When the torsional or twisting load is applied, all the initial right angles in the square lined up with the eraser sides change substantially, indicating shear. In contrast, the right angles in the 45° square do *not* change. When twisting in one direction, the parallel lines in the 45° square get shorter and farther apart. Reverse the twisting and they get longer and closer together. But, in neither case is there an angle change indicating shear.

Figure 4.22*b* shows the direct shear stresses acting on the faces of the element lined up with the eraser. Note that the *x* faces experience negative (counterclockwise) shear because the direction of load torque is such that it displaces the left face downward and the right face upward. Corresponding positive shear is, of course, required on the *y* faces in order to provide equilibrium. The direct stresses are plotted for *x* and *y* faces to establish the Mohr circle in 4.22*c*. Planes subjected to zero shear (also to the extreme values of tension and compression) are called *principal planes.* These are designated as #1 and #2 on the circle. A corresponding *principal element* is shown in Figure 4.22*d*.

Mohr's circle is named after Otto Mohr, a distinguished German structural engineer and professor who proposed it in 1880 and described it in a published article [4] in 1882. This graphical technique is extremely useful in solving problems and in visualizing the nature of stress states at points of interest.

4.9 *Combined Stresses—Mohr Circle Representation*

This topic can best be presented through the use of a typical example.

SAMPLE PROBLEM 4.3   Stresses in Stationary Shaft

Figure 4.23 represents a stationary shaft and pulley subjected to a 2000-lb static load. Determine the location of highest stresses in the 1-in.-diameter section, and calculate the stresses at that point.

SOLUTION

Known: A shaft of given geometry is subjected to a known combined loading.

Find: Determine the magnitude and location of the highest stresses.

Schematic and Given Data:

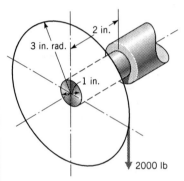

FIGURE 4.23
Shaft subjected to combined loading. For a solid 1-in.-diameter shaft: $A = \pi d^2/4 = 0.785$ in.^{2}; $I = \pi d^4/64 = 0.049$ in.^{4}; and $J = \pi d^4/32 = 0.098$ in.^{4} (see Appendix B-1).

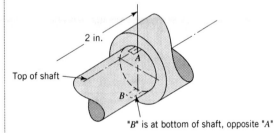

"*B*" is at bottom of shaft, opposite "*A*"

FIGURE 4.24
Location of highest stresses.

Assumptions:

1. The stress concentration at the 1-in.-diameter shaft step can be ignored.

2. The compressive stress on the shaft surface caused by atmospheric pressure has negligible effects.

Analysis:

1. The shaft is subjected to torsion, bending, and transverse shear. Torsional stresses are a maximum over the entire shaft surface. Bending stresses are a maximum at points *A* and *B*, shown in Figure 4.24. Note that both the bending moment and the distance from the neutral bending axis are a maximum at these two locations.

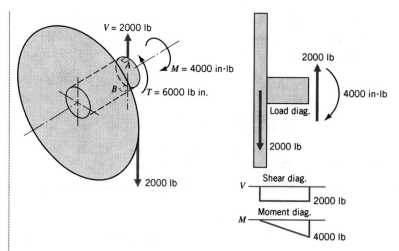

FIGURE 4.25
Free-body and load diagrams.

Transverse shear stresses are relatively small compared to bending stresses, and equal to zero at points *A* and *B* (see Section 4.7). Thus they can be neglected. Clearly it is the section containing points *A* and *B* that must be investigated.

2. In Figure 4.25, imagine the shaft to be cut off at the section containing *A* and *B*, and consider the member thus obtained as a *free body in equilibrium*. This is a convenient way of being certain that all loads acting on the cutting plane are identified. In this case there are the three loads, *M*, *T*, and *V*, as shown. Note that the free body is indeed in equilibrium, the summation of all forces and moments being zero. Also in Figure 4.25 are the load, shear, and moment diagrams for the isolated free body.

3. Compute the direct stresses associated with loads.
   Bending stresses (tension at *A*; compression at *B*):

   $$\sigma_x = \frac{Mc}{I} = \frac{(4000 \text{ in} \cdot \text{lb})\left(\frac{1}{2}\text{in.}\right)}{0.049 \text{ in.}^4} = 40{,}816 \text{ psi} \approx 40.8 \text{ ksi}$$

   Torsional stresses (over the entire surface):

   $$\tau_{xy} = \frac{Tr}{J} = \frac{(6000 \text{ lb} \cdot \text{in.})\left(\frac{1}{2}\text{in.}\right)}{0.098 \text{ in.}^4} = 30{,}612 \text{ psi} \approx 30.6 \text{ ksi}$$

4. Figure 4.26 shows the stresses acting on an element at *A*. (Stresses at *B* are the same except that the bending stress is compressive.) Note that the directions of the two counterclockwise shear stress vectors follow directly from the direction of twisting of the shaft. Then the clockwise direction of the shear vectors on the other pair of faces follows from the requirement of equilibrium. (Note: Subscripts used with the shear stresses in Figure 4.26 illustrate a common convention, but one that is not of importance in this text: τ_{xy} acts *on* an *x* face, in the *y* direction; τ_{yx} acts on a *y* face, in the *x* direction. No difficulties would be encountered if both were regarded as τ_{xy}, and the positive-clockwise rule is followed in order to keep the signs straight.)

   The isometric views are shown for direct comparison with previous figures. The direct view is the conventional way to show a stressed element. The three-

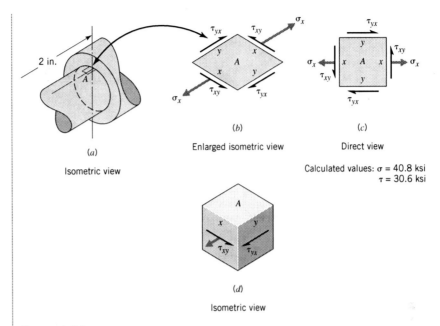

(b)
Enlarged isometric view

(c)
Direct view

(a)
Isometric view

Calculated values: σ = 40.8 ksi
τ = 30.6 ksi

(d)
Isometric view

FIGURE 4.26
Various views of element *A*.

dimensional representation shows how the stresses really act on *planes perpendicular to the surface*. The shaft surface itself is unloaded, except for atmospheric pressure, which is negligible.

5. Figure 4.26 shows all the stresses acting on an element at the most critical stress location. However, the analysis can be carried further. First, recall that the cubical element is infinitesimally small, and its *x* and *y* faces represent *only two* of the infinite number of planes perpendicular to the shaft surface passing through *A*. In general, there will be other planes subjected to higher levels of normal stress and shear stress. Mohr's circle provides a convenient means for determining and representing the normal and shear stresses acting on *all* planes through *A*, and perpendicular to the surface. This circle is constructed in Figure 4.27 by

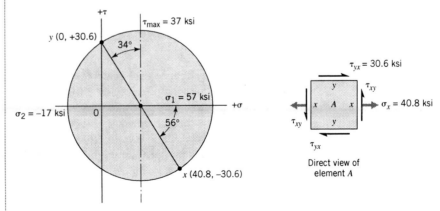

FIGURE 4.27
Mohr circle representation at point *A* of 4.25.

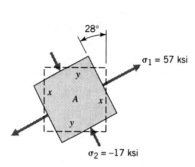

FIGURE 4.28
Principal element at A (direct view) shown in relation to x and y faces.

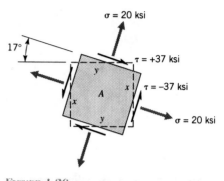

FIGURE 4.29
Maximum shear element at A (direct view) shown in relation to x and y faces.

first plotting points representing stresses on the x and y planes, connecting these points with a straight line, and then drawing the circle with the line xy as a diameter. The circle provides a convenient graphical solution for the magnitude and orientation of principal stresses σ_1 and σ_2. These stresses are shown on a *principal element* at point A, drawn in Figure 4.28. Note that the #1 principal plane is located by starting with the x plane and rotating counterclockwise half of the 56° measured on the circle, and so on.

6. Figure 4.28 shows the magnitude and orientation of the highest normal stresses. It may also be of interest to represent similarly the highest shear stresses. This is done in Figure 4.29. Observe again the rules of

   a. rotating in the *same direction* on the element and the circle, and

   b. using angles on the circle that are *twice* those on the element.

Comment: In support of neglecting the transverse shear stress in step 1, it is of interest to note that its maximum value at the neutral bending axis of the 1-in.-diameter shaft is $4V/3A = (4)(2000 \text{ lb})/[(3)(\pi)(1 \text{ in.})^2/4] = 3.4$ ksi

4.10   Stress Equations Related to Mohr's Circle

The derivation of the analytical expressions relating normal and shear stresses to the angle of the cutting plane is given in elementary texts on strength of materials and need not be repeated here. The important equations follow.

If the stresses on an element of given orientation are known (as in Figure 4.26), the principal stresses, principal directions, and maximum shear stress can be found from a Mohr circle plot or from the following equations,

$$\sigma_1, \sigma_2 = \frac{\sigma_x + \sigma_y}{2} \pm \sqrt{\tau_{xy}^2 + \left(\frac{\sigma_x - \sigma_y}{2}\right)^2} \qquad \textbf{(4.16)}$$

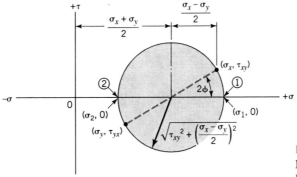

FIGURE 4.30
Mohr's circle illustrating
Eqs. 4.16, 4.17, and 4.18.

$$2\phi = \tan^{-1} \frac{2\tau_{xy}}{\sigma_x - \sigma_y} \tag{4.17}$$

$$\tau_{max} = \pm \sqrt{\tau_{xy}^2 + \left(\frac{\sigma_x - \sigma_y}{2}\right)^2} \tag{4.18}$$

where ϕ is the angle between the principal axes and the x and y axes (or the angle between the principal planes and the x and y planes). When ϕ is *positive*, the principal axes (or planes) are *clockwise* from the x and y axes (or planes).

When the principal stresses are known and it is desired to determine the stresses acting on a plane oriented at any angle ϕ from the #1 principal plane, the equations are

$$\sigma_\phi = \frac{\sigma_1 + \sigma_2}{2} + \frac{\sigma_1 - \sigma_2}{2} \cos 2\phi \tag{4.19}$$

$$\tau_\phi = \frac{\sigma_1 - \sigma_2}{2} \sin 2\phi \tag{4.20}$$

Equations 4.16 through 4.18 can readily be developed from the Mohr circle shown in Figure 4.30, and Eqs. 4.19 and 4.20 from Figure 4.31. This provides a welcome substitute for rote memory, and one that aids in understanding the physical significance of the equations.

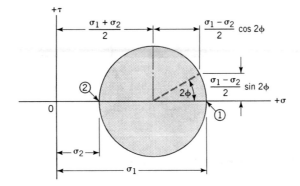

FIGURE 4.31
Mohr's circle illustrating
Eqs. 4.19 and 4.20.

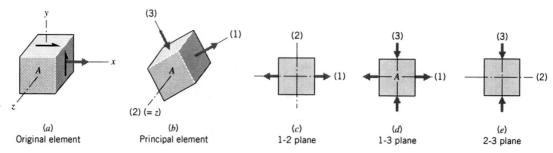

(a)	(b)	(c)	(d)	(e)
Original element	Principal element	1-2 plane	1-3 plane	2-3 plane

FIGURE 4.32

Elements representing the state of stress at point A.

4.11 Three-Dimensional Stresses

Since stresses exist only in real bodies that are three-dimensional, it is best always to think of stresses in three-dimensional terms. Uniaxial stress states (pure tension or compression) involve three principal stresses, but two of them are zero. Biaxial stresses (as pure shear, or the problem represented in Figures 4.23 through 4.29) involve one principal stress of zero. Forgetting about a zero principal stress can lead to serious errors, as is illustrated later in this section.

Let us extend the analysis of the state of stress at point *A* of Figure 4.24 by treating this as a three-dimensional problem. Figure 4.32 shows five views of stress elements at point *A*: (*a*) an oblique view, showing the original *x* and *y* planes and the stresses on these planes; (*b*) a principal element, obtained by rotating 28° about the *z* axis; (*c, d, e*) direct or true views of the 1–2, 1–3, and 2–3 planes of the principal element.

A complete Mohr circle representation of this state of stress is shown in Figure 4.33. The large circle between points 1 and 3 represents stresses on all planes through point *A*, which contain the 2, or *z*, axis. The small circle between 2 and 3 gives stresses on all planes containing the 1 axis, and the circle between 1 and 2 represents stresses on planes containing the 3 axis.

Although each of the three circles represents an infinite number of planes through point *A*, a higher order of infinity remains that does not contain *any* of the principal

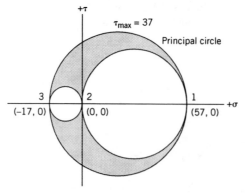

FIGURE 4.33

Complete Mohr circle representation of the stress state at point A of Figure 4.25.

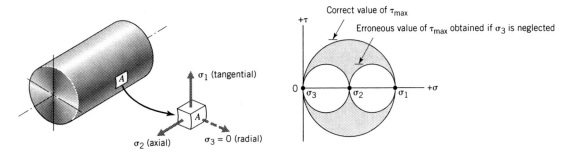

FIGURE 4.34

Example of biaxial stress where correct determination of τ_{max} requires taking σ_3 into consideration. Internally pressurized cylinder illustrates biaxial stress states where correct determination of τ_{max} requires taking σ_3 into account. Note that (1) for an element on the inside surface, σ_3 is negative and numerically equal to the internal fluid pressure and (2) for thin-wall cylinders $\sigma_2 \approx \sigma_1/2$.

axes. It can be shown that *all* such planes are subjected to stresses represented by points in the shaded area between the circles. The location of the specific point in this area that corresponds to any given plane is seldom of concern, but the interested reader can find the procedure involved in references such as [1, Section 3.7].

Since the largest of the three Mohr circles always represents the maximum shear stress as well as the two extreme values of normal stress, Mohr called this the *principal circle*.

A common example in which the maximum shear stress would be missed if we failed to include the zero principal stress in the Mohr plot is the outer surface of a pressurized cylinder. Here, the axial and tangential stresses are tensile principal stresses, and the unloaded outer surface ensures that the third principal stress is zero. Figure 4.34 illustrates both the correct value of maximum shear stress and the incorrect value obtained from a simple two-dimensional analysis. The same situation exists at the inner surface of the cylinder, except that the third principal stress (which acts on the surface) is not zero but a negative value numerically equal to the internal fluid pressure.

For the rare case in which there are significant shear stresses on *all* faces of the stress element, the reader is referred to detailed works on theoretical stress analysis—for example, [1,11].

4.12 *Stress Concentration Factors, K_t*

In Section 4.2, Figure 4.1*e* indicated lines of force flow through a tensile link. It was noted earlier that a uniform distribution of these lines (hence, a uniform distribution of stress) existed only in regions substantially removed from the ends. Near the ends, the force flow lines indicate a *concentration* of stress near the outer surface. This same stress concentration effect exists for bending and torsional loading. We now wish to evaluate the stress concentration associated with various geometric configurations so that the *maximum stresses* existing in a part can be determined.

The first mathematical treatments of stress concentration were published shortly after 1900 [5]. In order to handle other than very simple cases, experimental methods for measuring highly localized stresses were developed and used. In recent years, computerized finite-element studies have also been employed. The results of many of these studies are available in the form of published graphs, such as those in Figures 4.35 through 4.41. These give values of the *theoretical stress concentration factor*, K_t (based on a theoretical elastic, homogeneous, isotropic material), for use in the equations

$$\sigma_{\text{max}} = K_t \sigma_{\text{nom}} \quad \text{and} \quad \tau_{\text{max}} = K_t \tau_{\text{nom}} \qquad (4.21)$$

For example, the maximum stress for axial loading (of an ideal material) would be obtained by multiplying P/A by the appropriate value of K_t.

Note that the stress concentration graphs are plotted on the basis of *dimensionless ratios*, indicating that only the *shape* (not the size) of the part is involved. Also note that stress concentration factors are different for axial, bending, and torsional loading. Among the most extensive and authoritative references on stress concentration factors are those of R. E. Peterson [6,7].

In many situations involving notched parts in tension or bending, the notch not only increases the primary stress but also causes one or both of the other principal stresses to take on nonzero values. This is referred to as the *biaxial or triaxial effect of stress raisers* ("stress raiser" is a general term applied to notches, holes, threads, etc.). Although this is a small secondary effect that will not be pursued further in this book, it is desirable to be able to visualize how these additional stress components can arise. Consider, for example, a soft rubber model of the grooved shaft in tension illustrated in Figure 4.36*b*. As the tensile load is increased, there will be a tendency for the outer surface to pull into a smooth cylinder. This will involve an *increase* in the diameter and circumference of the section in the plane of the notch. The increased circumference gives rise to a *tangential* stress, which is a maximum at the surface. The increase in diameter is associated with the creation of *radial* stresses. (Remember, though, that this radial stress must be zero at the surface because there are no external radial forces acting there.)

Stress concentration factor graphs, such as those in Figures 4.35 through 4.41, pertain to the maximum stress, existing at the surface of the stress raiser. The lower values of stress elsewhere in the cross section are seldom of interest but, in simple cases, can be determined analytically from the theory of elasticity, or they can be approximated by finite-element techniques or by experimental procedures, such as photoelasticity. The variation in stress over the cross section (i.e., the stress *gradient*) is given for a few cases in [3].

4.13   *Importance of Stress Concentration*

It should be emphasized that the stress concentration factors given in the graphs are *theoretical* (hence, the subscript *t*) or *geometric* factors based on a theoretical homogeneous, isotropic, and elastic material. Real materials have microscopic irregularities causing a certain nonuniformity of microscopic stress distribution, even in notch-free parts. Hence, the introduction of a stress raiser may not cause as much *additional* damage as indicated by the theoretical factor. Moreover, real parts—even if free of stress raisers—have surface irregularities (resulting from processing and use) that can be considered as extremely small notches.

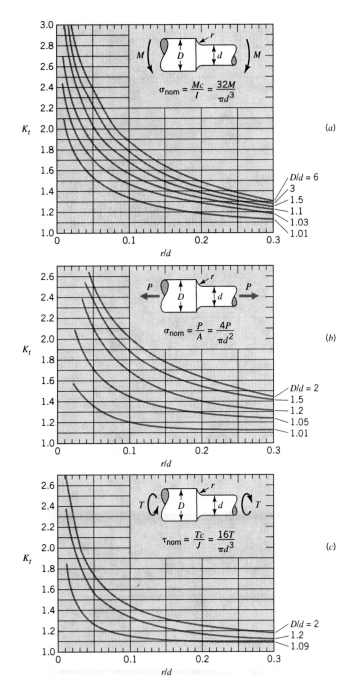

FIGURE 4.35
Shaft with fillet (*a*) bending; (*b*) axial load; (*c*) torsion [7].

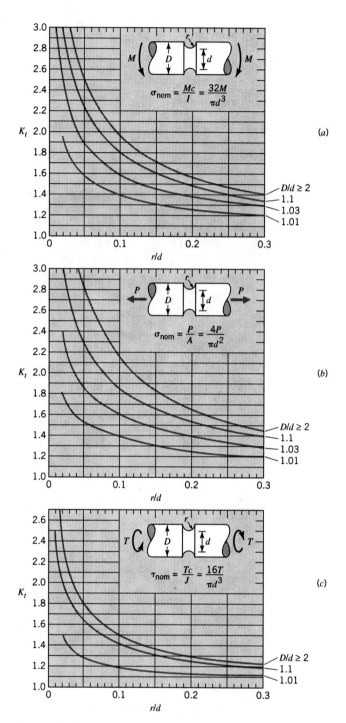

FIGURE 4.36

Grooved shaft (*a*) bending; (*b*) axial load; (*c*) torsion [7].

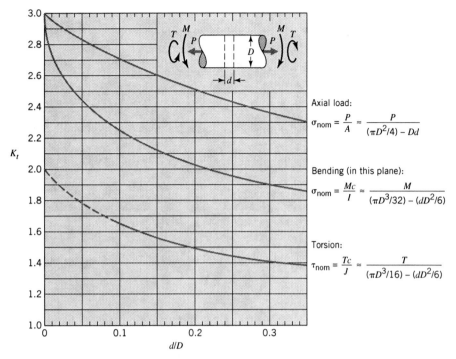

Axial load:

$$\sigma_{nom} = \frac{P}{A} \approx \frac{P}{(\pi D^2/4) - Dd}$$

Bending (in this plane):

$$\sigma_{nom} = \frac{Mc}{I} \approx \frac{M}{(\pi D^3/32) - (dD^2/6)}$$

Torsion:

$$\tau_{nom} = \frac{Tc}{J} \approx \frac{T}{(\pi D^3/16) - (dD^2/6)}$$

FIGURE 4.37
Shaft with radius hole [7].

The extent to which the engineer must take stress concentration into account depends on (1) the extent to which the real material deviates from the theoretical and (2) whether the loading is static, or involves impact or fatigue. For materials permeated with internal discontinuities, such as gray cast iron, stress raisers usually have little effect, regardless of the nature of loading. This is so because surface or geometric irregularities seldom cause more severe stress concentration than that already associated with the internal irregularities. For fatigue and impact loading of most engineering materials, stress concentration must be considered, as will be seen in subsequent chapters. For the case of static loading being treated in this chapter, stress concentration is important only with unusual materials that are both brittle and relatively homogeneous[2]; or for normally ductile materials that, under special conditions, *behave* in a brittle manner (see Chapter 6 for further discussion). For the usual engineering materials having some ductility (and under conditions such that they *behave* in a ductile manner), it is customary to ignore stress concentration for static loads. The basis for this is illustrated in the following discussion.

Figure 4.42*a* and *b* show two flat tensile bars each having a minimum cross-sectional area of *A*, and each made of a ductile material having the "idealized" stress–strain curve shown in Figure 4.42*e*. The load on the unnotched bar (Figure 4.42*a*) can be increased to a value equal to the product of area times yield

---

[2] A common example: When tearing open a package wrapped in clear plastic film, a sharp notch in the edge is *most* helpful!

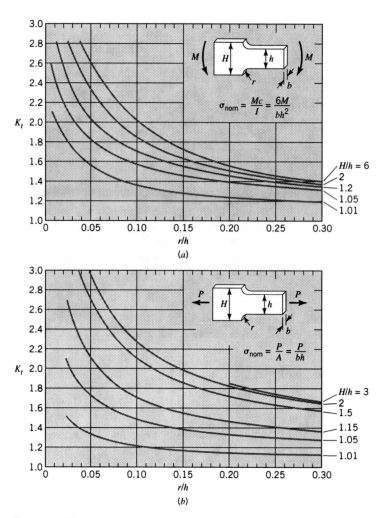

FIGURE 4.38
Bar with shoulder fillet (*a*) bending; (*b*) axial load [7].

strength before failure (gross yielding) occurs. This is represented in Figure 4.42*c*. Since the grooved bar in Figure 4.42*b* has a stress concentration factor of 2, yielding will *begin* at only half the load, as shown in Figure 4.42*d*. This is repeated as curve "a" of Figure 4.42*f*. As the load is increased, the stress distribution (shown in Figure 4.42*f*) becomes "b," "c," and finally "d." These curves reflect a continuous deepening of local yielding, which began at the root of the groove; but gross (or general) yielding involving the entire cross section is not ready to begin until "d" is reached. Note that the load associated with curve "d" is identical to the unnotched load capacity, shown in Figure 4.42*c*. Also note that curve "d" can be achieved without significant stretching of the part. The part as a whole cannot be significantly elongated without yielding the entire cross section, including the portion at the center. Thus, for most practical purposes, the grooved bar will carry the same static load as the ungrooved bar.

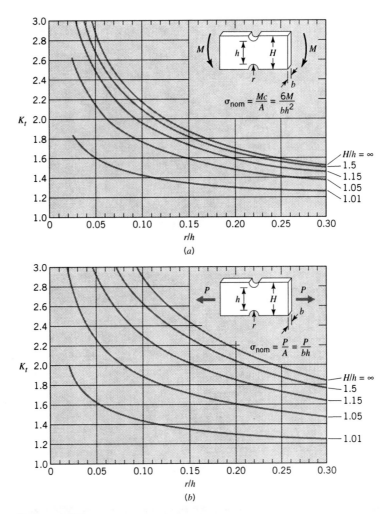

FIGURE 4.39
Notched flat bar (*a*) bending; (*b*) tension [7].

4.14 *Residual Stresses Caused by Yielding—Axial Loading*

When a part is yielded nonuniformly throughout a cross section, *residual stresses* remain in this cross section after the external load is removed. Consider, for example, the four levels of loading of the notched flat tensile bar shown in Figure 4.42*f*. This same bar and the four levels of loading are represented in the left column of Figure 4.43. Note that only *slight* yielding is involved—not major yielding such as often occurs in processing. The middle column in this figure shows the *change* in stress when the load is removed. Except for Figure 4.43*a*, where the load was not quite enough to cause yielding at the notch root, the stress change when the load is removed does not exactly cancel the stresses caused by applying the load. Hence,

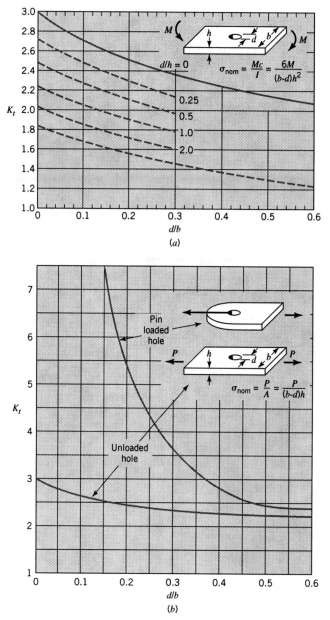

FIGURE 4.40
Plate with central hole (*a*) bending [7]; (*b*) axial hole [10].

residual stresses remain after the load is removed. These are shown in the right column of Figure 4.43.

Note that in each case shown in Figure 4.43, the stress *change* caused by removing the load is *elastic*.

It is often helpful in visualizing the development of residual stresses such as those shown in Figure 4.43 to imagine a column of small strain gages mounted from the top to the bottom of the notched section. If these gages are attached *while the load is*

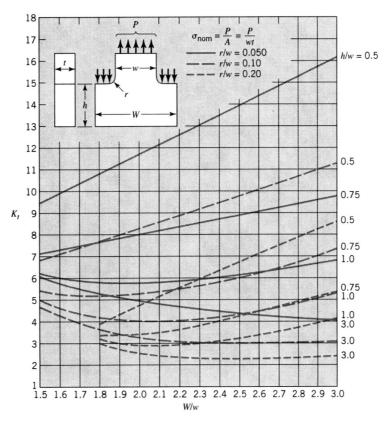

FIGURE 4.11
T-head member with an axial load [7].

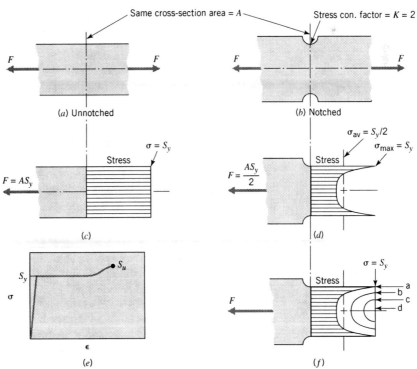

FIGURE 4.12
Tensile stress distribution of an unnotched and a notched ductile part.

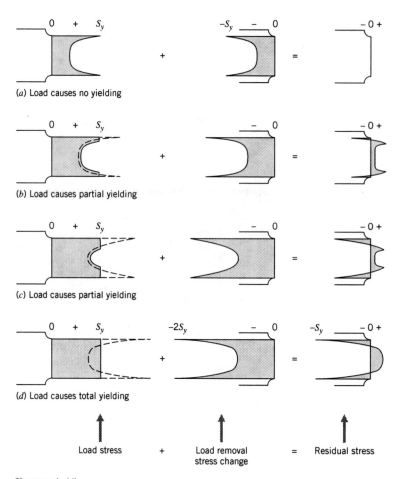

FIGURE 4.43

FIGURE 4.43
Residual stresses caused by yielding of a notched tensile bar of $K = 2$ for stress gradients a to d in 4.42*f*.

applied to the bar, they will initially all read zero, although the actual stresses in the cross section are as shown in the left column. As the tensile load is released, the gages will all indicate *compression*, as shown in the middle column of the figure. The *average* compressive stress indicated by the gages when the load is completely removed will, of course, be *P/A*, but the distribution of this compressive stress will be completely elastic, so long as no yielding occurs *during the load release*. This provision is satisfied in all the cases shown. Even in Figure 4.43*d*, where the elastic change in stress at the notch root is $2S_y$ (the average change in stress is S_y, and at the notch root it is KS_y), no yielding occurs. Assuming equal yield strengths in tension and compression, the notch root material goes from S_y in tension when the load is applied to S_y in compression when the load is released.

The elastic stress gradient curves associated with the various loads can be estimated graphically, as shown by the dotted lines in the left column of Figure 4.43. (Note that in each case the dotted curve corresponds to the same *average* stress as the solid curve, and that the maximum stress shown in the dotted curve is twice the average stress because $K = 2$.) After the dotted curves are sketched, the center column load release curves are obtained by merely changing the sign. Once this procedure is understood, the center column plots can be dispensed with and the residual stress curves obtained by merely subtracting the dotted curves from the solid curves in the left column.

Without determining the actual shape of the stress distribution curves (i.e., stress gradients), the residual stress curves obtained in Figure 4.43 are admittedly approximations. They do, however, reflect the correct surface residual stress and general shape of the residual stress distribution curve, and these are usually the matters of primary interest. It must be remembered, too, that this development of residual stress curves was based on assuming that the material conforms to the idealized stress–strain curve of Figure 4.42*e*. For this reason also, the residual stress curves in Figure 4.43 can be no better than good approximations.

4.15   *Residual Stresses Caused by Yielding— Bending and Torsional Loading*

Figure 4.44 illustrates residual stresses caused by the bending of an unnotched rectangular beam. The figure illustrates the specific case of a 25 × 50-mm beam made of steel having an idealized stress–strain curve with S_y = 300 MPa. Unknown moment M_1 produces the stress distribution shown in Figure 4.44*a*, with yielding to a depth of 10 mm. Let us first determine the magnitude of moment M_1.

If the distributed stress pattern is replaced with concentrated forces F_1 and F_2 at the centroids of the rectangular and triangular portions of the pattern, respectively, M_1 is equal to the sum of the couples produced by F_1 and F_2. The magnitude of F_1 is equal to the product of the average stress (300 MPa) times the area over which it acts (10 mm × 25 mm). Similarly, F_2 is equal to an average stress of 150 MPa times an area of 15 mm × 25 mm. The moment arms of the couples are 40 mm and 20 mm, respectively. Hence,

$$M_1 = (300 \text{ MPa} \times 250 \text{ mm}^2)(0.040 \text{ m}) + (150 \text{ MPa} \times 375 \text{ mm}^2)(0.020 \text{ m})$$

$$= 4125 \text{ N} \cdot \text{m}$$

Next, let us determine the residual stresses remaining after moment M_1 is removed. The elastic stress change when M_1 is removed is

$$\sigma = M/Z = 4125 \text{ N} \cdot \text{m}/(1.042 \times 10^{-5} \text{ m}^3)$$

$$= 3.96 \times 10^8 \text{ Pa} = 396 \text{ MPa}$$

The elastic stress distribution when the load is removed is shown in the center plot of Figure 4.44*b*. This, added to the load stress, gives the residual stress pattern shown at the right side of the figure.

The dotted line plotted on the load stress diagram of Figure 4.44*b* is the negative of the load removal stress. Since both the solid and dotted patterns on this diagram correspond to the same value of bending moment, we can observe the graphical relationship, which indicates that the moment of the solid pattern is equal to the moment of the dotted pattern. In retrospect, this fact could have been used to draw the dotted pattern fairly accurately without making any calculations. Notice how points on the load stress diagram serve to locate the points of zero and 62 MPa on the residual stress diagram.

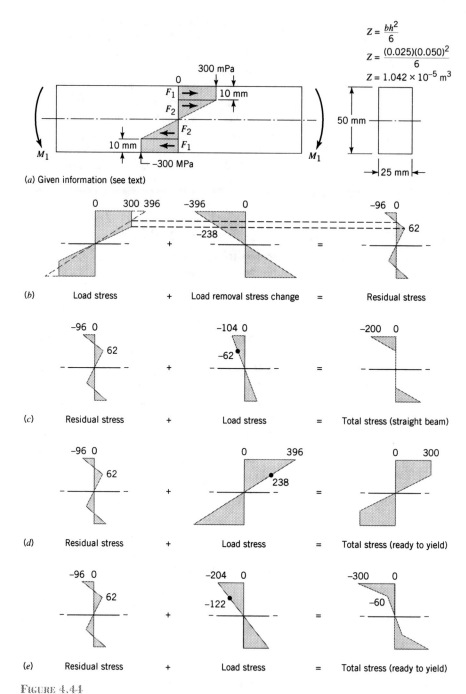

(a) Given information (see text)

(b)   Load stress   +   Load removal stress change   =   Residual stress

(c)   Residual stress   +   Load stress   =   Total stress (straight beam)

(d)   Residual stress   +   Load stress   =   Total stress (ready to yield)

(e)   Residual stress   +   Load stress   =   Total stress (ready to yield)

FIGURE 4.44
Residual stresses in an unnotched rectangular beam.

Note that at this point the beam is *slightly* bent. The outer portions that were yielded by the load do not want to come back to their initial positions, whereas the center portions that did not yield do. Thus, a balance of these opposing tendencies is reached, with the residual stress pattern satisfying the equilibrium requirements of

$\Sigma F = 0$ and $\Sigma M = 0$. We *know* the beam is slightly bent just by looking at the residual stress pattern. The center portion that was initially straight and stress-free has not yielded. It can again be straight only if the center core is stress-free.

Figure 4.44c shows that the desired center portion stress-free condition requires superimposing a load that develops a compressive stress of 62 MPa, 10 mm below the surface. With this load in place, total stresses are as shown at the right of the figure. Since center portion stresses are zero, the beam is indeed straight. Let us compute the magnitude of the moment required to hold the beam straight. It is already known that an elastic surface stress of 396 MPa is associated with a moment of 4125 N·m. By simple proportion, a stress of 104 MPa requires a moment of *1083 N·m*.

Let us now determine the *elastic* bending moment capacity of the beam *after the residual stresses have been established*. Figure 4.44d shows that a moment in the same direction as M_1 can be added that superimposes a surface stress of +396 MPa without yielding. From previous calculations, it is known that this stress is associated with a moment of *4125 N·m*. A moment's reflection indicates that this conclusion is obvious: The *release* of original moment $M_1 = 4125$ N·m caused no yielding; hence, it can be *reapplied* without yielding. Figure 4.44e shows that in the direction opposite the original moment M_1, a moment giving a surface stress of 204 MPa is all that can be elastically withstood. Again, by simple proportion, this corresponds to a moment of *2125 N·m*.

This study illustrates an important principle.

An overload causing yielding produces residual stresses that are favorable to future loads in the same direction and unfavorable to future loads in the opposite direction.

Furthermore, on the basis of the idealized stress–strain curve, the increase in load capacity in one direction is exactly equal to the decrease in load capacity in the opposite direction. These principles can also be illustrated for tensile loading, using Figure 4.43.

The example of Figure 4.44 could be carried a step further by considering the external moment required to straighten the beam permanently (so that the center section is again stress-free and therefore straight after the straightening moment is removed), and the new residual stress pattern resulting therefrom. This is done in [2].

Round bars overloaded in torsion can be treated in the same way as described in the preceding example for the rectangular bar overloaded in bending. The introduction of stress concentration in either bending or torsion requires no new concepts beyond those presented in this and the previous section.

4.16 Thermal Stresses

Thus far, only stresses caused by the application of external loads have been considered. Stresses can also be caused by constrained expansion and contraction due either to temperature changes or to a material phase change. In actual mechanical and structural parts, an accurate quantitative evaluation of these stresses is, in general, beyond the scope of this text. It is important, however, for the student to become familiar with the basic principles involved. From these, important qualitative information can often be gained.

When the temperature of an unrestrained homogeneous, isotropic body is uniformly changed, it expands (or contracts) uniformly in all directions, according to the relationship

$$\epsilon = \alpha \Delta T \tag{4.22}$$

where ϵ is the strain, α is the coefficient of thermal expansion, and ΔT is the temperature change. Values of α for several common metals are given in Appendix C-1. This uniform, unrestrained volume change produces no shear strain and no axial or shear stresses.

If restraints are placed on the member during the temperature change, the resulting stresses can be determined by (1) computing the dimensional changes that would take place in the *absence* of constraints, (2) determining the restraining loads necessary to *enforce* the restrained dimensional changes, and (3) computing the stresses associated with these restraining loads. This procedure is illustrated by the following sample problem.

SAMPLE PROBLEM 4.4   Thermal Stresses in a Tube

A 10-in. length of steel tubing (with properties of $E = 30 \times 10^6$ psi and $\alpha = 7 \times 10^{-6}$ per degree Fahrenheit) having a cross-sectional area of 1 in.^{2} is installed with "fixed" ends so that it is stress-free at 80°F. In operation, the tube is heated throughout to a uniform 480°F. Careful measurements indicate that the fixed ends separate by 0.008 in. What loads are exerted on the ends of the tube, and what are the resultant stresses?

SOLUTION

Known: A given length of steel tubing with a known cross-sectional area expands 0.008 in. from a stress-free condition at 80°F when the tube is heated to a uniform 480°F (see Figure 4.45).

Find: Determine the steel tubing loads and stresses.

Schematic and Given Data:

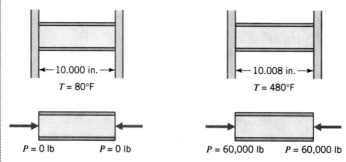

FIGURE 4.45
Sample Problem 4.4. Thermal expansion of a constrained tube.

Assumptions:

1. The tube material is homogeneous and isotropic.
2. The material stresses remain within the elastic range.

Analysis:

1. For the unrestrained tube

$$\epsilon = \alpha \Delta T = (7 \times 10^{-6})(400) = 2.8 \times 10^{-3}$$
$$\Delta L = L\epsilon = 10 \text{ in. } (2.8 \times 10^{-3}) = 0.028 \text{ in.}$$

2. Since the measured expansion was only 0.008 in., the constraints must apply forces sufficient to produce a deflection of 0.020 in. From the relationship

$$\delta = \frac{PL}{AE}$$

which is from elementary elastic theory, and reviewed in Chapter 5,

$$0.020 = \frac{P(10)}{(1)(30 \times 10^6)}, \quad \text{or} \quad P = 60,000 \text{ lb}$$

3. Because the area is unity, $\sigma = 60 \text{ ksi.}$

Comment: Since these answers are based on elastic relationships, they are valid only if the material has a yield strength of at least 60 ksi at *480°F*.

If stresses caused by temperature change are undesirably large, the best solution is often to reduce the constraint. For example, in Sample Problem 4.4 elimination or drastic reduction of the end fixity would correspondingly eliminate or drastically reduce the 60-ksi computed stress. This is commonly done by using expansion joints or telescopic joints with appropriate seals.

Thermal stresses also result from the introduction of *temperature gradients* within a member. For example, if a thick metal plate is heated in the center of one face with a torch, the hot surface is restrained from expanding by the cooler surrounding material; consequently, it is in a state of compression. Then the remote cooler metal is forced to expand, causing tensile stresses. A thick plate that is heated on both faces has the outer surface material in biaxial compression and the interior in biaxial tension. The laws of equilibrium require that all forces and moments arising from these internal stresses balance within themselves. If the forces and moments do not balance for the original geometry of the part, it will distort or warp to a size and shape that *does* bring about internal equilibrium. As long as all stresses so introduced are within the elastic limit at the temperatures involved, the part will revert to its original geometry when the initial temperature conditions are restored. If some portion of the part yields, this portion will not tend to revert to the initial geometry, and there will be warpage and internal (residual) stresses when initial temperature conditions are restored. The warpage or distortion of the part is such that it satisfies the requirements of equilibrium. This must be taken into account, for example, in the design of brake drums.

Residual stresses are commonly produced by the thermal gradients associated with heat treating, flame cutting, welding, and, to a lesser extent, by grinding and some machining operations. For example, when a uniformly heated part is quenched, the surface cools first, and at its lower temperature the surface has a relatively high yield strength. The subsequent thermal contraction of the core material is resisted by the outer skin, which is thereby placed in residual compression. The core is left in tri-axial tension, following the rule "what cools last is in tension." (Note that the surface stresses cannot be triaxial because of the unloaded exposed surface.)

This same principle explains why flame cutting and most welding operations tend to leave surfaces in residual tension: if heating occurs predominantly near the surface, the tendency for surface thermal expansion is resisted by the cooler core. Having a relatively low yield strength at high temperature, the surface yields in compression. Upon cooling, the skin tends to contract, but is again largely restrained by the core. Thus, the surface material is left in biaxial tension.

A related phenomenon producing residual stresses in steel is phase transformation. When steel with sufficient carbon content is quenched from above its critical temperature to form martensite, the new lattice structure is slightly less dense, causing the transformed material to expand slightly. With thorough hardening, the transformation normally occurs last in the interior. This causes undesirable residual tensile stresses in the surface. Special processing can cause the transformation to occur last in the outer skin, giving favorable residual compresive stresses in the surface material.

Residual stresses are added to any subsequent load stresses in order to obtain the total stresses. Furthermore, if a part with residual stresses is subsequently machined, the removal of residually stressed material causes the part to warp or distort. This is true because the removal of this material upsets the internal equilibrium of the part. Subsequent warpage *must* take place to arrive at a new geometry satisfying equilibrium requirements. In fact, a common (destructive) method for determining the residual stress in a particular zone of a part is to remove very carefully material from the zone and then to make a precision measurement of the resulting change in geometry.

Residual stresses are often removed by annealing. The unrestrained part is uniformly heated (to a sufficiently high temperature and for a sufficiently long period of time) to cause virtually complete relief of the internal stresses by localized yielding. The subsequent slow cooling operation introduces no yielding. Hence, the part reaches room temperature in a virtually stress-free state.

For a more detailed discussion of phenomena related to residual stresses, see [2].

4.17   *Importance of Residual Stresses*

In general, residual stresses are important in situations in which stress concentration is important. These include brittle materials involving all loading types, and the fatigue and impact loading of ductile as well as brittle materials. For the static loading of ductile materials, harmless local yielding can usually occur to relieve local high stresses resulting from either (or both) stress concentration or superimposed residual stress.

It is easy to overlook residual stresses because they involve nothing that ordinarily brings them to the attention of the senses. When one holds an unloaded machine part, for example, there is normally no way of knowing whether the stresses are all zero or whether large residual stresses are present. Usually there are no readily available means for determining residual stresses. However, a reasonable qualitative estimate can often be made by considering the thermal and mechanical loading history of the part, both during and after manufacture.

Almen and Black[3] cite an interesting example showing that residual stresses remain in a part as long as heat or external loading does not remove them by yielding. The Liberty Bell, cast in 1753, has residual tensile stresses in the outer surface because the casting cooled most rapidly from the *inside* surface (the principle that "*what cools last is in residual tension*"). After 75 years of satisfactory service, the bell cracked, probably as a result of fatigue from superimposed vibratory stresses caused by ringing the bell. Holes were drilled at the ends to keep the crack from growing, but the crack subsequently extended itself. Almen and Black cite this as proof that residual stresses are still present in the bell.

References

1. Durelli, A. J., E. A. Phillips, and C. H. Tsao, *Introduction to the Theoretical and Experimental Analysis of Stress and Strain*, McGraw-Hill, New York, 1958.

2. Juvinall, R. C., *Engineering Considerations of Stress, Strain, and Strength*, McGraw-Hill, New York, 1967.

3. Lipson, C., and R. C. Juvinall, *Handbook of Stress and Strength*, Macmillan, New York, 1963.

4. Mohr, O., *Zivilingenieur*, p. 113, 1882.

5. Neuber, Heinz, *Theory of Notch Stresses*, J. W. Edwards, Inc., Ann Arbor, Mich., 1946 (translation of the original German version published in 1937).

6. Peterson, R. E., *Stress Concentration Factors*, Wiley, New York, 1974.

7. Peterson, R. E., *Stress Concentration Design Factors*, Wiley, New York, 1953.

8. Young, W. C., *Roark's Formulas for Stress and Strain*, 6th ed., McGraw-Hill, New York, 1989.

9. Seely, F. B., and J. O. Smith, *Advanced Mechanics of Materials*, 2nd ed., Wiley, New York, 1952. (Also 5th ed. by Boresi, A. P., R. J. Schmidt, and O. M. Sidebottom, Wiley, New York, 1993.)

10. Smith, Clarence R., "Tips on Fatigue," Report NAVWEPS 00-25-559, Bureau of Naval Weapons, Washington, D.C., 1963.

11. Timoshenko, S., and J. N. Goodier, *Theory of Elasticity*, 2nd ed., McGraw-Hill, New York, 1951. (Also, Timoshenko, S., *Theory of Elasticity*, Engineering Societies Monograph, McGraw-Hill, New York, 1934.)

Problems

Section 4.2

4.1 The rectangular bar in Figure P4.1 is loaded in compression through two hardened steel balls. Estimate the maximum compressive stress in each of the sections A to D. Assume that an element of the shaft once deformed to the yield point will continue to deform with no increase in stress; i.e., the material follows an idealized stress–strain curve.

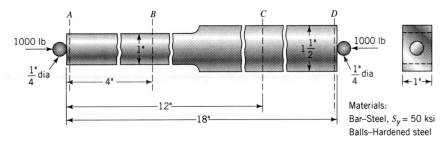

FIGURE P4.1

---

[3] John O. Almen and Paul H. Black, *Residual Stresses and Fatigue in Metals*, McGraw-Hill, New York, 1963.

4.2   For the axially loaded shaft in Figure P4.2, at which of the lettered sections is the average compressive stress equal to P/A? At which is the maximum stress equal to P/A?

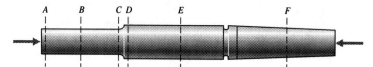

FIGURE P4.2

4.3   Figure 4.1 in Section 4.2 shows an axially loaded link in tension. At which cross sections is the average tensile stress equal to P/A? At which locations is the maximum stress equal to P/A?

Section 4.3

4.4   For the configuration shown in Figure 4.4 with load $P = 12{,}325$ lb and a pin manufactured from AISI 1040 steel with $S_u = 90.0$ ksi (where $S_{us} = 0.62\,S_u$), calculate the minimum diameter pin to avoid pin shear failure.

4.5D   Select a steel from Appendix C-4a and use $S_{us} = 0.62\,S_u$ to determine what force, P, is required to produce shear failure in a 0.375 in.-diameter bolt or pin.
   (a)   With the configuration shown in Figure 4.3?
   (b)   With the configuration shown in Figure 4.4?

4.6   What force, P, is required to produce shear failure in a 30-mm-diameter bolt or pin made of a ductile metal having $S_{us} = 200$ MPa:
   (a)   With the configuration shown in Figure 4.3?
   (b)   With the configuration shown in Figure 4.4?

Section 4.4

4.7   A 2-in.-diameter steel propeller shaft of an experimental high-speed boat transmits 2500 hp at 2000 rpm. Bending and axial loads are negligible.
   (a)   What is the nominal shear stress at the surface?
   (b)   If a hollow shaft of inside diameter 0.9 times outside diameter is used, what outside diameter would be required to give the same outer-surface stress?
   (c)   How do the weights of the solid and hollow shafts compare?

4.8D   Select a diameter of a steel driveshaft that transmits 250 hp at 5000 rpm. Bending and axial loads are negligible.
   (a)   What is the nominal shear stress at the surface?
   (b)   If a hollow shaft of inside diameter 0.9 times outside diameter is used, what outside diameter would be required to give the same outer-surface stress?
   (c)   How do the weights of the solid and hollow shafts compare?

4.9   A 30-mm-diameter shaft transmits 700 kW at 1500 rpm. Bending and axial loads are negligible.
   (a)   What is the nominal shear stress at the surface?
   (b)   If a hollow shaft of inside diameter 0.8 times outside diameter is used, what outside diameter would be required to give the same outer-surface stress?
   (c)   How do weights of the solid and hollow shafts compare?

4.10D   Select a steel from Appendix C-4a and an rpm between 1250 and 2000 rpm for a 40-mm-diameter shaft transmitting 500 kW. Bending and axial loads are negligible. Assume $\tau \leq 0.2\, S_u$ for safety.

    (a)   What is the nominal shear stress at the surface?

    (b)   If a hollow shaft of inside diameter 0.8 times outside diameter is used, what outside diameter would be required to give the same outer-surface stress?

    (c)   How do weights of the solid and hollow shafts compare?

4.11   Power from a 3200 hp motor is transmitted by a $2\frac{1}{2}$-in.-diameter shaft rotating at 2000 rpm. Bending and axial loads are negligible.

    (a)   What is the nominal shear stress at the surface?

    (b)   If a hollow shaft of inside diameter 0.85 times outside diameter is used, what outside diameter would be required to give the same outer-surface stress?

    (c)   How do weights of the solid and hollow shafts compare?

4.12   Estimate the torque required to produce a maximum shear stress of 570 MPa in a hollow shaft having an inner diameter of 20 mm and an outer diameter of 25 mm—see Figure P4.12.

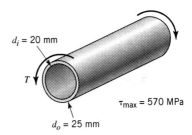

$d_i = 20$ mm

T

$\tau_{max} = 570$ MPa

$d_o = 25$ mm

FIGURE P4.12

4.13   The same torque is applied on both a solid square shaft of cross section $b \times b$ and a solid round shaft of radius r. For both shafts to have equal outer-surface maximum shear stress values, what would be the ratio b/r? For this ratio, compare the weight of the two shafts and also the ratio of strength to weight—see Figure P4.13.

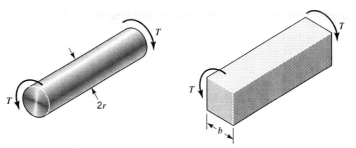

T

$2r$

T

T

T

b

FIGURE P4.13

4.14   What torque is required to produce a maximum shear stress of 400 MPa:

    (a)   In a round shaft of 40-mm diameter?

    (b)   In a square shaft, 40 mm on a side?

4.15   Compare the torque-transmitting strength of a solid round shaft with that of a solid square shaft of the same size (circle diameter equal to side of square). Compare the weight of the two shafts and also the ratio of strength to weight.

4.16   A straight bar of solid rectangular cross section and one of solid round cross section are subjected to tensile, bending, and torsional loads. Surface stresses are to be computed for each load and each bar. Discuss briefly any inherent limitations in applying the stress formulas $\sigma = P/A$, $\sigma = My/I$, $\tau = Tr/J$ to this problem.

4.17   A 2-in.-diameter straight round shaft is subjected to a bending of 2000 ft · lb.

(a)   What is the nominal bending stress at the surface?

(b)   If a hollow shaft of inside diameter 0.5 times outside diameter is used, what outside diameter would be required to give the same outer-surface stress? (Note: If the hollow shaft is too thin, buckling will occur. See Section 5.15.)

4.18   Determine the bending stress at the surface of a 3-in.-diameter shaft subjected to a bending moment of 3200 ft · lb.

4.19   A bending moment of 2000 N · m is applied to a 40-mm-diameter shaft. Estimate the bending stress at the shaft surface. If a hollow shaft of outside diameter 1.15 times inside diameter is used, determine the outside diameter required to give the same outer-surface stress.

4.20   What bending moment is required to produce a maximum normal stress of 400 MPa:

(a)   In a straight round rod of 40-mm diameter?

(b)   In a straight square rod, 40 mm on a side (with bending about the X axis as shown for a rectangular section in Appendix B-2)?

4.21   The rectangular beam shown in Figure P4.21 has an initial curvature, $\bar{r}$, equal to twice the section depth, h. How do the extreme-fiber-bending stresses for the beam compare with those of an otherwise identical straight beam?

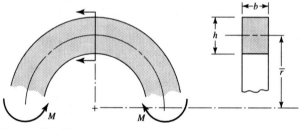

FIGURE P4.21

4.22   Determine the location and magnitude of the maximum tensile stress in the S hook shown in Figure P4.22. (Note: The lower portion experiences the larger bending moment, but the upper part has a smaller radius of curvature; hence, both locations must be investigated.)

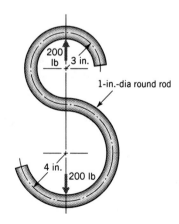

FIGURE P4.22

4.23 Repeat Problem P4.22 except that the smaller radius of curvature is 5 in. and the larger radius of curvature is 7 in.

4.24 Critical section *AA* of a crane hook (Figure P4.24) is considered, for purposes of analysis, to be trapezoidal with dimensions as shown. Determine the resultant stress (bending plus direct tension) at points *P* and *Q*.

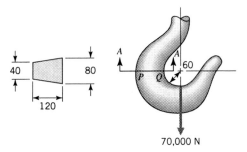

FIGURE P4.24

4.25 Repeat Problem 4.24 for a hook having a circular cross section (with the cross-sectional area equal to that in Problem 4.24).

4.26 Prove that the centroidal distance ($\bar{c}$) from the *X* axis for the trapezoid shown in Figure P4.26 is $(h)(2b + a)/(3)(b + a)$.

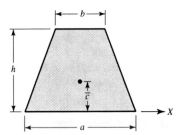

FIGURE P4.26

4.27 Figure P4.27 shows a portion of a C-clamp. What force *F* can be exerted by the screw if the maximum tensile stress in the clamp is to be limited to 30 ksi?

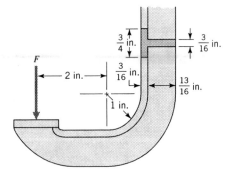

FIGURE P4.27

4.28   For the rocker arm shown in Figure P4.28, determine the maximum tensile stress in section *AA*.

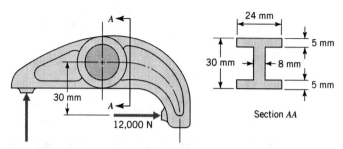

FIGURE P4.28

Section 4.7

4.29   A solid square-section beam, 60 mm on a side, is used in place of the beam in Sample Problem 4.2. What is the location and magnitude of the maximum shear stress? Use Eq. 4.12 and check the result with Eq. 4.14.

4.30   Using Eq. 4.12, derive Eq. 4.13.

4.31   Using Eq. 4.12, derive Eq. 4.14.

4.32   For the 8-in. I beam shown (Figure P4.32), compute the maximum transverse shear stress when the beam is simply supported at each end and subjected to a load of 1000 lb in the center. Compare your answer with the approximation obtained by dividing the shear load by the area of the web (only) with the web considered to extend for the full 8-in. depth.

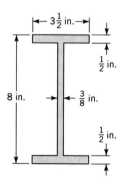

FIGURE P4.32

4.33   Figure P4.33 shows a plastic beam having a box section, where the top plate is cemented in place, as indicated. All dimensions are in millimeters. For the 12-kN load shown, what is the shear stress acting on the cemented joint?

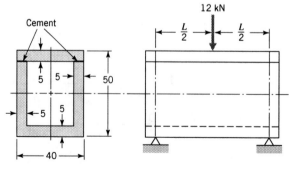

FIGURE P4.33

4.34   The shaft shown in Figure P4.34 is 200 mm long between self-aligning bearings A and B. Belt forces are applied to a sheave in the center, as shown. The left end of the shaft is connected to a clutch by means of a flexible coupling. Nothing is attached to the right end.

(a)   Determine and make a sketch showing the stresses acting on the top and side elements, *T* and *S*, located adjacent to the sheave. (Neglect stress concentration.)

(b)   Represent the states of stress at *T* and *S* with three-dimensional Mohr circles.

(c)   At location *S*, show the orientation and stresses acting on a principal element, and on a maximum shear element.

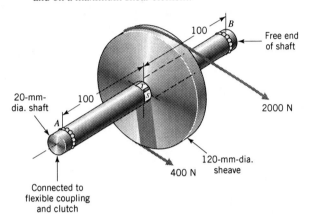

FIGURE P4.34

4.35   Repeat Problem 4.34, except that the sheave diameter is 140 mm.

4.36   We wish to analyze the stresses in a bicycle crankshaft. (This is the horizontal shaft, supported in the frame by two ball bearings, which connects the two pedal crank arms.) Obtain whatever dimensions you need by measuring an actual bicycle of standard adult size.

(a)   Show, with the aid of a simple sketch, the most severe loading condition normally encountered by this shaft. Show all important dimensions, and state any assumptions made concerning the loading.

(b)   Show on your sketch the location of greatest stress in this shaft, and make a Mohr circle representation of this state of stress. (Neglect stress concentration.)

4.37   Figure P4.37 shows a hand crank with static vertical load applied to the handle.

(a)   Copy the drawing and mark on it the location of highest bending stress. Make a three-dimensional Mohr circle representation of the stresses at this point. (Neglect stress concentration.)

(b)   Mark on the drawing the location of highest combined torsional and transverse shear stress. Make a three-dimensional Mohr circle representation of the stresses at this point, again neglecting stress concentration.

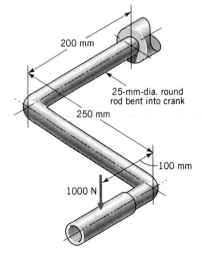

FIGURE P4.37

175

4.38   Repeat Problem 4.37, but change the 200-mm dimension to 50 mm.

4.39   Figure P4.39 shows an electric motor loaded by a belt drive. Copy the drawing and show on both views the location or locations on the shaft of the highest stress. Make a complete Mohr circle representation of the stress state at this location. (Neglect stress concentration.)

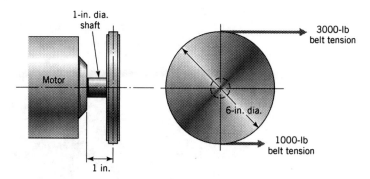

FIGURE P4.39

4.40   Repeat Problem 4.39, except that the pulley diameter is 5 in.

4.41   Figure P4.41 shows a 1-in. solid round shaft supported by self-aligning bearings at *A* and *B*. Attached to the shaft are two chain sprockets that are loaded as shown. Treat this as a static loading problem, ignoring fatigue and stress concentration. Identify the specific shaft location subjected to the most severe state of stress, and make a Mohr circle representation of this stress state.

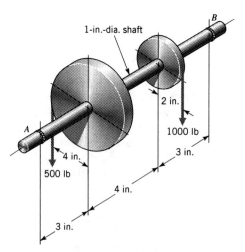

FIGURE P4.41

4.42   Repeat Problem 4.41 except that the pulleys are 3 in. apart.

176

4.43 Repeat Problem 4.41, except use Figure P4.43.

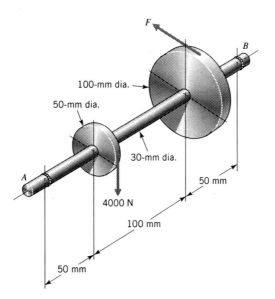

FIGURE P4.43

4.44 Figure P4.44 shows a small pressurized cylinder, attached at the one end and loaded with a pipe wrench at the other. The internal pressure causes a tangential stress of 400 MPa and an axial stress of 200 MPa that act on an element at point *A*. The pipe wrench superimposes a bending stress of 100 MPa and a torsional stress of 200 MPa.

(a) Make a Mohr circle representation of the state of stress at point *A*.

(b) What is the magnitude of the maximum shear stress at *A*?

(c) Make a sketch showing the orientation of a principal element (with respect to the original element drawn at *A*), and show all stresses acting on it.

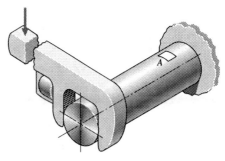

FIGURE P4.44

[Ans.: (b) 278 MPa]

4.45 Determine the maximum shear stress at point *A*, for the pressurized cylinder, shown in Figure P4.44. The cylinder is attached at one end and loaded with a pipe wrench at the other, so that it is subjected to a bending stress of 75 MPa and a torsional stress of 100 MPa. The internal pressure causes a tangential stress of 100 MPa and an axial stress of 60 MPa that act on an element at point *A*.

4.46 An internally pressurized section of round steel tubing is subjected to tangential and axial stresses at the surface of 200 and 100 MPa, respectively. Superimposed on this is a torsional stress of 50 MPa. Make a Mohr circle representation of the surface stresses.

4.47 Represent the surface stresses on a Mohr circle of an internally pressurized section of round steel tubing that is subjected to tangential and axial stresses at the surface of 400 and 250 MPa, respectively. Superimposed on this is a torsional stress of 200 MPa.

4.48　Repeat Problem 4.47, except that the torsional stress is 150 MPa.

4.49　Draw the Mohr circle for the stresses experienced by the surface of an internally pressurized steel tube that is subjected to tangential and axial stresses in the outer surface of 45,000 and 30,000 psi, respectively, and a torsional stress of 18,000 psi—see Figure P4.49.

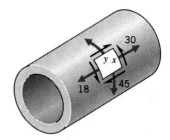

FIGURE P4.49

4.50　A cylinder is internally pressurized to a pressure of 100 MPa. This causes tangential and axial stresses in the outer surface of 400 and 200 MPa, respectively. Make a Mohr circle representation of the stresses in the outer surface. What maximum shear stress is experienced by the outer surface?

[Ans.: 200 MPa]

4.51　Determine the maximum shear stress at the outer surface of an internally pressurized cylinder where the internal pressure causes tangential and axial stresses in the outer surface of 300 and 150 MPa, respectively.

4.52　Figure P4.52 shows a cylinder internally pressurized to a pressure of 7000 psi. The pressure causes tangential and axial stresses in the outer surface of 30,000 and 20,000 psi, respectively. Determine the maximum shear stress at the outer surface.

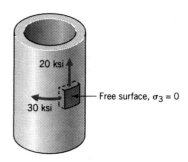

FIGURE P4.52

4.53　Repeat Problem 4.52, except that the cylinder is pressurized to 10,000 psi.

4.54　The inner surface of a hollow cylinder internally pressurized to 100 MPa experiences tangential and axial stresses of 600 and 200 MPa, respectively. Make a Mohr circle representation of the stresses in the inner surface. What maximum shear stress exists at the inner surface?

[Ans.: 350 MPa]

4.55　The inner surface of a hollow cylinder internally pressurized to 100 MPa is subjected to tangential and axial stresses of 350 MPa and 75 MPa, respectively as shown in Figure P4.55. Represent the inner-surface stresses using a Mohr circle and determine the maximum shear tress.

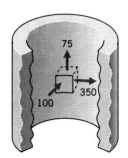

FIGURE P4.55

4.56   The inner surface of a hollow cylinder is subjected to tangential and axial stresses of 40,000 and 24,000 psi, respectively. Determine the maximum shear stress at the inner surface, if the cylinder is pressurized to 10,000 psi.

Sections 4.12–4.14

4.57   Find the maximum value of stress at the hole and semicircular notch shown in Figure P4.57.

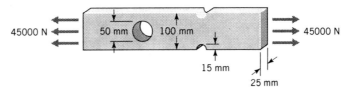

FIGURE P4.57

4.58   For Figure P4.58, what is the value of the maximum stress at both the hole and the notch?

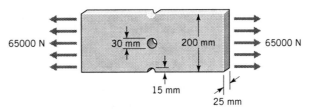

FIGURE P4.58

4.59   A shaft is supported by bearings at locations A and B and is loaded with a downward 1000-N force as shown in Figure P4.59. Find the maximum stress at the shaft fillet. The critical shaft fillet is 70 mm from B.

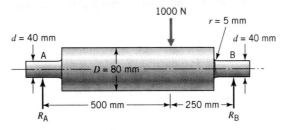

FIGURE P4.59

4.60   A notched flat bar (as shown in Figure 4.39) has a stress concentration factor for tensile loads of 2. Its cross-sectional area in the plane of the notches is 0.5 in.^{2}. The material is steel, with tensile and compressive yield strengths of 30 ksi. Assume an idealized stress–strain curve. The bar is initially free of residual stress.

(a)   Make a drawing showing the approximate shape of the stress distribution curve when the bar is loaded to 5000-lb tension and also after the load is removed.

(b)   Repeat for a 10,000-lb load.

(c)   Repeat for a 15,000-lb load.

4.61   Repeat Problem 4.60, except that the loading causes compression.

4.62   Repeat Problem 4.60, except use a stress concentration factor of 3.

4.63   Repeat Problem 4.60, except that the stress concentration factor is 3 and the loading causes compression.

4.64   A 20 × 60-mm ($h \times b$) rectangular bar with a 10-mm-diameter central hole (as shown in Figure 4.40) is made of steel having tensile and compressive yield strengths of 600 MPa. Assume an idealized stress–strain curve. The bar is initially free of residual stress. Make a drawing showing the approximate stress distribution in the plane of the hole (Figure P4.64):

(a)   When a tensile force of 400 kN is applied to each end of the bar.

(b)   After the load is removed.

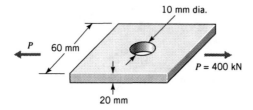

FIGURE P4.64

4.65   Repeat Problem 4.64, except that the bar is loaded in compression.

4.66   A 10 × 40-mm ($h \times b$) steel rectangular bar (having compressive and tensile yield strengths of 300 MPa) has a 6-mm-diameter central hole (as shown in Figure 4.40). Assume that the bar is initially free of residual stress and that the steel material has an idealized stress–strain curve. Make a sketch showing the approximate stress distribution in the plane of the hole:

(a)   When a tensile force of 100 kN is applied to each end of the bar.

(b)   After the load is removed.

4.67   Repeat Problem 4.66, except that the bar is loaded in compression.

4.68   A notched bar (illustrated in Figure 4.39) has a stress concentration factor for tensile loading of 2.5. It is made of ductile steel (assume an idealized stress–strain curve) with tensile and compressive yield strengths of 200 MPa. The bar is loaded in tension with *calculated* notch root stresses varying with time as shown in Figure P4.68. Copy the drawing and add to it a curve showing the variation with time of *actual* notch root stresses.

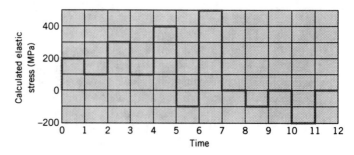

FIGURE P4.68

4.69   Repeat Problem 4.68, except use a stress concentration factor of 3.

4.70   Three notched tensile bars (see Figure 4.39) have stress-concentration factors of 1, 1.5, and 2.5, respectively. Each is made of ductile steel having S_y = 100 ksi, has a rectangular cross section with a minimum area of 1 in.^{2}, and is initially free of residual stress. Draw the shape of the stress-distribution curve for each case when (*a*) a tensile load of 50,000 lb is applied, (*b*) the load is increased to 100,000 lb, and (*c*) the load is removed.

Section 4.15

4.71   Two rectangular beams are made of steel having a tensile yield strength of 80 ksi and an assumed idealized stress–strain curve. Beam A has a uniform 1 × 0.5-in. section. Beam B has a 1 × 0.5-in. section that blends symmetrically into a 1.5 × 0.5-in. section with fillets giving a stress concentration factor of 3. The beams are loaded in bending in such a way that $Z = I/c = bh^2/6 = 0.5(1)^2/6 = \frac{1}{12}$ in.^{3}

    (a) For each beam, what moment, M, causes (1) initial yielding and (2) complete yielding?

    (b) Beam A is loaded to cause yielding to a depth of $\frac{1}{4}$ in. Determine and plot the distribution of residual stresses that remain after the load is removed.

    [Ans.: (a1) beam A, 6667 in · lb, beam B, 2222 in · lb; (a2) 10,000 in · lb for both beams]

4.72   Two rectangular beams are made of steel having a tensile yield strength of 550 MPa and an assumed idealized stress–strain curve. Beam A has a uniform 25 mm × 12.5-mm section. Beam B has a 25 mm × 12.5-mm section that blends symmetrically into a 37.5 mm × 12.5-mm section with fillets giving a stress concentration factor of 2.5. The beams are loaded in bending in such a way that $Z = I/c = bh^2/6 = 12.5(25)^2/6 = 1.3$ m^3.

    (a) For each beam, what moment, M, causes (1) initial yielding and (2) complete yielding?

    (b) Beam A is loaded to cause yielding to a depth of 6.35 mm. Determine and plot the distribution of residual stresses that remain after the load is removed.

Section 4.16

4.73   A 12-in. length of aluminum tubing (with properties of $E = 10.4 \times 10^6$ psi and $\alpha = 12 \times 10^{-6}$ per degree Fahrenheit) having a cross-sectional area of 1.5 in.^{2} is installed with "fixed" ends so that it is stress-free at 60°F. In operation, the tube is heated throughout to a uniform 260°F. Careful measurements indicate that the fixed ends separate by .008 in. What loads are exerted on the ends of the tube, and what are the resultant stresses?

4.74   A 250-mm length of steel tubing (with properties of $E = 207 \times 10^9$ Pa and $\alpha = 12 \times 10^{-6}$ per degree Celsius) having a cross-sectional area of 625 mm^2 is installed with "fixed" ends so that it is stress-free at 26°C. In operation, the tube is heated throughout to a uniform 249°C. Careful measurements indicate that the fixed ends separate by 0.20 mm. What loads are exerted on the ends of the tube, and what are the resultant stresses?

CHAPTER 5

Elastic Strain, Deflection, and Stability

5.1 *Introduction*

Elastic strain, deflection, stiffness, and stability are considerations of basic importance to the engineer. Deflection or stiffness, rather than stress, is often the controlling factor in the design of a part. Machine tool frames, for example, must be extremely rigid to maintain manufacturing accuracy. When the frames are made massive enough to satisfy rigidity requirements, the stresses may be insignificantly low. Other parts may require great stiffness in order to eliminate vibration problems. Excessive deflection can cause interference between components and disengagement of gears.

Another important aspect of elastic strains is their involvement in experimental techniques for measuring stresses. Stress is not, in general, a directly measurable quantity; strain is. When the elastic constants of a material are known, experimentally determined strain values can be transposed into corresponding stress values by means of the elastic stress–strain relationships reviewed in Section 5.5.

Figures 5.1a through d illustrate elastically stable systems. In such systems a small disturbance of the equilibrium illustrated will be corrected by elastic restoring forces, moments, or both. Such may not be the case in the slender column shown in Figure 5.1e. Here, if the column is slender enough, the elastic modulus low enough,

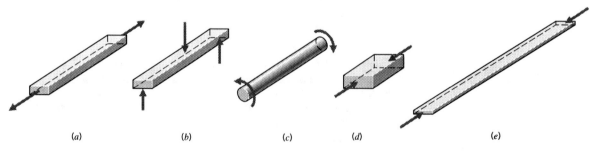

        (a)   (b)   (c)   (d)   (e)

FIGURE 5.1
(*a–d*) Elastically stable and (*e*) potentially elastically unstable loaded members.

and the load large enough, then the compression member will be *elastically unstable* and the slightest disturbance will cause *buckling* or collapse. This is true even though the *P/A* stress may be *well below* the elastic limit of the material. Sections 5.10–5.15 in this chapter deal with this phenomenon.

Section 5.16 introduces the subject of finite element analysis.

5.2 Strain Definition, Measurement, and Mohr Circle Representation

Figure 5.2 shows strains experienced by an element subjected to uniaxial tension. Equations defining the three linear components of strain are given on the figure. The loaded element experiences no change in any of the initial right angles. Shear strains γ_{xy}, γ_{xz}, and γ_{yz} are therefore zero, and the element shown is a principal element. Because of this, ϵ_x, ϵ_y, and ϵ_z are also ϵ_1, ϵ_2, and ϵ_3, where subscripts 1, 2, and 3 denote the principal directions. The negative values shown for ϵ_y and ϵ_z result from the material's having a positive Poisson's ratio.

Figure 5.3 shows a similar element subjected to pure shear. The resulting shear strains are defined on the figure. The double subscript notation corresponds to the convention mentioned briefly in Section 4.9 in connection with Figure 4.26. As was true in the case of shear stresses, there is no need here to be concerned with a distinction between γ_{xy} and γ_{yx}.

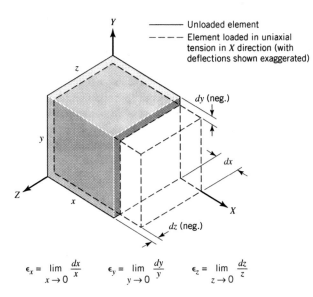

——— Unloaded element
– – – Element loaded in uniaxial tension in *X* direction (with deflections shown exaggerated)

$$\epsilon_x = \lim_{x \to 0} \frac{dx}{x} \qquad \epsilon_y = \lim_{y \to 0} \frac{dy}{y} \qquad \epsilon_z = \lim_{z \to 0} \frac{dz}{z}$$

FIGURE 5.2
Linear strain illustrated for uniaxial tensile loading.

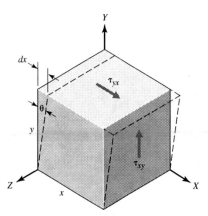

FIGURE 5.3
Shear strain illustrated for pure shear loading.

γ_{xy} (shown counterclockwise, hence negative)
γ_{yx} (shown clockwise, hence positive) } absolute value $= \lim_{y \to 0} \frac{dx}{y} = \tan \theta \approx \theta$

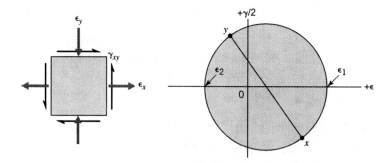

FIGURE 5.4
**Mohr strain circle drawn
for known values of ϵ_x, ϵ_y,
and γ_{xy}.**

Figure 5.4 illustrates how a Mohr strain circle can be plotted from a knowledge of ϵ_x, ϵ_y, and γ_{xy}. The procedure is identical to that used with the Mohr stress circle except that care must be taken to plot as ordinates only *half* the shear strain, γ. Analytical stress equations (Eqs. 4.15 through 4.19) have direct counterparts for strain, with ϵ being substituted for σ, and $\gamma/2$ substituted for τ.

When experimentally determining stresses at critical points on machine and structural parts, we begin by measuring strains, and then compute the corresponding stresses for materials of known elastic constants. If the directions of the principal axes are known, principal strains ϵ_1 and ϵ_2 can be measured directly, by using electrical resistance strain gages of the single-element type (Figure 5.5a) or two-element rosettes

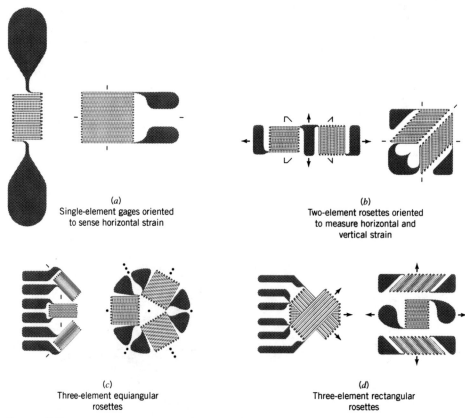

(a)
Single-element gages oriented
to sense horizontal strain

(b)
Two-element rosettes oriented
to measure horizontal and
vertical strain

(c)
Three-element equiangular
rosettes

(d)
Three-element rectangular
rosettes

FIGURE 5.5

Grid configurations of typical metal foil electrical resistance strain gages.

(Figure 5.5*b*). If principal directions are not known, we could theoretically determine ϵ_1 and ϵ_2 by first measuring arbitrarily oriented strains ϵ_x, ϵ_y, and γ_{xy}, and then determining ϵ_1 and ϵ_2 from a Mohr circle plot as in Figure 5.4. Unfortunately, direct experimental measurement of shear strain is not normally practical. Hence, use is made of three-element strain gage rosettes, illustrated in Figures 5.5*c* and *d*. The rationale associated with this is as follows.

First, note that the conventional Mohr circle construction—either for stress, as shown in Figure 4.27, or for strain, as shown in Figure 5.4—provides a convenient graphical solution of three equations in three unknowns. The unknowns are two principal stress (or strain) values and the angle between the principal planes and the reference planes (usually designated by *x* and *y*). A solution requires three known values. These are σ_x, σ_y, and τ_{xy} (or ϵ_x, ϵ_y, and γ_{xy}). Three-element rosettes permit solutions for the same three unknowns, but the "knowns" are all *linear* strains. No simple graphical Mohr-circle-type solution is available, so an analytical solution is used. Such a solution is available when given three linear strains in *any* direction [5], but only the two commonly used arrangements will be considered here: equiangular rosettes (Figure 5.5*c*), and rectangular rosettes (Figure 5.5*d*).

An interactive guide to strain gage technology is online at http://www.vishay.com/test-measurements. The Web site contains technical literature on strain gages, instrumentation, and photoelastic products as well as calculators for strain gage technology. For example, calculators are provided for determining principal strains with equiangular (delta) and rectangular strain gage rosettes.

5.3　*Analysis of Strain—Equiangular Rosettes*

All equiangular rosettes can be represented diagrammatically by Figure 5.6*a*, which shows individual gages at 0°, 120°, and 240°, in *counterclockwise progression*. Angle α is measured from the 0° gage to the as-yet-unknown principal axes. Figures 5.6*b* and *c* show other combinations of gage orientations that are equivalent. Using the preceding notation, we have for principal strain magnitude and direction the equations [3]

$$\epsilon_{1,2} = \frac{\epsilon_0 + \epsilon_{120} + \epsilon_{240}}{3} \pm \sqrt{\frac{(2\epsilon_0 - \epsilon_{120} - \epsilon_{240})^2}{9} + \frac{(\epsilon_{120} - \epsilon_{240})^2}{3}} \quad (5.1)$$

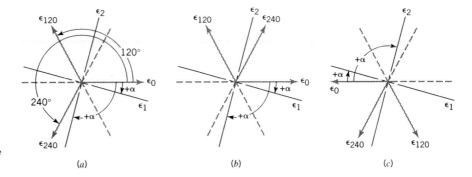

FIGURE 5.6

Equiangular strain rosette representations.

(*a*)　　　　　(*b*)　　　　　(*c*)

$$\tan 2\alpha = \frac{\sqrt{3}(\epsilon_{120} - \epsilon_{240})}{2\epsilon_0 - \epsilon_{120} - \epsilon_{240}} \tag{5.2}$$

A *positive* value of α means that we measure *clockwise* from the ϵ_0 gage orientation to each of the two principal axis orientations given by Eq. 5.2. To determine which direction goes with which principal axis, use the rule that the higher principal strain always lies within 30° of the algebraically highest of ϵ_0, ϵ_{120}, and ϵ_{240}. The use and interpretation of Eqs. 5.1 and 5.2 are illustrated by the following example.

SAMPLE PROBLEM 5.1   Equiangular Strain Gage Rosette

The following strains are obtained from an equiangular strain gage rosette:

$$\epsilon_0 = -0.00075 \text{ m/m}$$
$$\epsilon_{120} = +0.0004 \text{ m/m}$$
$$\epsilon_{240} = +0.00185 \text{ m/m}$$

Determine the magnitude and orientation of the principal strains, and check the results by plotting a Mohr circle.

SOLUTION

Known: The three strain values from an equiangular strain gage rosette are given.

Find: Calculate the magnitude and orientation of the principal strains. Plot a Mohr circle representation of the strains.

Schematic and Given Data:

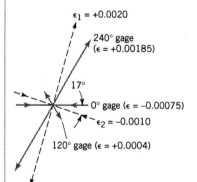

$\epsilon_1 = +0.0020$

240° gage
($\epsilon = +0.00185$)

17°

0° gage ($\epsilon = -0.00075$)

$\epsilon_2 = -0.0010$

120° gage ($\epsilon = +0.0004$)

FIGURE 5.7
Vector representation of Sample Problem 5.1 solution.

Assumption: The three known strains are all linear strains.

Analysis:

1. From direct substitution in Eq. 5.1,

$$\epsilon_{1,2} = 0.0005 \pm 0.0015, \qquad \epsilon_1 = 0.0020 \text{ m/m}, \qquad \epsilon_2 = -0.0010 \text{ m/m}$$

2. From Eq. 5.2,
$$\tan 2\alpha = +0.67, \qquad 2\alpha = 34°, 214°, \qquad \alpha = 17°, 107°$$

3. The principal strain axes are 17° and 107° clockwise from the 0° gage axis. According to the 30° rule, it is the axis of ϵ_2 that is 17° from ϵ_0 (also, it is intuitively apparent that since ϵ_0 is the only negative gage reading, the principal strain closest to it will be the negative principal strain).

4. A vector representation of the magnitudes and directions of the gage readings and the principal strains is shown in Figure 5.7.

5. The correctness of the solution is verified in Figure 5.8, where a Mohr circle is drawn based on the computed values of ϵ_1 and ϵ_2. Points are marked on the circle corresponding to the angular orientations of ϵ_0, ϵ_{120}, and ϵ_{240}, as shown in Figure 5.7 (remembering that actual angles are doubled when representing them on the circle). Since the abscissas of these three points correspond to the given gage readings, the solution is correct.

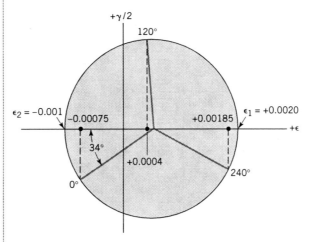

FIGURE 5.8
Mohr circle check of Sample Problem 5.1 solution.

Comment: A careful study of Figures 5.7 and 5.8 is helpful in gaining an intuitive understanding of the significance of the calculations performed with Eqs. 5.1 and 5.2 and of the associated conventions for gage labeling and for discriminating between orientations of ϵ_1 and ϵ_2.

5.4 Analysis of Strain—
Rectangular Rosettes

Figure 5.9a shows the basic configuration of the rectangular rosette, with three gage directions progressing *counterclockwise* at 45° increments from an arbitrarily oriented 0° gage. As with the equiangular rosette, there are several possible versions of the basic rectangular orientation. Two others are shown in Figures 5.9b and c. Again,

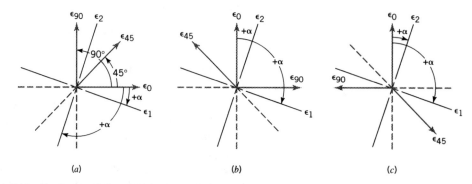

FIGURE 5.9

Rectangular strain rosette representations.

angle α is measured from the 0° gage direction to each of the principal directions. The equations for principal strain magnitude and direction are [5]

$$\epsilon_{1,2} = \frac{\epsilon_0 + \epsilon_{90}}{2} \pm \sqrt{\frac{(\epsilon_0 - \epsilon_{45})^2 + (\epsilon_{45} - \epsilon_{90})^2}{2}} \qquad (5.3)$$

$$\tan 2\alpha = \frac{\epsilon_0 - 2\epsilon_{45} + \epsilon_{90}}{\epsilon_0 - \epsilon_{90}} \qquad (5.4)$$

As with the equiangular rosette, a positive value of α means that we measure *clockwise* from the ϵ_0 gage to a principal axis. Discrimination between the two principal axes can be based on the rule that the algebraically greater principal strain makes an angle of less than 45° with the algebraically larger of strains ϵ_0 and ϵ_{90}.

SAMPLE PROBLEM 5.2   Rectangular Strain Gage Rosette

Readings obtained from a rectangular rosette are as shown in Figure 5.10a (the readings are in micrometers per meter, which is, of course, the same as microinches per inch). Determine the magnitude and orientation of the principal strains, and check the result by plotting a Mohr circle.

SOLUTION

Known: The three strain values from a rectangular rosette are given.

Find: Calculate the magnitude and orientation of the principal strains. Plot a Mohr circle to check the results.

Schematic and Given Data:

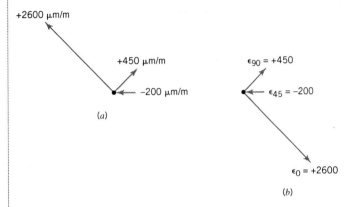

(a)

(b)

FIGURE 5.10
Sample Problem 5.2 given data. (a) Gage readings.
(b) Equivalent rosettes.

Assumption: The three known strains are all linear strains.

Analysis:

1. First note that in order to conform with the 45° increment counterclockwise progression, the gages must be labeled as shown in Figure 5.10*b*.
2. Substitution in Eqs. 5.3 and 5.4 gives

$$\epsilon_{1,2} = 1525 \pm 2033, \quad \epsilon_1 = 3558\ \mu m/m, \quad \epsilon_2 = -508\ \mu m/m$$

$$\tan 2\alpha = 1.605, \quad 2\alpha = 58°, 238°, \quad \alpha = 29°, 119°$$

These results are represented in Figure 5.11.

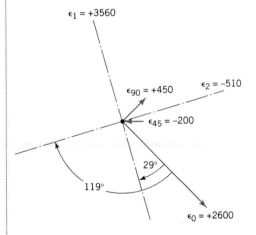

FIGURE 5.11
Vector representation of Sample Problem 5.2
solution.

189

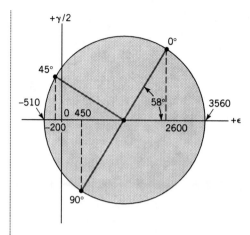

FIGURE 5.12
Mohr circle check of Sample Problem 5.2 solution.

3. A Mohr circle is drawn in Figure 5.12, based on the computed values of ϵ_1 and ϵ_2. Points are marked on the circle corresponding to the angular orientations of ϵ_0, ϵ_{45}, and ϵ_{90} shown in Figure 5.11. The abscissas of these points are found to check with the given gage readings.

Comment: Again, a careful study of Figures 5.11 and 5.12 is advised in order to gain a clear understanding of the physical situation.

5.5   *Elastic Stress–Strain Relationships and Three-Dimensional Mohr Circles*

Elastic, or more precisely, *linearly elastic*, stress–strain relationships for the general case of triaxial stress are given in various references, such as [3]. For the frequently encountered *biaxial stress* case (where ϵ_1 and ϵ_2 are determined experimentally), these reduce to

$$\sigma_1 = \frac{E}{1-\nu^2}(\epsilon_1 + \nu\epsilon_2)$$

$$\sigma_2 = \frac{E}{1-\nu^2}(\epsilon_2 + \nu\epsilon_1) \qquad \textbf{(5.5)}$$

$$\sigma_3 = 0$$

$$\epsilon_3 = \frac{-\nu}{1-\nu}(\epsilon_1 + \epsilon_2)$$

Or, if principal stresses are known and strains are to be computed,

$$\epsilon_1 = \frac{1}{E}(\sigma_1 - \nu\sigma_2)$$

$$\epsilon_2 = \frac{1}{E}(\sigma_2 - \nu\sigma_1)$$

$$\epsilon_3 = -\frac{\nu}{E}(\sigma_1 + \sigma_2)$$

(5.6)

For the case of *uniaxial stress* these equations reduce to

$$\left.\begin{array}{l} \sigma_1 = E\epsilon_1 \\ \sigma_2 = \sigma_3 = 0 \end{array}\right\}$$

(5.7a)

$$\left.\begin{array}{l} \epsilon_1 = \dfrac{\sigma_1}{E} \\[2mm] \epsilon_2 = \epsilon_3 = -\dfrac{\nu\sigma_1}{E} \end{array}\right\}$$

(5.7b)

A common serious error is to use $\sigma = E\epsilon$ for all stress states. For example, suppose that the equiangular strain gage rosette in Sample Problem 5.1 was mounted on an aluminum member of elastic constants $E = 71 \times 10^9$ Pa, $\nu = 0.35$. From $\epsilon_1 = 0.0020$ and $\epsilon_2 = -0.0010$, Eq. 5.5 for the biaxial stress state gives $\sigma_1 = 134$ MPa, $\sigma_2 = -24$ MPa. The erroneous computation of principal stresses by merely multiplying each principal strain by E gives $\sigma_1 = 142$ MPa and $\sigma_2 = -71$ MPa.

To complete the determination of states of stress and strain for Sample Problem 5.1 with aluminum material, we need only compute $\epsilon_3 = -0.0005$ from either Eq. 5.5 or Eq. 5.6. The complete Mohr circle representation of states of stress and strain is plotted in Figure 5.13.

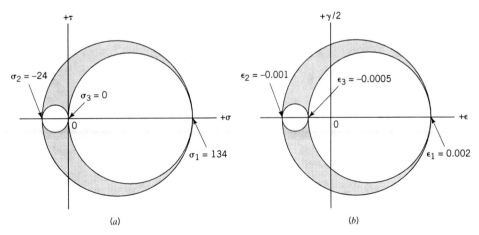

(a)   (b)

FIGURE 5.13

State of (a) stress and (b) strain for Sample Problem 5.1 and aluminum material.

5.6   *Deflection and Spring Rate—Simple Cases*

The basic deflection and spring rate formulas are given in Table 5.1, supplemented, in the case of torsion, by Table 5.2. Derivations are not included, because we have presumably covered these in previous courses. No effort should be made to memorize these equations. Instead, we should be sure to understand the rationale and pattern behind them—then most of the equations will be memorized automatically.

TABLE 5.1   Deflection and Stiffness Formulas for Straight Bars (Rods, Beams) of Uniform Section

Number	Case	Deflection	Spring Rate
1.	Tension or compression Cross-section area = A	$\delta = \dfrac{PL}{AE}$	$k = \dfrac{P}{\delta} = \dfrac{AE}{L}$
2.	Torsion K'^a = section property. For solid round section, $K' = J = \pi d^4/32$.	$\theta = \dfrac{TL}{K'G}$ For solid round bar and deflection in degrees, $\theta° = \dfrac{584TL}{d^4G}$	$K = \dfrac{T}{\theta} = \dfrac{K'G}{L}$
3.	Bending (angular deflection) I = moment of inertia about neutral bending axis	$\theta = \dfrac{ML}{EI}$	$K = \dfrac{M}{\theta} = \dfrac{EI}{L}$
4.	Bending (linear deflection) I = moment of inertia about neutral bending axis	$\delta = \dfrac{ML^2}{2EI}$	$k = \dfrac{M}{\delta} = \dfrac{2EI}{L^2}$
5.	Cantilever beam loaded at end I = moment of inertia about neutral bending axis	$\delta = \dfrac{PL^3}{3EI}$	$k = \dfrac{P}{\delta} = \dfrac{3EI}{L^3}$

Note: See Appendixes A-4 and A-5 for appropriate SI units and prefixes.
[a] See Table 5.2 for values of K' for other sections.

TABLE 5.2 Formulas for Torsional Deflection—
Case 2 of Table 5.1

$\theta = \dfrac{TL}{K'G}$ where values for K' are the following.

Cross Section	Formula for K'
	$K' = J = \dfrac{\pi d^4}{32}$
	$K' = J = \dfrac{\pi}{32}(d_o^4 - d_i^4)$
	$K' = \dfrac{\pi dt^3}{32}$
	$K' = \dfrac{\pi a^3 b^3}{a^2 + b^2}$
	$K' = 0.0216a^4$
	$K' = 2.69a^4$
	$K' = \dfrac{ab^3}{16}\left[\dfrac{16}{3} - 3.36\dfrac{b}{a}\left(1 - \dfrac{b^4}{12a^4}\right)\right]$
	$K' = 0.1406a^4$

Note that the first three cases involve the deflection at the point of load application and in the direction of load application. In each of these cases the equation merely states that deflection varies linearly with load (which it must, for the linear elastic portion of the stress–strain curve) and with length, and inversely with a geometric rigidity property of the cross section and with the appropriate elastic rigidity property of the material. "Spring rate" is also known as *spring constant* or *spring scale*. For linear deflections the spring rate is designated by k (measured in pounds per inch, newtons per meter, etc.). For angular deflections, the symbol K is used (with units of lb · ft per radian, N · m per radian, etc.).

In case 4, note that the length must be squared. This must be so because linear deflection increases both with length and with end slope, the latter being itself a function of length. In case 5, length must be *cubed* because the bending moment is an additional factor increasing with length. Incidentally, in case 5 the equation given for deflection results *only* from bending stresses, the contribution to deflection made by transverse shear being considered negligible. Castigliano's method, treated in Section 5.8, enables us to evaluate the shear contribution. For now, let us merely note that the shear contribution to deflection follows exactly the pattern of cases 1, 2, and 3: the shear deflection varies linearly with shear load and length, and inversely with shear modulus of elasticity and with a geometric shear rigidity property of the cross section. The geometric shear rigidity property is roughly equal to the area for most sections (it is equal to five-sixths times the area for a rectangular section).

Tables that give deflection equations for beams with a wide variety of loading conditions are contained in various handbooks and references, such as [4].

5.7 *Beam Deflection*

Beams are structural members, subjected to transverse loads. Examples include machinery shafts, building floor joists, leaf springs, automobile frame members and numerous other machine and structural components. A beam often requires a larger cross section to limit deflection than it does to limit stress. Hence, many steel beams are made of low-cost alloys because these have the same modulus of elasticity (thus, the same resistance to elastic deflection) as stronger, high-cost steels.

The reader has undoubtedly studied previously one or more of the many methods for computing beam deflection (as area–moment, integration by singularity functions, graphical integration, and numerical integration). Appendix D contains a summary of equations for deflection (as well as shear and moment) pertaining to beams of uniform section with commonly encountered loads. More complete tables are given in many handbooks, such as [4]. When more than one load is applied to a beam (and its response is within the linear elastic range), the deflection at any point on the beam is the sum of the individual deflections produced at that point by each of the loads acting singly. This *method of superposition* (used with information such as that provided in Appendix D) often provides the easiest and quickest solution to beam deflection problems involving several loads.

For various reasons, many beams do not have a uniform cross section. For example, machinery rotating shafts are usually "stepped," as shown in Figure 5.14, in order to accommodate the bearings and other parts assembled on the shaft. The calculation of deflections in such beams is tedious using conventional methods. Fortunately, these problems can be solved readily on a computer. Appendix D-4 gives a computer program for determining the deflection of stepped shafts.

Now, because of computers, it is unusual for an engineer to solve stepped-shaft deflection problems by "longhand" methods. The following sample problem is included primarily to help the student understand the fundamental mathematical manipulations involved. Such an understanding is vital to the intelligent engineering use of the computer. Moreover, it is always well for the engineer to have the satisfaction of knowing how to solve the problem without a computer, if this should sometimes be necessary for simple cases.

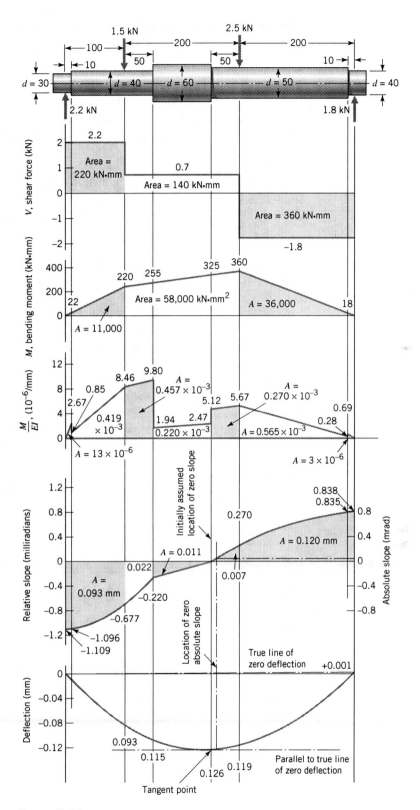

FIGURE 5.14
Deflection determination for an end-supported stepped steel shaft with two concentrated loads (Sample Problem 5.3).

The solution to Sample Problem 5.3 is based directly on the fundamental equations:

$$\text{Load intensity at any point } x = \frac{d^4\delta}{dx^4}EI = w$$

$$\text{Shear force at any point } x = \frac{d^3\delta}{dx^3}EI = V$$

$$\text{Bending moment at any point } x = \frac{d^2\delta}{dx^2}EI = M \qquad (5.8)$$

$$\text{Slope at any point } x = \frac{d\delta}{dx} = \theta$$

$$\text{Deflection at any point } x = \delta$$

The concepts involved in integrating or differentiating to obtain any one of the preceding quantities from any of the others are fundamental, and the engineering student is urged to study the following sample problem carefully. An understanding of the solution to this problem will carry over to other fields that use essentially the same differential equations. A prominent example is in dynamics, where successive time derivatives of displacement give velocity, acceleration, and jerk.

SAMPLE PROBLEM 5.3   Deflection for a Stepped Shaft

The stepped shaft at the top of Figure 5.14 is made of steel ($E = 207$ GPa) and loaded (as by gears or pulleys mounted on the shaft) with the 1.5- and 2.5-kN forces shown. It is simply supported by bearings at each end. Determine the deflection at all points along the shaft.

SOLUTION

Known: A stepped shaft with given loads and geometry.

Find: Determine the deflection at all points along the shaft.

Schematic and Given Data: See Figure 5.14.

Assumptions:

1. The zero slope of the deflection curve occurs at the midportion of the shaft.
2. The shaft deflection is elastic.

Analysis:

1. The bearing-supporting forces (2.2 and 1.8 kN) and the shear and moment diagrams are determined as in Figure 2.11.

2. Note carefully the key factors involved in the graphical integration of any curve (as the shear diagram) to obtain the next lower curve (as the moment diagram).

   a. The *difference in ordinate values* at any two points along the lower curve (as the moment diagram) is equal to the *area under the curve* above it (as the shear diagram) between these two points.

   b. The absolute value of the ordinate of the lower curve is determined from known end conditions. For example, the moment at the bearing supports is known to be zero.

   c. The *slope* at any point on the lower curve is equal to the *ordinate* of the curve above.

3. To account for the differences in diameter along the shaft, each segment of the moment curve is divided by the product *EI* for that segment. (Values of *I* for the 30-, 40-, 50-, and 60-mm segments are 39,761, 125,664, 306,796, and 636,173 mm^4, respectively.)

4. When integrating the *M/EI* curve to obtain slope, we encounter the problem that the location of zero slope is not known at this time. Visualizing or sketching a rough deflection curve makes it clear that zero slope occurs somewhere in the midportion of the shaft. Accordingly, an "initially assumed location of zero slope" is chosen as shown. (Note: Final accuracy is not affected by this assumption—zero slope could even be assumed at a bearing support.) Because of the assumption, it is necessary to call the ordinate "*relative* slope."

5. Integration of the slope curve to obtain deflection begins with the known location of zero deflection at the left bearing support. *If the estimated location of zero slope is correct, the calculated deflection at the right support will also come out to zero.* In this instance the assumed zero-slope location is only slightly off. To correct for this, connect the two known points of zero deflection with the "true line of zero deflection." Values of true deflection at any point *must be measured perpendicularly from this line.*

6. Finally, the correct location of zero slope is determined by drawing a line tangent to the deflection curve, parallel to the "true line of zero deflection." This enables the "absolute slope" scale to be added.

Comment: In this case negligible error would have been introduced by eliminating the steps at the shaft ends; that is, the problem could have been simplified by carrying out the 40- and 50-mm diameters to the ends.

Shaft design and analysis are discussed further in Chapter 17.

5.8 *Determining Elastic Deflections by Castigliano's Method*

Situations frequently develop that make it necessary to compute elastic deflections not covered by the simple cases given in Table 5.1, and involving more than the bending loading treated in the previous section. Castigliano's method is selected here for dealing with these situations. It is selected because of its versatility in handling a wide

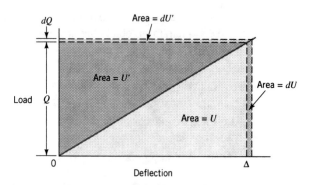

General load–deflection curve for elastic range.

range of deflection problems, and because it is also useful in determining redundant reactions (treated in the next section). The theorem underlying the method was published as part of a thesis written by Alberto Castigliano while a student at the Turin (Italy) Polytechnic Institute in the mid-nineteenth century.

Figure 5.15 shows an elastic load–deflection curve for the completely general case. The load can be any force or moment with the displacement being the corresponding linear or angular displacement. The light-blue area (U) under the curve is equal to the stored elastic energy. The darker blue area (U') is known as the complementary energy. By simple geometry,

$$U = U' = Q\Delta/2$$

that is, stored elastic energy is equal to deflection times average force. The additional energy associated with incremental load dQ is

$$dU' = dU = \Delta\, dQ$$

Solving for the deflection, Δ, we have

$$\Delta = dU/dQ$$

In the general case, Q may be only one of many loads acting on the member. The deflection in the direction of Q and at the point where Q is applied is found by taking the derivative while all other loads are held constant. Thus the general equation for deflection, which constitutes Castigliano's theorem, is

$$\Delta = \partial U/\partial Q \qquad (5.9)$$

The great importance of this simple equation justifies restating it in words.

When a body is elastically deflected by any combination of loads, the deflection at any point and in any direction is equal to the partial derivative of strain energy (computed with all loads acting) with respect to a load located at that point and acting in that direction.

The theorem can be used to find a deflection at any point and in any direction, even if there is no load at that point and in that direction. It is only necessary to apply an *imaginary* load (force or moment), commonly designated as Q, at the point and in

TABLE 5.3 Summary of Energy and Deflection Equations for Use with Castigliano's Method

Load Type (1)	Factors Involved (2)	Energy Equation for Special Case Where All Three Factors Are Constant with x (3)	General Energy Equation (4)	General Deflection Equation (5)
Axial	P, E, A	$U = \dfrac{P^2 L}{2EA}$	$U = \displaystyle\int_0^L \dfrac{P^2}{2EA}\,dx$	$\Delta = \displaystyle\int_0^L \dfrac{P(\partial P/\partial Q)}{EA}\,dx$
Bending	M, E, I	$U = \dfrac{M^2 L}{2EI}$	$U = \displaystyle\int_0^L \dfrac{M^2}{2EI}\,dx$	$\Delta = \displaystyle\int_0^L \dfrac{M(\partial M/\partial Q)}{EI}\,dx$
Torsion	T, G, K'	$U = \dfrac{T^2 L}{2GK'}$	$U = \displaystyle\int_0^L \dfrac{T^2}{2GK'}\,dx$	$\Delta = \displaystyle\int_0^L \dfrac{T(\partial T/\partial Q)}{GK'}\,dx$
Transverse shear (rectangular section)	V, G, A	$U = \dfrac{3V^2 L}{5GA}$	$U = \displaystyle\int_0^L \dfrac{3V^2}{5GA}\,dx$	$\Delta^{a} = \displaystyle\int_0^L \dfrac{6V(\partial V/\partial Q)}{5GA}\,dx$

[a]Change constant $\frac{6}{5}$ to 1 for quick *estimates* involving nonrectangular sections [3].

the direction desired and to solve for deflection as a function of Q. After this expression is obtained, Q is equated to zero to obtain the final answer.

In all but the simplest cases, the expression for U in Eq. 5.9 will involve more than one term, each of which expresses the energy associated with one component of loading. The equations for elastic strain energy associated with the various types of loading are summarized in the third and fourth columns of Table 5.3. To review where these come from, consider the case of axial loading. As was noted in Figure 5.15,

$$U = Q\Delta/2$$

For the particular case with an axial load, designated as P, and an axial deflection, designated δ,

$$U = P\delta/2 \tag{a}$$

But, from case 1 in Table 5.1,

$$\delta = PL/AE \tag{b}$$

Substitution of Eq. b into Eq. a gives

$$U = P^2 L/2EA \tag{c}$$

For a bar of length L that has a varying cross section and possibly a varying modulus of elasticity,

$$U = \int_0^L \frac{P^2}{2EA}\,dx \tag{d}$$

The other equations in Table 5.3 are similarly derived (see [3]).

The most straightforward application of Castigliano's method consists of (1) obtaining the proper expression for all components of energy, using the equations for U in Table 5.3, and then (2) taking the appropriate partial derivative to obtain deflection. It is recommended that the student work one or two problems in this way to be sure that the basic procedure is clearly understood. A shorter and more expedient solution can often be obtained by applying the technique of differentiating under the integral sign, represented by the deflection equations in the final column of Table 5.3.

Sample Problems 5.4 and 5.5 illustrate a comparison of the preceding two procedures. Several examples are included to illustrate the wide variety of problems to which Castigliano's theorem can be applied. The student is urged to study each of them carefully. Note that the key part of the solution is always setting up the proper expressions for load. After that, the mathematical manipulation is routine.

SAMPLE PROBLEM 5.4   Simply Supported Beam with Concentrated Center Load

Determine the deflection at the center of a centrally loaded beam, shown in Figure 5.16.

SOLUTION

Known: A simply supported rectangular beam of known geometry is centrally loaded with a given concentrated force.

Find: Determine the deflection at the center of the beam.

Schematic and Given Data:

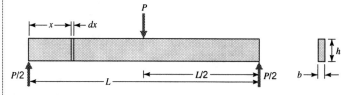

FIGURE 5.16
Sample Problem 5.4—simply loaded, simply supported beam.

Assumption: The deflections are elastic.

Analysis 1:

1. First, compute energy; then take the partial derivative to get deflection. The beam experiences two kinds of loading—bending and shear—with magnitudes at any point x (see Figure 5.16) of

$$M = \frac{P}{2}x \quad \text{and} \quad V = \frac{P}{2}$$

2. Correspondingly, the equation for energy has two terms:

$$U = 2 \int_0^{L/2} \frac{M^2}{2EI} \, dx + \int_0^L \frac{3V^2}{5GA} \, dx$$

$$= 2 \int_0^{L/2} \frac{P^2 x^2}{8EI} \, dx + \int_0^L \frac{3(P/2)^2}{5GA} \, dx$$

$$= \frac{P^2}{4EI} \int_0^{L/2} x^2 \, dx + \frac{3P^2}{20GA} \int_0^L dx$$

$$= \frac{P^2 L^3}{96EI} + \frac{3P^2 L}{20GA}$$

3. Taking the partial derivative to obtain deflection, we have

$$\delta = \frac{\partial U}{\partial P} = \frac{PL^3}{48EI} + \frac{3PL}{10GA}$$

Comments: Before continuing, three points in this analysis merit attention.

1. The equation for bending load, $M = Px/2$, is valid only between $x = 0$ and $x = L/2$. The simplest way to handle this situation was to recognize that the beam is symmetrical about the center, with energy in the right and left halves being equal. Hence, we accounted for bending energy by integrating between 0 and $L/2$ and doubling.

2. Since V, G, and A are all constant with x, we could obtain the transverse shear energy term more quickly by using the equation in column 3 of Table 5.3. (This is illustrated in Analysis 2.)

3. The final answer, consisting of two terms, may surprise those who recognize the first term *only* as being the traditional deflection equation for this case. Obviously, when one uses only the first term, the deflection caused by transverse shear is neglected. As will be seen in Sample Problem 5.5, this is justified in almost all cases. However, it is important for the engineer to be *aware* of neglecting the shear term. And whenever there is any doubt about the shear term being negligible, Castigliano's method enables us to evaluate its magnitude quickly.

Analysis 2:

1. Compute deflection by differentiating the bending term under the integral sign, and using column 3 of Table 5.3 for the shear term.

2. As in the first solution, write the equations for the two kinds of loading present (at any location x along the beam):

$$M = \frac{P}{2}x \quad \text{and} \quad V = \frac{P}{2}$$

3. Again, handling the bending term by integrating over half the length and then doubling, we determine deflection directly:

$$\delta = 2 \int_0^{L/2} \frac{M(\partial M/\partial P)}{EI}\, dx + \frac{\partial}{\partial P}(U \text{ for transverse shear})$$

$$= \frac{2}{EI} \int_0^{L/2} \frac{Px}{2}\frac{x}{2}\, dx + \frac{\partial}{\partial P}\left(\frac{3(P/2)^2 L}{5GA}\right)$$

$$= \frac{2}{EI} \int_0^{L/2} \frac{Px^2}{4}\, dx + \frac{3PL}{10GA}$$

$$= \frac{P}{2EI}\left[\frac{(L/2)^3}{3} - 0\right] + \frac{3PL}{10GA}$$

$$= \frac{PL^3}{48EI} + \frac{3PL}{10GA}$$

SAMPLE PROBLEM 5.5   Comparison of Bending and Shear Terms in Sample Problem 5.4

Using the formula derived in Sample Problem 5.4, evaluate the magnitude of the two deflection terms when $P = 5000$ N, $L = 400$ mm, $b = 25$ mm, $h = 50$ mm, and the beam is made of steel, having $E = 207$ GPa and $G = 80$ GPa (Figure 5.17).

SOLUTION

Known: The formula is given for the deflection of a simply supported beam with known concentrated central load and known geometry.

Find: Determine the magnitude of the bending and the shear deflection terms.

Schematic and Given Data:

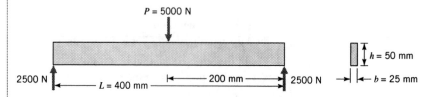

FIGURE 5.17
Sample Problem 5.5—simply loaded, simply supported beam.

Assumption: The deflections are elastic.

Analysis: The deflection at the center of a centrally loaded beam is

$$\delta = \frac{PL^3}{48EI} + \frac{3PL}{10GA}$$

$$= \frac{5000(0.400)^3}{48(207 \times 10^9)\left[\dfrac{25(50)^3}{12} \times 10^{-12}\right]} + \frac{3(5000)(0.400)}{10(80 \times 10^9)(0.025)(0.050)}$$

$$= (1.237 \times 10^{-4}) + (6.000 \times 10^{-6}) = 1.297 \times 10^{-4} \text{ m}$$

Comments:

1. This problem suggests the general rule that

   For rectangular-section beams of length at least eight times depth, transverse shear deflection is less than 5 percent of bending deflection.

2. It is unusual for transverse shear to make a significant contribution to *any* engineering deflection problem.

SAMPLE PROBLEM 5.6   Use of Dummy Load

Determine the vertical deflection at the free end of the 90° bent cantilever shown in Figure 5.18.

SOLUTION

Known: The general geometry and loading of a cantilever beam with a 90° bend is known.

Find: Determine the vertical deflection at the free end of the beam.

Schematic and Given Data:

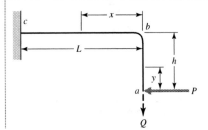

FIGURE 5.18

Sample Problem 5.6—end-loaded, 90° bent cantilever beam.

Assumptions:

1. The deflections are elastic.
2. The transverse shear deflection term is negligible.

Analysis:

1. Since there is no given load acting *at the point* and *in the direction* of the desired deflection, such a load *must* be added (Q in Figure 5.18).
2. If transverse shear is neglected, four components of energy are present.

   i. Bending in portion *ab*, where $M_{ab} = Py$ (note that y was arbitrarily defined so as to give a simple expression for M_{ab}).

   ii. Bending in portion *bc*, where $M_{bc} = Qx + Ph$ (again, x was arbitrarily defined for convenience).

   iii. Tension in *ab*, of magnitude Q.[1]

   iv. Compression in *bc*, of magnitude P.[1]

3. Deflection for each of the four terms i through iv is determined as

$$\delta = \int_0^h \frac{M_{ab}(\partial M_{ab}/\partial Q)}{EI}\,dy + \int_0^L \frac{M_{bc}(\partial M_{bc}/\partial Q)}{EI}\,dx$$

$$+ \int_0^h \frac{Q(\partial Q/\partial Q)}{EA}\,dx + \int_0^L \frac{P(\partial P/\partial Q)}{EA}\,dx$$

$$= \int_0^h \frac{(Py)(0)}{EI}\,dy + \int_0^L \frac{(Qx + Ph)x}{EI}\,dx + \frac{Qh}{EA} + \int_0^L \frac{P(0)}{EA}\,dx$$

4. Now that the partial derivatives have been taken, we can set

$$Q = 0$$

to simplify the remaining mathematics:

$$\delta = 0 + \int_0^L \frac{Phx}{EI}\,dx + 0 + 0, \qquad \delta = \frac{PhL^2}{2EI}$$

Comment: The solution to this problem by (1) evaluating energy, U, and then (2) taking the partial derivative, is of comparable length and constitutes a good exercise for those not previously acquainted with Castigliano's method.

---

[1] It is noted in Sample Problem 5.8 that axial loading terms are almost always negligible if bending terms, torsion terms, or both are present. The axial loading terms are included here to illustrate general procedure.

SAMPLE PROBLEM 5.7   Tangential Deflection of a Split Ring

Figure 5.19*a* shows a piston ring being expanded by a tool to facilitate installation. The ring is sufficiently "thin" to justify use of the straight-beam bending formula. Derive an expression relating the separating force F and the separation δ. Include all terms.

SOLUTION

Known: The general geometry and force of separation for a piston ring is known.

Find: Develop an expression relating separating force and deflection.

Schematic and Given Data:

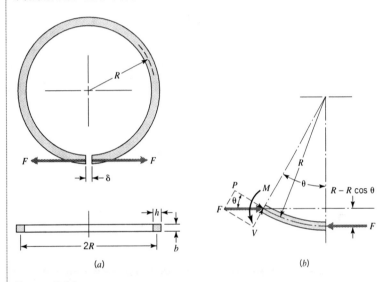

FIGURE 5.19
Sample Problem 5.7—piston ring loaded by an expander.

Assumptions:

1. The deflections are elastic.
2. The ring remains in the plane of the applied loads (no buckling).

Analysis:

1. Figure 5.19*b* shows a typical segment of the ring bounded by angle θ (defined in the figure) as a free body. The deflection has three components: those caused by bending, axial load (compression in the bottom half, tension in the top), and transverse shear. Corresponding equations are

$$M = FR(1 - \cos \theta)$$
$$P = F \cos \theta$$
$$V = F \sin \theta$$

2. The preceding equations are valid for all values of θ. Hence, we can integrate from 0 to 2π:

$$\delta = \frac{1}{EI}\int_0^{2\pi} M\frac{\partial M}{\partial F}R\,d\theta + \frac{1}{EA}\int_0^{2\pi} P\frac{\partial P}{\partial F}R\,d\theta + \frac{6}{5GA}\int_0^{2\pi} V\frac{\partial V}{\partial F}R\,d\theta$$

$$= \frac{1}{EI}\int_0^{2\pi} FR(1-\cos\theta)R(1-\cos\theta)R\,d\theta + \frac{1}{EA}\int_0^{2\pi} F(\cos^2\theta)R\,d\theta$$

$$+ \frac{6}{5GA}\int_0^{2\pi} F(\sin^2\theta)R\,d\theta$$

$$= \frac{FR^3}{EI}\int_0^{2\pi} (1-2\cos\theta+\cos^2\theta)\,d\theta + \frac{FR}{EA}\int_0^{2\pi}\cos^2\theta\,d\theta$$

$$+ \frac{6FR}{5GA}\int_0^{2\pi}\sin^2\theta\,d\theta$$

$$= \frac{FR^3}{EI}(2\pi-0+\pi) + \frac{RF\pi}{EA} + \frac{6FR\pi}{5GA}$$

$$= \frac{3\pi FR^3}{EI} + \frac{\pi FR}{EA} + \frac{6\pi FR}{5GA}$$

Comments:

1. In the preceding solution the values of the definite integrals were written directly, without the bother (and possibility for error) of integrating the expressions and then substituting upper and lower limits. Evaluation of definite integrals such as these can be accomplished expediently by taking advantage of the elementary graphical interpretations in Figure 5.20. Such figures can be reproduced readily from the simplest concepts of integral calculus, thereby avoiding dependence on memory or integral tables.

2. Note that the ring is symmetrical about the vertical but not the horizontal axis. Hence, we could have integrated between 0 and π and then doubled each integral, but we could not have integrated between 0 and $\pi/2$ and then multiplied by 4.

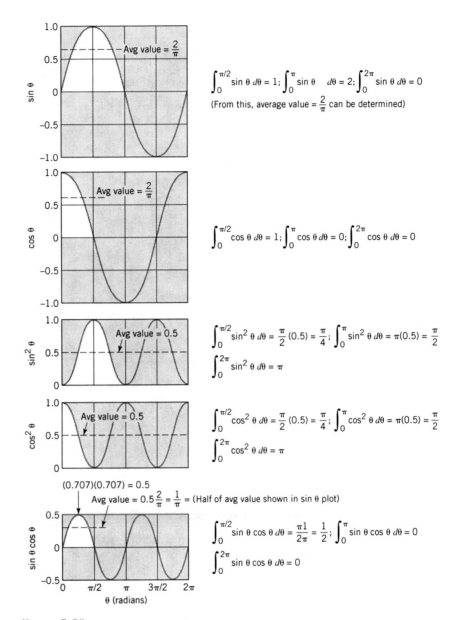

$$\int_0^{\pi/2} \sin\theta\, d\theta = 1; \int_0^{\pi} \sin\theta\ \ d\theta = 2; \int_0^{2\pi} \sin\theta\, d\theta = 0$$

(From this, average value = $\frac{2}{\pi}$ can be determined)

$$\int_0^{\pi/2} \cos\theta\, d\theta = 1; \int_0^{\pi} \cos\theta\, d\theta = 0; \int_0^{2\pi} \cos\theta\, d\theta = 0$$

$$\int_0^{\pi/2} \sin^2\theta\, d\theta = \frac{\pi}{2}\,(0.5) = \frac{\pi}{4}; \int_0^{\pi} \sin^2\theta\, d\theta = \pi(0.5) = \frac{\pi}{2}$$

$$\int_0^{2\pi} \sin^2\theta\, d\theta = \pi$$

$$\int_0^{\pi/2} \cos^2\theta\, d\theta = \frac{\pi}{2}\,(0.5) = \frac{\pi}{4}; \int_0^{\pi} \cos^2\theta\, d\theta = \pi(0.5) = \frac{\pi}{2}$$

$$\int_0^{2\pi} \cos^2\theta\, d\theta = \pi$$

$$\int_0^{\pi/2} \sin\theta\cos\theta\, d\theta = \frac{\pi 1}{2\pi} = \frac{1}{2}; \int_0^{\pi} \sin\theta\cos\theta\, d\theta = 0$$

$$\int_0^{2\pi} \sin\theta\cos\theta\, d\theta = 0$$

FIGURE 5.20

Graphical evaluation of defining integrals, such as those encountered in Sample Problem 5.7.

SAMPLE PROBLEM 5.8   Comparison of Terms in Solution to Sample Problem 5.7

Determine the numerical values for deflection in Sample Problem 5.7 if $R = 2$ in., $b = 0.2$ in., $h = 0.3$ in., and the ring is made of cast iron, having $E = 18 \times 10^6$ psi and $G = 7 \times 10^6$ psi.

SOLUTION

Known: The dimension and material properties for a piston ring are given.

Find: Determine the magnitude of the deflection.

Schematic and Given Data:

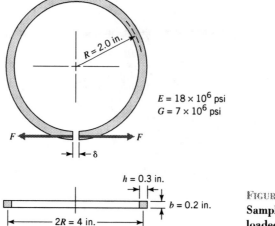

$E = 18 \times 10^6$ psi
$G = 7 \times 10^6$ psi

$h = 0.3$ in.

$b = 0.2$ in.

$2R = 4$ in.

FIGURE 5.21a
Sample Problem 5.8—piston ring
loaded with force F.

Assumptions:

1. The deflections are elastic.

2. The ring remains in a plane with the applied loads (no buckling).

Analysis: For the dimensions given, A = 0.06 in.^{2} and I = 0.00045 in.^{4}. Substitution of these values in the deflection equation of Sample Problem 5.7 gives

$$\delta = (930 + 0.58 + 1.79)F \times 10^{-5} \text{ in.}$$

Comments:

1. The analysis reveals that the first term in the deflection equation contributes 99.7% of the deflection.

2. This problem illustrates the general rule that

   If bending terms, torsion terms, or both are present, axial and transverse shear terms are almost always negligible.

   Note the hedging is saying "*almost* always." A nice thing about Castigliano's method is that should an unusual situation be encountered for which axial and transverse shear terms may be important, they can readily be evaluated.

3. Inspection of the first term in the deflection equation reveals that the approximate deflection is $\delta = 3\pi FR^3/EI$. The effect of the ring radius R, width h, and the modulus of elasticity E, can be explored by computing and plotting the deflection for $h = 0.2$ to 0.5, $R = 1.0$ to 3.0, and a modulus of elasticity E of copper, cast iron, and steel, with $F = 1$ lb—see Figures 5.21*b* and *c*.

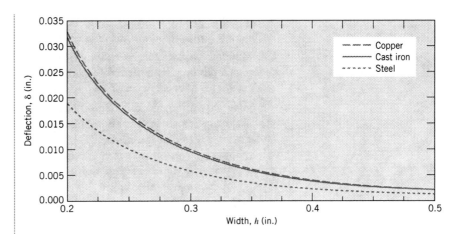

FIGURE 5.21*b*
Deflection of piston ring versus ring width ($F = 1$ lb).

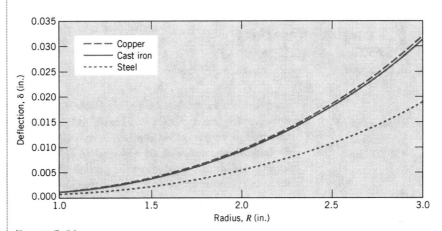

FIGURE 5.21*c*
Deflection of piston ring versus ring radius ($F = 1$ lb).

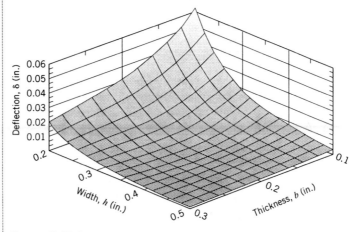

FIGURE 5.21*d*
Deflection of piston ring versus ring thickness b, and ring width h.

4. Analytically, since $I = bh^3/12$, deflection $\delta \sim 1/h^3$. The plot of δ vs. h shown in Figure 5.21b also reveals this relationship.

5. The effect of thickness b and width h on deflection δ can be explored by computing and plotting the deflection for $b = 0.1$ to 0.3, $h = 0.2$ to 0.5, $R = 2.0$, and a modulus of elasticity E of cast iron, with $F = 1$ lb—see Figure 5.21d.

6. An important additional required calculation is to determine whether yielding of the piston ring takes place during deflection, because yielding would make the deflection equation invalid. Since the radius of curvature of the beam (ring) is large compared to the beam (ring) thickness, a straight beam analysis can be employed. The maximum bending stress is given by $\sigma = Mc/I + F/A$, where $M = 2FR$. As an example, with $F = 1$ lb, $b = 0.2$ in., $h = 0.3$ in., $R = 2$ in., $\delta = 932.37 \times 10^{-5}$ in., we have $\sigma = 1333.33 + 16.67 = 1350$ psi.

5.9 *Redundant Reactions by Castigliano's Method*

As noted in Chapter 2, a redundant reaction is a supporting force or moment that is not necessary for equilibrium. Thus, as the magnitude of a redundant reaction is varied, deflections change but equilibrium remains. Castigliano's theorem tells us that the deflection associated with any reaction (or applied load) that can be varied without upsetting equilibrium is equal to the partial derivative of total elastic energy with respect to that reaction (or load). In the previous section, the loads were all known and a desired deflection solved for. In this section, the deflection is known and we will solve for the corresponding load. Again, the procedure is best understood by careful study of typical sample problems.

SAMPLE PROBLEM 5.9   Guy Wire Tension to Prevent Pole Deflection

Figure 5.22 represents a pole supporting an eccentric mass. The pole is "fixed" at the bottom and supported horizontally by a guy wire at point a. What tension F in the guy wire is required to make the pole deflection equal to zero where the wire is attached?

SOLUTION

Known: The geometry is given for a pole that supports a known eccentric mass and is loaded horizontally by a guy wire that makes the pole deflection zero at the point of wire attachment.

Find: Determine the tension in the guy wire.

Schematic and Given Data:

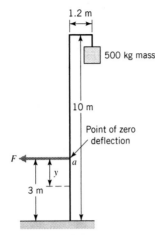

1.2 m

500 kg mass

10 m

Point of zero
deflection

F

a

y

3 m

FIGURE 5.22
Sample Problem 5.9—eccentrically loaded,
redundantly supported column.

Assumptions:

1. The deflections are elastic.

2. No buckling takes place.

3. The pole is on the earth, where the acceleration of gravity is 9.8 m/s².

Analysis:

1. Since the gravitational acceleration is 9.8 m/s², the gravitational force on the mass is 4900 N.

2. Tension F is a redundant reaction (i.e., the pole would be in equilibrium without the guy wire), and the deflection at the point where F is applied and in the direction of F is to be zero. Hence, the partial derivative of the total elastic energy in the system with respect to F must be zero.

3. Before writing the complete expression for energy, let us omit terms that will later drop out because their partial derivatives with respect to F are zero. This will be true of all terms representing energy in the pole above point a and the term for compression of the pole below a. The only remaining terms represent the bending energy below a.

4. Defining y for convenience as shown in Figure 5.22, we have, for this bending term,

$$M = (4900 \text{ N})(1.2 \text{ m}) - Fy \quad \text{or} \quad M = 5880 - Fy$$

5. Bending energy below point a is

$$U = \int_0^3 \frac{M^2}{2EI} \, dy = \frac{1}{2EI} \int_0^3 (5880^2 - 11{,}760Fy + F^2y^2) \, dy$$

$$= \frac{1}{2EI}(5880^2 \times 3 - 52{,}920F + 9F^2)$$

6. The horizontal deflection at point a is

$$\delta = 0 = \frac{\partial U}{\partial F} = \frac{1}{2EI}(-52{,}920 + 18F)$$

Because E and I can only have finite values, the term in parentheses must be equal to zero, giving $F = 2940$ N.

Comment: Note the seemingly remarkable result that the answer is completely independent of E and I. The stiffness of the pole is not a factor *so long as the deflection does not cause the moment arm of the gravity force to differ significantly from 1.2 m.* This is a condition that applies to all Castigliano problems. The load equations are written in terms of a given geometry. To the degree that subsequent deflections alter the geometry, errors are introduced into the load equations that cause corresponding errors in the computed deflection. Although this should be kept in mind, it is seldom a cause for concern in engineering problems.

SAMPLE PROBLEM 5.10   Deflection of Redundantly Supported Bracket

Determine the deflection at the load P for the three-sided bracket shown in Figure 5.23. The bracket has the same material and cross section throughout.

SOLUTION

Known: The general geometry is given for a three-sided bracket loaded at the center.

Find: Develop an expression for the deflection at the location of the applied load.

Schematic and Given Data:

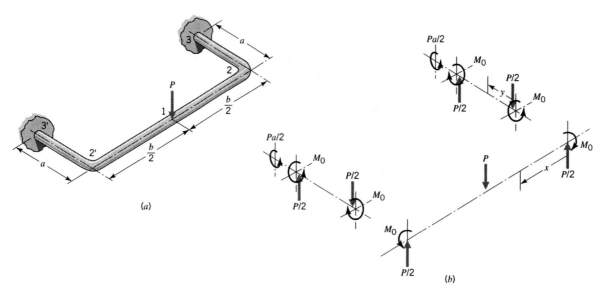

FIGURE 5.23
Sample Problem 5.10—centrally loaded rectangular bracket.

Assumptions:

1. The deflections are elastic.
2. The deflection contribution from transverse shear can be ignored.

Analysis:

1. Figure 5.23*b* shows an exploded view of each portion of the bracket as free bodies in equilibrium. All loads can be expressed in terms of *P* and dimensions *a* and *b* *except* for redundant moment M_0. We *must* determine an expression for M_0 before Castigliano's theorem can be applied to determine the deflection.

2. To visualize more clearly the redundant moment M_0, we may find it helpful to consider the following. Imagine that instead of being welded to the fixed vertical support, the bracket slips into bushings or bearings mounted in this support. Then, when load *P* is applied, deflections in the bracket will cause a slight rotation of the ends that extend inside the bushings. Now, imagine that with load *P* applied, pipe wrenches are placed adjacent to the fixed support on each end of the bracket, and just enough torque is applied to rotate the ends back to their original positions. The wrenches are then providing the redundant reaction torque, M_0. With the bracket welded to the vertical support before the load is applied, this redundant torque is applied to the bracket by the support, through the weld.

3. Castigliano's method will now be used to determine M_0 as the torque necessary to enforce zero angular deflection at the points of bracket attachment.

4. When writing expressions for the various load terms, take advantage of symmetry; energies in the right and left halves of the bracket are identical. Dimensions *x* and *y* in Figure 5.23*a* may be defined as desired, and this is done to simplify the load equations. With transverse shear assumed to be negligible, three sources of energy are present. Considering the right side only, these are

   Bending between 1 and 2, where $M_{1,2} = -M_0 + Px/2$.

   Bending between 2 and 3, where $M_{2,3} = Py/2$.

   Torsion between 2 and 3, where $T_{2,3} = M_0$.

5. Writing directly the equation for a zero angular deflection at the point where M_0 is applied, we have

$$\theta = 0 = 2\int_0^{b/2} \frac{M_{1,2}(\partial M_{1,2}/\partial M_0)}{EI}\, dx + 2\int_0^{a} \frac{M_{2,3}(\partial M_{2,3}/\partial M_0)}{EI}\, dy + 2\frac{T_{2,3}a}{GK'}$$

Canceling the 2's and substituting values gives

$$0 = \frac{1}{EI}\int_0^{b/2}\left(-M_0 + \frac{Px}{2}\right)(-1)\, dx + \frac{1}{EI}\int_0^{a} \frac{Py}{2}(0)\, dy + \frac{M_0 a}{GK'}$$

Integrating and substituting limits gives

$$0 = \frac{1}{EI}\left(\frac{M_0 b}{2} - \frac{Pb^2}{16}\right) + 0 + \frac{M_0 a}{GK'}$$

Solving for M_0, we have

$$M_0\left(\frac{b}{2EI} + \frac{a}{GK'}\right) = \frac{Pb^2}{16EI}$$

which reduces to

$$M_0 = \frac{Pb^2 GK'}{8(bGK' + 2aEI)}$$

6. In proceeding to determine the deflection, we find the algebra a bit more manageable by letting $M_0 = PZ$, where Z is a constant defined by

$$Z = \frac{b^2 GK'}{8(bGK' + 2aEI)} \qquad \text{(e)}$$

7. The same three energy terms are involved as before. This time the partial derivative is taken with respect to P, and the result is the desired deflection:

$$\delta = \frac{2}{EI}\int_0^{b/2} M_{1,2}\frac{\partial M_{1,2}}{\partial P}\,dx + \frac{2}{EI}\int_0^a M_{2,3}\frac{\partial M_{2,3}}{\partial P}\,dy$$

$$+ \frac{2}{GK}\int_0^a T_{2,3}\frac{\partial T_{2,3}}{\partial P}\,dy$$

$$= \frac{2}{EI}\int_0^{b/2}\left(-PZ + \frac{Px}{2}\right)\left(-Z + \frac{x}{2}\right)dx + \frac{2}{EI}\int_0^a \frac{Py}{2}\frac{y}{2}$$

$$+ \frac{2}{GK}\int_0^a (PZ)(Z)\,dy$$

Evaluation of the three definite integrals yields

$$\delta = \frac{P}{EI}\left(Z^2 b - \frac{Zb^2}{4} + \frac{b^2}{48}\right) + \frac{P}{EI}\frac{a^3}{6} + \frac{2PZ^2 a}{GK'}$$

8. Substitution of Eq. e into the preceding gives, after routine but admittedly tedious algebra,

$$\delta = \frac{P}{48EI}(b^2 + 8a^3) - \frac{Pb^4 GK'}{64EI(bGK' + 2aEI)}$$

Comment: At first glance, this sample problem might appear to belong more properly in Section 5.8. Careful study shows, of course, that the desired deflection cannot be computed without *first* evaluating the redundant torsional reaction.

5.10 Euler Column Buckling—Elastic Instability

We normally think of deflections within the elastic range as varying linearly with load. Several notable exceptions occur, all of which involve subjecting relatively long, thin portions of material to compressive stress. Perhaps the most common of these are long, slender columns loaded in compression. Examples include columns in buildings, structural compression links (as in bridges), piston connecting rods, coil springs in compression, and jack screws. These correspond to the general case treated by Leonhard Euler (pronounced *oil'er*) in 1744 when he published the first known treatise on elastic stability.

Euler's analysis pertains to Figure 5.24, which shows a long, slender column—such as an ordinary yardstick—loaded in compression. Euler assumed the ideal case of a perfectly straight column, with the load precisely axial, the material perfectly homogeneous, and stresses within the linear elastic range. If such a column is loaded below a certain value, P_{cr}, any slight lateral displacement given to the column (as shown exaggerated in Figure 5.24) results in an internal elastic restoring moment more than adequate to restore straightness to the column when the lateral displacing force is removed. The column is then *elastically stable*. When P_{cr} is exceeded, the slightest lateral displacement results in an eccentric bending moment Pe, greater than the internal elastic restoring moment and the column collapses. Thus, loads in excess of P_{cr} render the column *elastically unstable*.

Euler's classical equation for P_{cr} is derived in almost all texts in strength of materials. We give it here without repeating the derivation:

$$P_{cr} = \frac{\pi^2 EI}{L_e^2} \tag{5.10}$$

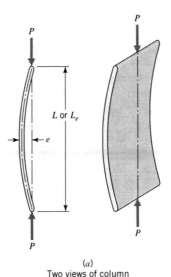

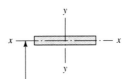

Axis of least I and ρ becomes neutral bending axis when buckling occurs. With column formulas, always use I and ρ with respect to this axis.

(b)
Column cross section

FIGURE 5.24
Initially straight column in Euler buckling.

(a)
Two views of column

where

> E = modulus of elasticity
>
> I = moment of inertia of the section with respect to the buckling–bending axis. This is the *smallest* value of I about any axis, as illustrated in Figure 5.24.
>
> L_e = equivalent length of column. This is the same as the actual length, L, for the hinged end connections shown in Figure 5.24. Values of L_e for columns having other end conditions are given in the next section.

Substituting into Eq. 5.10 the relationship $I = A\rho^2$ (i.e., moment of inertia = area times radius of gyration squared[2]) gives

$$S_{cr} = \frac{P_{cr}}{A} = \frac{\pi^2 E}{(L_e/\rho)^2} \quad \text{or} \quad \frac{S_{cr}}{E} = \frac{\pi^2}{(L_e/\rho)^2} \qquad (5.11)$$

where the ratio, L_e/ρ, is known as the *slenderness ratio* of the column. Note that this equation gives the value of the P/A stress at which the column becomes elastically unstable. It has nothing to do with the yield strength or ultimate strength of the material.

Equation 5.11 is plotted in Figure 5.25 using log-log coordinates. Note that this single straight line represents a general relationship that applies to all (elastic) materials. Being dimensionless, Eq. 5.11 is equally usable for either SI or English units. The plot shows that the critical buckling P/A load, as a percentage of the modulus of elasticity, depends only on the slenderness ratio.

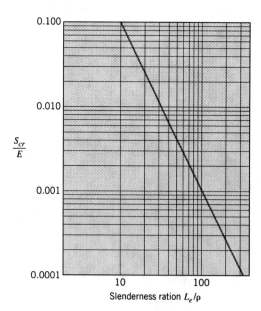

FIGURE 5.25
Log-log plot of Euler Eq. 5.11 (dimensionless, hence applies to all materials within their elastic range).

---

[2] Various symbols are used for radius of gyration, the most common one being r. The symbol ρ is used here (and in some other references) to avoid confusion with the actual radius of a round-section column.

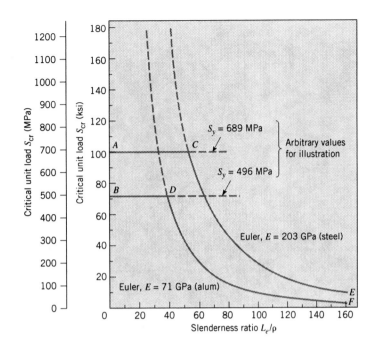

FIGURE 5.26
Euler column buckling curves illustrated for two values of E and S_y.

Euler curves corresponding to the elastic modulus of steel and of aluminum are plotted on linear coordinates in Figure 5.26. Also shown are direct compressive yield curves for $S_y = 496$ MPa (72 ksi) and $S_y = 689$ MPa (100 ksi). A steel compression member having a yielding strength of 689 MPa would, according to Euler theory, fail if its combination of loading and geometry plotted above curve *ACE*. Similarly, an aluminum member having a yield strength of 496 MPa would theoretically fail under conditions plotting above curve *BDF*. We will see in Section 5.11 that in real life, failures would be expected to occur at lower values of *P/A*, particularly in the regions of transition points *C* and *D*.

5.11 *Effective Column Length for Various End Conditions*

Euler's analysis indicates that the theoretical shape of the deflection curve in Figure 5.24 is one-half sine wave. In order to use a single Euler equation—as (5.10) or (5.11)—for all end conditions, it is customary to work with *equivalent* column length, defined as the length of an equivalent column, pinned at both ends (or the length corresponding to a half sine wave, or the length between points of zero bending moment).

Figure 5.27 shows the most common types of column end conditions. The theoretical values of equivalent length correspond to *absolute rigidity* of all fixed ends (i.e., zero rotation due to the bending reaction). In actual practice this can only be

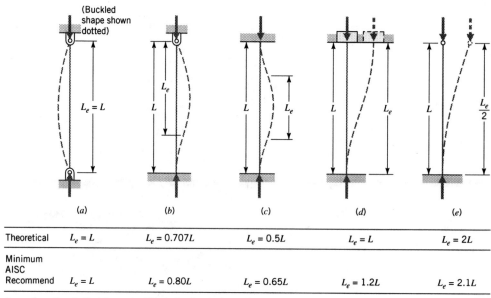

Theoretical	$L_e = L$	$L_e = 0.707L$	$L_e = 0.5L$	$L_e = L$	$L_e = 2L$
Minimum AISC Recommend	$L_e = L$	$L_e = 0.80L$	$L_e = 0.65L$	$L_e = 1.2L$	$L_e = 2.1L$

Source: From *Manual of Steel Construction*, 7th ed., American Institute of Steel Construction, Inc., New York, 1970, pp. 5–138.

FIGURE 5.27
Equivalent column lengths for various end conditions.

approached; hence, columns having one or both ends fixed always have equivalent lengths longer than the theoretical. The "minimum AISC recommendations" tabulated in Figure 5.27 apply to end constructions where "ideal conditions are approximated." When fixed end attachments are less rigid, judgment must be used. If rigidity is questionable, it is sometimes prudent to make the conservative assumption that bending rigidity of the "fixed" support is negligible and therefore equivalent to a pinned end.

5.12 *Column Design Equations—*
J. B. Johnson Parabola

Because of inevitable deviations from the ideal situation represented by the curves *ACE* and *BDF* in Figure 5.26, column failures occur at smaller loads than predicted by theory, particularly in the vicinity of points *C* and *D*. Many empirical modifications have been proposed to deal with this. Some of these are embodied in codes that pertain to the design of specific equipment involving columns. Perhaps the most widely used modification is the parabola proposed by J. B. Johnson around the turn of the 20th century. This is shown for two cases in Figure 5.28. The equation of the parabola is

$$S_{cr} = \frac{P_{cr}}{A} = S_y - \frac{S_y^2}{4\pi^2 E}\left(\frac{L_e}{\rho}\right)^2 \qquad \textbf{(5.12)}$$

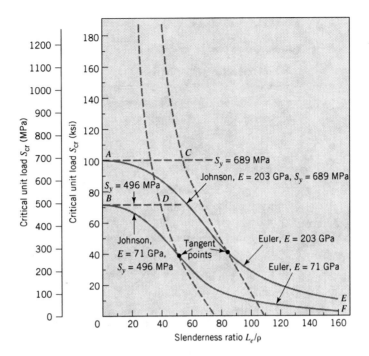

FIGURE 5.28
Euler and Johnson column curves illustrated for two values of E
and S_y (used in Sample Problems 5.11 and 5.12).

Although there is much scatter in the test data, the Johnson parabola has been found to agree reasonably well with experimental results.

As illustrated in Figure 5.28, the parabola is always tangent to the Euler curve at the point $(S_{cr}, L_e/\rho)$ where

$$S_{cr} = \frac{S_y}{2} \quad \text{and} \quad \frac{L_e}{\rho} = \left(\frac{2\pi^2 E}{S_y} \right)^{1/2} \tag{5.13}$$

This tangency point often serves to distinguish between "intermediate" columns (parabola range) and "long" columns (Euler range). "Short" columns are commonly regarded as those having L_e/ρ less than 10, in which case the critical unit load can be taken as S_y.

Equation 5.12 was written to correspond to the general equation of a parabola:

$$y = a - bx^2$$

Sometimes constants other than those of Eq. 5.12 are used in order to obtain a better fit with specific experimental data.

219

SAMPLE PROBLEM 5.11   Determine the Required Diameter of a Steel Connecting Rod

An industrial machine requires a solid, round connecting rod 1 m long (between pinned ends) that is subjected to a maximum compressive force of 80,000 N. Using a safety factor of 2.5, what diameter is required if steel is used, having properties of S_y = 689 MPa, E = 203 GPa?

SOLUTION

Known: A 1-m-long steel rod (Figure 5.29) of known elastic modulus, yield strength, and safety factor is compressed by a specified force.

Find: Determine the rod diameter.

Schematic and Given Data:

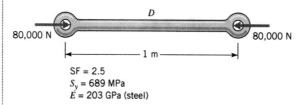

SF = 2.5
S_y = 689 MPa
E = 203 GPa (steel)

FIGURE 5.29
Solid round steel connecting rod in compression (used in Sample Problem 5.11).

Assumptions:
1. The rod is straight.
2. The pinned ends act to create an effective rod length of 1 m.
3. The rod does not fail from compressive stress.
4. The buckling capacity of the material corresponds to line *AE* of Figure 5.28.
5. The Euler relationship applies.

Analysis: As assumed, the material corresponds to line *AE* of Figure 5.28, rod construction corresponds to $L_e = L = 1$ m. In addition, tentatively assuming that the Euler relationship applies, we have

$$\frac{P}{A} = \frac{\pi^2 E}{(L_e/\rho)^2}$$

where the *design overload, P,* is 80,000 N × 2.5 or 200,000 N and where *A* is the cross-sectional area and ρ the radius of gyration. For the solid round section specified here,

$$A = \pi D^2/4, \qquad \rho = D/4$$

Hence,

$$\frac{4P}{\pi D^2} = \frac{\pi^2 E D^2}{16 L_e^2}, \qquad 64 P L_e^2 = \pi^3 E D^4$$

$$D = \left(\frac{64 P L_e^2}{\pi^3 E}\right)^{1/4} = \left[\frac{64(200,000)(1)^2}{\pi^3(203 \times 10^9)}\right]^{1/4} = 0.0378 \text{ m}$$

Comments:

1. The calculated diameter gives a slenderness ratio of

$$\frac{L_e}{\rho} = \frac{1}{0.0378/4} = 106$$

2. Figure 5.28 shows that with the calculated slenderness ratio we are well beyond the tangent point on curve *AE* and into the range where the Euler relationship can indeed be applied. Hence, the final answer (slightly rounded off) is 38 mm.

SAMPLE PROBLEM 5.12   Required Diameter of an Aluminum Connecting Rod

---

Repeat Sample Problem 5.11, except reduce the length to 200 mm and use aluminum with properties of S_y = 496 MPa, E = 71 GPa.

SOLUTION

Known: A 200-mm-long aluminum rod (Figure 5.30) of known elastic modulus, yield strength, and safety factor is compressed by a specified force.

Find: Determine the rod diameter.

Schematic and Given Data:

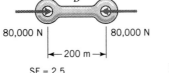

80,000 N   80,000 N

|← 200 m →|

SF = 2.5
S_y = 496 MPa
E = 71 GPa (aluminum)

FIGURE 5.30

Aluminum connecting rod (used in Sample Problem 5.12).

Assumptions:

1. The rod is straight.
2. The pinned ends act to create an effective rod length of 200 mm.
3. The rod does not fail from compressive stress.
4. The buckling capacity of the material corresponds to line *AE* of Figure 5.28.
5. The Euler relationship applies.

Analysis:

1. Again, with the assumption that the column is in the Euler range,

$$D = \left(\frac{64PL_e^2}{\pi^2 E}\right)^{1/4} = \left[\frac{64(200,000)(0.2)^2}{\pi^3(71 \times 10^9)}\right]^{1/4} = 0.0220 \text{ m}$$

$$\frac{L_e}{\rho} = \frac{0.20}{0.0220/4} = 36.4$$

2. Figure 5.28 shows that with the calculated slenderness ratio we have too "short" a column for the Euler relationship to apply, and the Johnson equation is applicable:

$$\frac{P}{A} = S_y - \frac{S_y^2}{4\pi^2 E}\left(\frac{L}{\rho}\right)^2, \qquad A = \frac{\pi D^2}{4}, \qquad \rho = \frac{D}{4}$$

$$\frac{200,000(4)}{\pi D^2} = (496 \times 10^6) - \frac{(496 \times 10^6)^2}{4\pi^2(71 \times 10^9)}\frac{(0.2)^2(16)}{D^2}$$

$$\frac{254,648}{D^2} = (496 \times 10^6) - \frac{56,172}{D^2}$$

$$D = \left(\frac{254,648 + 56,172}{496 \times 10^6}\right)^{1/2} = 0.025 \text{ m}$$

$$\frac{L_e}{\rho} = \frac{0.2(4)}{0.025} = 32$$

Comments:

1. The Euler equation predicted a required diameter of 22 mm, whereas the applicable Johnson equation shows that the required diameter will be greater than 22 mm, that is, 25 mm.

2. Compared with the answer to the previous sample problem in which the rod was 1 m long and made of steel, the result is about as expected.

5.13   *Eccentric Column Loading—the Secant Formula*

If the line of action of the resultant column load *P* does not pass through the centroidal axis of the cross section, the column is loaded eccentrically. The distance between the load axis and the column axis is the eccentricity *e*. When the eccentric moment *Pe* is taken into account, the following analytical equation, known as the *secant formula*, can be derived[3]:

---

[3] See almost any basic text in stength of materials.

$$S_{cr} = \frac{P_{cr}}{A} = \frac{S_y}{1 + (ec/\rho^2)\sec[(L_e/\rho)\sqrt{P_{cr}/4AE}]} \tag{5.14}$$

where c is the distance from the neutral bending plane to the extreme fiber, and where ec/ρ^2 is known as the *eccentricity ratio*.

It is important to note that Eq. 5.14 pertains to buckling *in the plane of bending moment Pe*. Hence, the radius of gyration, ρ, must be taken with respect to the corresponding bending axis. If this is not also the least radius of gyration, then we must also check for buckling about the axis of least ρ, using the procedures for concentric column loading described in the preceding sections.

To illustrate this point, suppose the column shown in Figure 5.24 is loaded with a force whose line of action is displaced a small distance along the X axis. Although this eccentricity increases any tendency to buckle about the Y axis, it has no effect on buckling about the X axis. If the column section shown were more nearly square, it is easy to visualize buckling about the Y axis for eccentricities (along the X axis) greater than some critical value, and buckling about the X axis for smaller eccentricities.

The secant formula is inconvenient to use for design purposes because of the involved way the various column dimensions appear in the equation. Curves, such as those in Figure 5.31, can be prepared for eccentrically loaded column design and analysis involving a material with specific values of E and S_y.

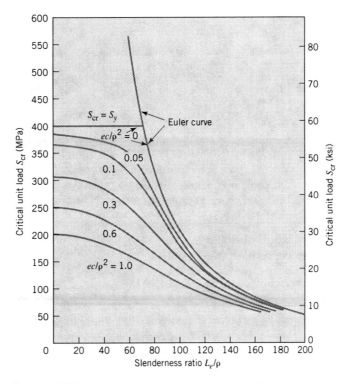

FIGURE 5.31

Comparison of secant and Euler formulas for $E = 207$ GPa, $S_y = 400$ MPa.

The secant formula can also be used with centrally loaded columns if we assume that some estimated small eccentricity would inevitably be present in any realistic situation. An assumed eccentricity equal to $L_e/400$ is sometimes suggested [8]. For "centrally" loaded structural columns, an assumed eccentricity ratio (ec/ρ^2) of 0.025 is often used, as the result of an extensive study in 1933 by a Committee of the American Society of Civil Engineers.[4]

5.14   *Equivalent Column Stresses*

As noted previously, column formulas (as the Euler and the Johnson) provide equations for S_{cr} with which an applied P/A load can be compared. We can think of S_{cr} as being related to S_y by the equation

$$S_{cr} = \frac{S_y}{\alpha} \qquad \textbf{(a)}$$

where α is a factor by which the compressive strength is reduced because of buckling tendencies. For extremely short columns (as $L_e/\rho < 10$), α is essentially unity. For longer columns, α takes on increasing values.

In the Euler range, it follows from Eq. 5.11 that

$$\alpha = \frac{S_y}{S_{cr}} = \frac{S_y(L_e/\rho)^2}{\pi^2 E} \qquad \textbf{(5.15)}$$

Similarly, in the Johnson range and using Eq. 5.12, we have

$$\alpha = \frac{S_y}{S_{cr}} = \frac{4\pi^2 E}{4\pi^2 E - S_y(L_e/\rho)^2} \qquad \textbf{(5.16)}$$

It is sometimes convenient to use α as a stress multiplier. Then, we compare $\alpha P/A$ directly with S_y. This concept is particularly useful when working with combined stresses. For example, if a direct compressive stress is involved in the calculation of σ_x or σ_y in Eqs. 4.15 through 4.17, use $\alpha P/A$ to make allowance for the buckling tendency.

5.15   *Other Types of Buckling*

Columns designed for structures requiring very high strength–weight ratios frequently use nonferrous materials not having a sharply defined yield point. For these materials in particular, the gradual onset of yielding, as S_{cr} is approached, progressively reduces the slope of the stress–strain curve, with a resulting reduction in effective elastic modulus, E. Methods have been developed based on the "tangent modulus" concept for dealing more effectively with this situation.

---

[4]Report of a Special Committee on Steel Column Research, *Trans. Amer. Soc. Civil Engrs.*, **98** (1933).

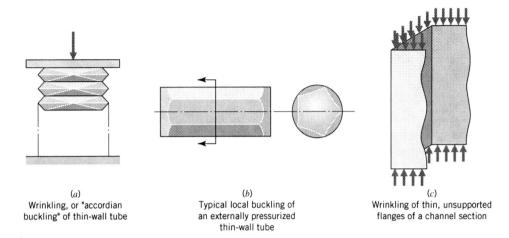

(a)
Wrinkling, or "accordian buckling" of thin-wall tube

(b)
Typical local buckling of an externally pressurized thin-wall tube

(c)
Wrinkling of thin, unsupported flanges of a channel section

FIGURE 5.32
Examples of local buckling.

The buckling stability of a long column of circular cross section can be greatly increased with no increase in weight by redistributing the same material into a tubular cross section. There is a limit to how far one can go in this direction because tubing with a very thin wall tends to buckle locally—wrinkling in accordion fashion—while the axis of the column itself may remain straight. This is illustrated in Figure 5.32*a* and can readily be demonstrated using an ordinary sheet of paper and a little transparent tape. The proportions are not at all critical, but try rolling an 8 1/2 × 11-in. sheet into a tube 8 1/2 in. long with either single thickness plus small overlap (about 3 1/4-in. diameter) or double thickness (about 1 1/3-in. diameter). If the paper is of reasonable quality, the resulting "column" will easily support the weight of this book. Pushing down on the book, using care to keep the load concentric, will cause a wrinkling, or "accordion-type" failure. The best failure patterns are usually obtained by pushing the book down quickly.

If a thin-wall tube is subjected to external pressure (as in boiler tubes, oil well casings, vacuum tanks, suction pipes, etc.), the circumferential compressive stresses can cause local buckling in the form of flutes or longitudinal corrugations, as shown in Figure 5.32*b*. When we attempt to bend a thin-wall tube into a circular arc, common experience tells us that local buckling tends to occur on the compression side. The desired bending can sometimes be accomplished by providing lateral support to the compression surface, either externally by a special bending fixture, or internally by filling with sand or other suitable material.

A thin plate bent in the form of an angle or channel can fail in local buckling or wrinkling, as shown in Figure 5.32*c*. Similar failure can occur in a thin I-beam flange which is bent and subjected to compression. A thin I-beam web can "wrinkle" when high shear stress subjects it to compression. Shear-induced stress causes similar wrinkling in components fabricated by means of stress-skin construction, such as aircraft panels. (This may be permitted, to a degree, without harm.)

Appropriate formulas for dealing with a wide variety of local buckling situations have been summarized by Roark and Young [4]. Analytical treatments are given in advanced texts, as [5].

It is interesting to note that many columns appear in nature.[5] Plant stems are generally tubular, and well into the Euler range with values of L_e/ρ equal to 150 or more. Wall thicknesses are adequate to provide greater reserve for local buckling than for general Euler buckling. The long bones of vertebrates provide interesting studies in column design. An example is the eccentrically loaded human femur, the thigh bone.

5.16   *Finite Element Analysis*[6]

5.16.1   Introduction

For generations, a matter of concern to engineers has been the determination of stress and strains in machines and structures. Although Castigliano's method of Sections 5.8–5.9 computes elastic deflections and loads for more difficult problems than those simple cases given in Table 5.1, the finite element method will solve problems when the component geometry is complex and cannot be modeled accurately with standard strength of materials analyses. In these complex cases, the determination of stresses, strains, deformations, and loads favors the finite element method, an approach that has broad applicability to different types of analyses (deformation, stress, plasticity, stability, vibration, impact, fracture, etc.), as well as to different classes of structures—shells, joints, frames—and components—gears, bearings, and shafts, for examples.

The basic philosophy of the finite element method is discretization and approximation. Simply, the finite element method is a numerical approximation technique that divides a component or structure into discrete regions (the finite elements) and the response is described by a set of functions that represent the displacements or stresses in that region. The finite element method requires formulation, solution processes, and a representation of materials, geometry, boundary conditions, and loadings.

To treat adequately the subject of finite element analysis would require a far more lengthy presentation than could possibly be justified in this text. Yet the subject is so important that any engineer concerned with the design and development of mechanical and structural components should have at least a knowledge of its basic principles. It is with this purpose in mind that the following introductory materials on the finite element method are presented. We hope that the interested student will find an opportunity to continue his or her study in this area.

5.16.2   Steps of Finite Element Analysis

Machine components can involve complicated geometric parts fabricated from different materials. In order to determine stresses, strains, and safety factors, a component is divided into basic elements, each being of simple geometric shape and made of a single material. Detailed analysis of each element is then possible. By knowing

---

[5] See *Mechanical Design in Organisms* by Wainwright, Biggs, Currey, and Gosline, Wiley, New York, 1975.
[6] This section is adapted from Y. C. Pao, *Elements of Computer-Aided Design and Manufacturing*, Wiley, New York, 1984.

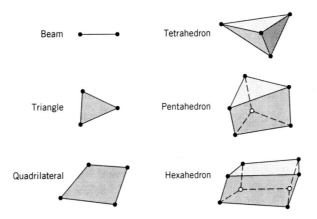

Beam

Triangle

Quadrilateral

Tetrahedron

Pentahedron

Hexahedron

FIGURE 5.33
Finite elements.

the physical interrelationships of the elements based on how they are assembled together, an approximate but relatively accurate evaluation of the behavior of the component can be determined. Some basic finite element shapes are shown in Figure 5.33.

Usually included in the finite element method of stress analysis are the following steps:

1. Divide the part into discrete elements.
2. Define the properties of each element.
3. Assemble the element stiffness matrices.
4. Apply known external loads at nodes.
5. Specify part support conditions.
6. Solve the system of simultaneous linear algebraic equations.
7. Calculate stresses in each element.

Steps 1, 2, 4, 5, and 7 typically require input from the user of the finite element analysis program.

As stated, the component (structure) is divided into an assemblage of individual finite elements. The material properties of each element are defined. The forces and displacements at the joints (nodes) are identified for each member. Each element has its nodal forces, and when the members are connected, all the nodal forces combined together at a joint equal the actual loads applied at that joint. For a stationary component, the forces at each node must be in static equilibrium. Equations are developed to relate the nodal forces to the nodal displacements, and these equations beside forces and deflections usually involve the modulus of elasticity of the member, and its cross-sectional area and length. A *stiffness coefficient* is used to relate nodal force to nodal displacement. The total force can be written in terms of the deflections and the stiffness coefficients. The stiffness matrix $[k^{(j)}]$ of each element is assembled into a *structural stiffness matrix* $[K]$ that will model the structure. The structural stiffness matrix equation is

$$[K]\{\delta\} = \{F\} \tag{a}$$

where $\{\delta\}$ is the displacement vector and $\{F\}$ is the force vector. From the solution to Eq. (a), we obtain the nodal forces and the support reactions. From the forces, geometry, and material properties, we can then calculate the stresses in each element.

5.16.3   Finite Element Analysis—Concluding Remarks

With the use of computers and available finite element analysis programs, results can be obtained for complex models. However, days can be spent "building" a finite element model. Finite elements are generally most appropriate when the component geometry is complex and the problem cannot be modeled accurately in a much shorter time with standard strength of materials analyses.

Because of the capability of finite element methods to solve complex problems, there may be a tendency of engineers to believe computed results without using straightforward analytical checks of the answers. It is therefore important to question the results of a finite element analysis and not to accept an answer assuming the computer output is correct. Students and practicing engineers should always verify and confirm the finite element analysis results by another method until the limitations of the finite element analysis model are understood. Also, the loads used in the analysis are often not well known, the loading system is often idealized, and material properties are assumed uniform throughout. If the initial assumptions or the initial model before calculations are incorrect, then the conclusions can be inaccurate by orders of magnitude. Computer output, like other calculated values, must therefore be used with caution.

References

1. Durelli, A. J., E. A. Phillips, and C. H. Tsao, *Introduction to the Theoretical and Experimental Analysis of Stress and Strain*, McGraw-Hill, New York, 1958.

2. Meier, J. H., "Strain Rosettes," in *Handbook of Experimental Stress Analysis*, M. Hetenyi (ed.), Wiley, New York, 1950.

3. Juvinall, R. C., *Engineering Considerations of Stress, Strain, and Strength*, McGraw-Hill, New York, 1967.

4. Roark, R. J., and W. C. Young, *Formulas for Stress and Strain*, 5th ed., McGraw-Hill, New York, 1975.

5. Seely, F. B., and J. O. Smith, *Advanced Mechanics of Materials*, 2nd ed., Wiley, New York, 1952. (Also 5th ed. by A. P. Boresi, R. J. Schmidt, and O. M. Sidebottom, Wiley, New York, 1993.)

6. Shanley, F. R., *Strength of Materials*, McGraw-Hill, New York, 1957.

7. Timoshenko, S., and J. N. Goodier, *Theory of Elasticity*, 2nd ed., McGraw-Hill, New York, 1951.

8. Timoshenko, S., and G. H. McCullough, *Elements of Strength of Materials*, Van Nostrand, New York, 1935.

9. Young, W. C., *Roark's Formulas for Stress and Strain*, 6th ed., McGraw-Hill, New York, 1989.

10. Cook, R., et al., *Concepts and Applications of Finite Element Analysis*, 4th ed., Wiley, New York, 2001.

Problems

Sections 5.2–5.4

5.1D   Obtain manufacturers' data on three different types of strain gages or photoelastic products that could be used to measure the strain (stress). Explain the basic operating principles of each product and compare the advantages and disadvantages of each. Consider sensitivity, accuracy, calibration, and cost.

5.2   An equiangular strain gage rosette is mounted on a free and unloaded surface of a component. The strains obtained from the rosette are $\epsilon_0 = -0.0005$ m/m, $\epsilon_{120} = +0.0003$ m/m, and $\epsilon_{240} = +0.001$ m/m. Gage orientation angles are measured counterclockwise. Find the magnitude and orientation (with respect to the 0° gage), of the principal strains and check the results by plotting a Mohr circle.

5.3   The following readings are obtained from an equiangular strain gage rosette mounted on a free and unloaded surface of a part: $\epsilon_0 = +950$, $\epsilon_{120} = +625$, and $\epsilon_{240} = +300$.

Gage orientation angles are measured counterclockwise, and strain values are in micrometers per meter (or microinches per inch)—see Figure P5.3. Determine the magnitude of the principal strains and their orientation with respect to the 0° gage. Check the results with a Mohr circle.

[Ans.: $\epsilon_1 = 0.0010$, $\epsilon_2 = 0.00025$, ϵ_1 is 15° clockwise from 0° gage]

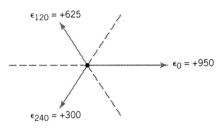

FIGURE P5.3

5.4   An equiangular strain gage rosette mounted on a free and unloaded surface of a part provides the following readings: $\epsilon_0 = +1900$, $\epsilon_{120} = +1250$, and $\epsilon_{240} = +600$. Gage orientation angles are measured counterclockwise, and strain values are in micrometers per meter (or microinches per inch). Determine the magnitude of the principal strains and their orientation with respect to the 0° gage. Check the results with a Mohr circle.

[Ans.: $\epsilon_1 = 0.0020$, $\epsilon_2 = 0.0005$, ϵ_1 is 15° clockwise from 0° gage]

5.5D For the strains obtained from an equiangular strain gage rosette on a homogeneous material given in Sample Problem 5.1, use the calculator given at http://www.vishay.com/test-measurements (Interactive Guide to Strain Gage Technology) to determine the magnitude and orientation of the principal strains. Compare the results with Sample Problem 5.1.

5.6   The following readings are obtained from a rectangular strain gage rosette mounted on a free and unloaded surface: $\epsilon_0 = +2000$, $\epsilon_{90} = -1200$, $\epsilon_{225} = -400$. Gage orientation angles are measured counterclockwise, and strain values are in micrometers per meter. Determine the magnitude of the principal strains and their orientation with respect to the 0° gage. Check the results with a Mohr circle.

5.7   Repeat Problem 5.6 except use gage orientations and readings of $\epsilon_0 = -300$, $\epsilon_{135} = -380$, and $\epsilon_{270} = -200$ (see Figure P5.7).

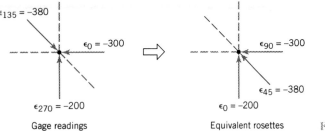

Gage readings   Equivalent rosettes   FIGURE P5.7

5.8   An equiangular strain gage rosette is mounted on a free and unloaded surface of a part made of steel. When loaded the gages read $\epsilon_0 = +1900$, $\epsilon_{120} = -700$, and $\epsilon_{240} = +300$ micrometers per meter. Determine all principal stresses and strains and draw Mohr circles for both stress and strain.

5.9   Repeat Problem 5.8 except use a rectangular rosette mounted on a magnesium part and gage readings of $\epsilon_0 = -625$, $\epsilon_{90} = 1575$, and $\epsilon_{135} = -390$ micrometers per meter. (Gage angles are measured counterclockwise.)

5.10   Determine values of principal stresses and maximum shear stress for the following:
   (a)   Sample Problem 5.1, if the material is steel.
   (b)   Sample Problem 5.2, if the material is aluminum.
   (c)   Problem 5.3, if the material is titanium.
   (d)   Problem 5.6, if the material is steel.
   (e)   Problem 5.7, if the material is aluminum.

5.11   What is the torsional spring constant (torque per degree of angular deflection) in N · m/deg. for a solid round steel shaft 400 mm long if its diameter is
   (a)   30 mm?
   (b)   20 mm?
   (c)   30 mm for half its length and 20 mm for the other half?

5.12   Figure P5.12 shows one end of a spring attached to a pivoting rigid link. What is the spring constant (newtons force per millimeter deflection):
   (a)   With respect to a horizontal force applied at *A*?
   (b)   With respect to a horizontal force applied at *B*?
   (c)   With respect to a horizontal force applied at *C*?

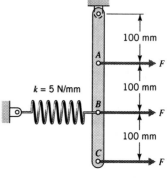

FIGURE P5.12

5.13   What are the angular and linear displacements of point *A* of Figure P5.13?

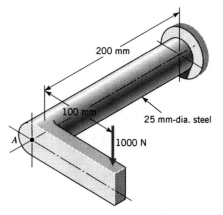

FIGURE P5.13

5.14   Figure P5.14 shows a simply supported steel shaft subjected to two loads. Determine the deflection at all points along the shaft.

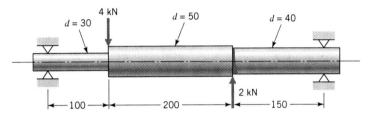

4 kN

$d = 30$ $d = 50$ $d = 40$

2 kN

|←— 100 —→|←——— 200 ———→|←— 150 —→|

FIGURE P5.14

5.15   The bracket in Figure P5.15 is loaded with a force in the Y direction, as shown. Derive an expression for the deflection of the free end in the Y direction.

[Ans.: $Fb^3/3EI + Fa^3/3EI + Fb^2a/GJ$ plus generally negligible transverse shear terms]

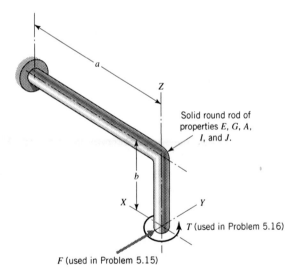

a

Z

Solid round rod of properties E, G, A, I, and J.

b

X Y

T (used in Problem 5.16)

F (used in Problem 5.15)

FIGURE P5.15

5.16   The bracket in Figure P5.15 is loaded with a torque about the Z axis, as shown. Derive an expression for the resulting deflection of the free end in the Y direction.

[Ans.: $Ta^2/2EI$]

5.17   Figure P5.17 shows a steel shaft supported by self-aligning bearings and subjected to a uniformly distributed load. Using Castigliano's method, determine the required diameter d to limit the deflection to 0.2 mm. (You may assume that transverse shear is negligible.)

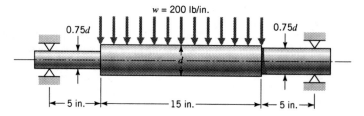

5.18   The structure shown (Figure P5.18) is fabricated by welding together three pieces of square rod or tubing, each having the same cross-sectional area A, moment of inertia I, and modulus of elasticity E. Derive an expression for the deflection between the points where force is applied. Omit terms that are likely to be negligible but enumerate any such terms. (You may want to use symmetry.)

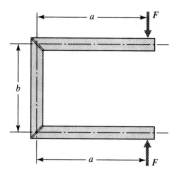

FIGURE P5.18

5.19   The helical lock washer in Figure P5.19 has material elastic properties of E and G, and cross-sectional properties of A, I, and K' (J if the section is circular). What is its spring rate with respect to the force P, which tends to flatten it? You may neglect terms expected to be unimportant, but enumerate terms neglected.

[Partial ans.: $\delta = \pi P R^3/EI + 3\pi P R^3/K'G + 12\pi P R/5GA$]

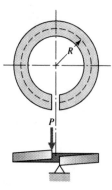

FIGURE P5.19

5.20 The triangular plate cantilever beam shown (Figure P5.20) represents an idealization of a leaf spring (more about these in Chapter 12). Using Castigliano's method, derive an expression for the deflection of the loaded end, assuming that transverse shear will contribute negligibly.

[Ans.: $\delta = 6FL^3/Ebh^3$]

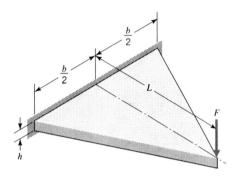

FIGURE P5.20

Section 5.9

5.21 In order to reduce the deflection of the I-beam cantilever shown (Figure P5.21), a support is to be added at S.

    (a) What vertical force at S is needed to reduce the deflection at this point to zero?

    (b) What force is needed to cause an upward deflection at S of 5 mm (thereby perhaps reducing the end deflection to a desired value)?

    (c) What can you say about the effect of these forces at S on the bending stresses at the point of beam attachment?

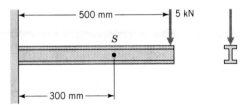

FIGURE P5.21

Sections 5.10–5.12

5.22 A solid round steel rod with $S_y = 350$ MPa is 1 m long and 70 mm in diameter. With a safety factor of 4, what axial compressive load can be applied if

    (a) Both ends are hinged?

    (b) Both ends are built in, as in Figure 5.27c?

5.23 A 1 × 2-in. bar is 20 in. long and made of aluminum having $S_y = 25$ ksi. With a safety factor of 4, what axial compressive load can be applied if

    (a) Both ends are hinged?

    (b) One end is built in and the other is unsupported, as in Figure 5.27e?

5.24   A steel angle iron, loaded in compression, is added to a structure in order to increase its rigidity. Although the two ends are attached by rivets, the end fixity is sufficiently questionable that pinned ends (Figure 5.27a) are to be assumed. The length is 1.2 m, and the yield strength 350 MPa. The radius of gyration about centroidal axis parallel to either side is 8 mm, but the minimum radius of gyration (about a centroidal axis at 45° to the sides) is only 5 mm. What compressive load can be carried with a safety factor of 3?

5.25   The 3-in. I beam shown in Figure P5.25 has cross-sectional properties of $A = 1.64$ in.^{2}, $I_{11} = 2.5$ in.^{4}, and $I_{22} = 0.46$ in.^{4}. It is made of steel having $S_y = 42$ ksi. Find the safe axial compressive load based on a safety factor of 3 for pinned ends and unsupported lengths of (a) 10 in., (b) 50 in., (c) 100 in., and (d) 200 in.

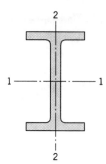

FIGURE P5.25

5.26   A 20-mm-diameter steel rod of $S_y = 350$ MPa is loaded as a column with pinned ends. If sufficiently short, it can carry a limiting load of $S_y A = 110$ kN. How long can the rod be and still carry the following percentages of this 110 kN load: (a) 90%, (b) 50%, (c) 10%, (d) 2%?

5.27   Figure P5.27 shows a boom and tie-rod arrangement supporting a load of 6 kN. The tie-rod is made of steel having a tensile yield strength of 400 MPa.

(a)   What is the safety factor of the tie-rod with respect to static yielding?

(b)   What is the safety factor of the tie-rod if the vertical rod is rotated 180° so that the 6-kN load acts upward?

(c)   What conclusion do you draw with respect to the relative desirability of designing machines with column members loaded in tension versus loaded in compression?

[Ans.: (a) 5.3, (b) none, it will buckle]

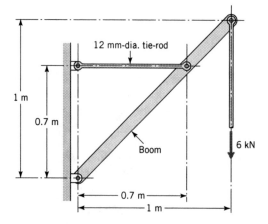

FIGURE P5.27

CHAPTER 6

Failure Theories, Safety Factors, and Reliability

6.1 Introduction

Previous chapters have dealt with the determination of loads (Chapter 2), with the stresses and deflections caused by those loads (Chapters 4 and 5), and with the ability of representative materials to resist *standard* test loads (Chapter 3). The present chapter is concerned with (1) predicting the capability of materials to withstand the infinite combination of *nonstandard* loads to which they are subjected as fabricated machine and structural components and (2) the selection of appropriate *safety factors* to provide the required safety and reliability. As with the earlier chapters, the concern in this chapter is primarily with static loads.

Reliability is a matter of extreme importance in the engineering of a product, and this point is becoming increasingly recognized. On the other hand, it is important that components not be *overdesigned* to the point of making them unnecessarily costly, heavy, bulky, or wasteful of resources.

The fundamental concept of designing every component of a machine to satisfy a given life and reliability requirement without overdesigning a single part was perhaps never so well phrased as by Oliver Wendell Holmes in 1858 when he wrote "The One-Hoss Shay." This classical bit of literary (and perhaps technical) heritage is all the more remarkable because Holmes was not an engineer but a physician and professor of anatomy at the Harvard Medical School. He was the son of a Congregational minister, and the father of Oliver Wendell Holmes, Jr., the noted Supreme Court Justice.

In his remarkable poem, reproduced here, Holmes tells of a colonial deacon possessed of such uncanny engineering genius that he was able to design and build a little one-horse carriage so that every single component had a useful life of exactly 100 years (to the minute!), at the end of which time they all failed, causing the little wagon to collapse in a heap of rubble! (Imagine, if we could only design automobiles this way—so that they ran trouble-free for, say, 200,000 miles, at the expiration of which the owner had better be driving into a convenient junkyard!)

The One-Hoss Shay (The Deacon's Masterpiece)
Oliver Wendell Holmes

Have you heard of the wonderful one-hoss shay,
That was built in such a logical way,
It ran a hundred years to a day,
And then, of a sudden, it—ah, but stay,
I'll tell you what happened without delay,
Scaring the parson into fits,
Frightening people out of their wits,—
Have you ever heard of that, I say?

Seventeen hundred and fifty-five,
Georgiuus Secundus was then alive,—
Snuffy old drone from the German hive.
That was the year when Lisbon-town
Saw the earth open and gulp her down,
And Braddock's army was done so brown,
Left without a scalp to its crown.
It was on the terrible Earthquake-day
That the Deacon finished the one-hoss shay.

Now in building of chaises, I tell you what,
There is always **somewhere** a weaker spot,—
In hub, tire, felloe,[1] in spring or thill,[2]
In panel, or crossbar, or floor, or sill,
In screw, bolt, thoroughbrace,[3]—lurking still,
Find it somewhere you must and will,—
Above or below, or within or without,—
And that's the reason, beyond a doubt,
A chaise breaks down, but doesn't wear out.

But the Deacon swore (as Deacons do),
With an "I dew vum," or an "I tell yeou,"
He would build one shay to beat the taown
'N' the keounty 'n' all the kentry raoun',
It should be so built that it **couldn'** break daown:
—"Fur," said the Deacon, "'t's mighty plain
Thut the weakes' place mus' stan' the strain;
'N' the way t' fix it, uz I maintain,
Is only jest
T' make that place uz strong uz the rest."

So the Deacon inquired of the village folk
Where he could find the strongest oak,
That couldn't be split nor bent nor broke,—
That was for spokes and floor and sills;
He sent for lancewood to make the thills;
The crossbars were ash, from the straightest trees,
The panels of white-wood, that cuts like cheese,
But lasts like iron for things like these;
The hubs of logs from the "Settler's ellum,"—

Last of its timber,—they couldn't sell 'em,
Never an axe had seen their chips,
And the wedges flew from between their lips,
Their blunt ends frizzled like celery tips;

Step and prop-iron, bolt and screw,
Spring, tire, axle, and linchpin[4] too,
Steel of the finest, bright and blue;
Thoroughbrace bison-skin, thick and wide;
Boot, top, dasher, from tough old hide
Found in the pit when the tanner died.
That was the way he "put her through."—
"There!" said the Deacon, "naow she'll dew!"

Do! I tell you, I rather guess
She was a wonder, and nothing less!
Colts grew horses, beards turned gray,
Deacon and Deaconess dropped away,
Children and grandchildren—where were they?
But there stood the stout old one-hoss shay
As fresh as on Lisbon-earthquake-day!

EIGHTEEN HUNDRED;—it came and found
The Deacon's masterpiece strong and sound.
Eighteen hundred increased by ten;—
"Hahnsum kerridge" they called it then.
Eighteen hundred and twenty came;—
Running as usual; much the same.
Thirty and forty at last arrive,
and then come fifty, and FIFTY-FIVE.

Little of all we value here
Wakes on the morn of its hundredth year
Without both feeling and looking queer.
In fact, there's nothing that keeps its youth,
So far as I know, but a tree and truth.
(This is a moral that runs at large;
Take it.—You're welcome.—No extra charge.)

FIRST OF
NOVEMBER—the-Earthquake-day,—
There are traces of age in the one-hoss shay.
A general flavor of mild decay,
But nothing local, as one may say.
There couldn't be,—for the Deacon's art
Had made it so like in every part
That there wasn't a chance for one to start.
For the wheels were just as strong as the thills,
And the floor was just as strong as the sills,
And the panels just as strong as the floor,
And the whipple-tree neither less nor more.
And the back-cross bar as strong as the fore,
And spring and axle and hub **encore**.
And yet, as a whole, it is past a doubt
In another hour it will be **worn out!**

First of November, 'Fifty-five'!
This morning the parson takes a drive.
Now, small boys, get out of the way!

Here comes the wonderful one-hoss shay,
Drawn by a rat-tailed, ewe-necked bay.
"Huddup!" said the parson. Off went they.

The parson was working his Sunday text,
*Had got to **fifthly**, and stopped perplexed*
At what the—Moses—was coming next
All at once the horse stood still,
Close by the meet'n' house on the hill.
—First a shiver, and then a thrill.
Then something decidedly like a spill,—
And the parson was sitting up on a rock,
At half-past nine by the meet'n' house clock,—

Just the hour of the Earthquake shock!
—What do you think the parson found,
When he got up and stared around?
The poor old chaise in a heap or mound,
As if it had been to the mill and ground!
You see, of course, if you're not a dunce,
How it went to pieces all at once,—
All at once, and nothing first,—
Just as bubbles do when they burst.

End of the wonderful one-hoss shay,
Logic is logic. That's all I say.

---

[1] Rim.
[2] Shaft on each side of horse.
[3] Leather strap between front and rear spring, supporting body (one on each side).
[4] Pin through axle to keep the wheel on.

6.2   Types of Failure

Failure of a loaded member can be regarded as any behavior that renders it unsuitable for its intended function. At this point we are concerned only with *static* loading, saving for later chapters impact, fatigue, and surface wear (all of which, incidentally, the deacon must have been intimately concerned with in the design of his masterpiece). Static loading can result in objectionable deflection and elastic instability (Chapter 5) as well as *plastic distortion* and *fracture*, with which the present chapter is concerned.

Distortion, or plastic strain, is associated with shear stresses and involves slip (or sliding) along natural slip planes. Failure is defined as having occurred when the plastic deformation reaches an arbitrary limit, such as the 0.2 percent offset in a standard tensile test. Often, appreciably more yielding can occur without harm, as (1) in localized areas of stress concentration and (2) in some members subjected to bending or torsion where yielding is restricted to the outer surface. The definition of failure by distortion is arbitrary, and not always easy to apply (i.e., how much distortion is too much?). Fracture, on the other hand, is clearly defined as the separation or fragmentation of a member into two or more pieces. It normally constitutes a "pulling apart," associated with a tensile stress.

In general, materials prone to distortion failure are classed as *ductile*, and those prone to fracture without significant prior distortion as *brittle*. Unfortunately, there is an intermediate "gray area" wherein a given material can fail in either a ductile or a brittle manner depending on circumstances. It is well known that materials that are normally ductile can fracture in a brittle manner at sufficiently low temperatures. Other factors promoting brittle fracture are sharp notches and impact loading. An important concept in this connection is that of *transition temperature*—that is, a fairly narrow temperature range above which the material and associated geometry and loading conditions produce ductile failure, with brittle fracture occurring at lower temperatures. Also, in general, where the yield strength of a material is close in magnitude to the ultimate strength or

FIGURE 6.1

S.S. Schenectady. T-2 tanker, broken in two in fitting-out dock, Portland, Oregon, January 16, 1943. (Courtesy Ship Structures Committee, U.S. Government.)

elongation is less than 5%, the material will not absorb significant energy in the plastic region and brittle fracture can occur.

For generations, a matter of concern to engineers and metallurgists has been the brittle fracture of structural steels that behave in a completely ductile manner during the ordinary laboratory strength tests. Figure 6.1 shows a rather spectacular example of a World War II tanker broken in two by a brittle fracture, despite the normal ductility associated with the grade of steel used. The mechanisms of brittle fracture are the concern of a relatively new discipline, *fracture mechanics.*

To treat adequately the subject of fracture mechanics would require a far more lengthy presentation than could possibly be justified in this text. Yet the subject is so important that any engineer concerned with the design and development of mechanical and structural components should have at least a knowledge of its basic principles. It is with this purpose in mind that the next two sections are presented. We hope that the interested student will find an opportunity to continue his or her study in this area (see [1,9,10]).

6.3   *Fracture Mechanics—Basic Concepts*

The fracture mechanics approach begins with the assumption that all real materials contain cracks of some size—even if only submicroscopic. If brittle fracture occurs, it is because the conditions of loading and environment (primarily temperature) are such that they cause an almost instantaneous propagation to failure of one or more of

TABLE 6.1   Strength Properties of 1-in.-Thick Plates—Values of K_{Ic}, Critical Stress Intensity Factor

Material	Temperature	S_u (ksi)	S_y (ksi)	K_{Ic} (ksi $\sqrt{\text{in.}}$)
7075-T651 Aluminum	Room	78	70	27
Ti-6Al-4V (annealed)	Room	130	120	65
D6AC Steel	Room	220	190	70
D6AC Steel	−40°F	227	197	45
4340 Steel	Room	260	217	52

Source: A. Gomza, Grumman Aerospace Corporation.

the original cracks. If there is fatigue loading, the initial cracks may grow very slowly until one of them reaches a *critical size* (for the loading, geometry, material, and environment involved), at which time total fracture occurs.

Theoretically, the stress concentration factor at the base of a crack approaches infinity because the radius at the crack root approaches zero (as with *r/d* approaching zero in Figure 4.35). This means that if the material has any ductility, yielding will occur within some small volume of material at the crack tip, and the stress will be redistributed. Thus, the effective stress concentration factor is considerably less than infinity, and furthermore it varies with the intensity of the applied nominal stress. In the fracture mechanics approach, one does not attempt to evaluate an effective stress concentration *per se*; rather, a *stress intensity factor, K*, is evaluated. This can be thought of as a measure of the effective local stress at the crack root. Once evaluated, *K* is then compared with a *limiting value of K* that is necessary for crack propagation in that material. This limiting value is a characteristic of the material, called *fracture toughness*, or *critical stress intensity factor* K_c, which is determined from standard tests. *Failure* is defined as whenever the stress intensity factor, *K*, exceeds the critical stress intensity factor, K_c. Thus, a *safety factor, SF*, for failure by fracture can be defined as K_c/K.

Most currently available values of *K* and K_c are for *tensile loading*, which is called *mode I*. Accordingly, these values are designated as K_I and K_{Ic}. Modes II and III pertain to shear loading. The treatment here will be concerned primarily with mode I.

Most available values of K_{Ic} (as those in Table 6.1) are for relatively *thick* members, such that the material at the crack root is approximately in a state of *plane strain*. That is, material that surrounds the crack and is under low stress resists "Poisson's ratio" contraction at the crack root, thereby enforcing $\epsilon_3 \approx 0$ in the thickness direction. Crack root material in sufficiently *thin* members is free to contract in the thickness direction, giving $\sigma_3 \approx 0$ or a condition of *plane stress*. The plane *strain* tensile loading, with σ_3 being tensile, offers less opportunity for redistributing high crack root stresses by shear yielding. (This is evident by considering three-dimensional Mohr stress circles for $\sigma_3 = 0$ and for $\sigma_3 = $ a positive value.) Because of this, values of K_{Ic} for plane *strain* are substantially lower than those for plane *stress*. Thus, the more readily available plane strain values of K_{Ic} are often used for conservative calculations when the value of K_{Ic} for the actual thickness is not known.

6.4   *Fracture Mechanics—Applications*

6.4.1   Thin Plates

Figure 6.2*a* shows a "thin" plate (e.g., the "skin" of an airplane) with a central crack of length $2c$ extending through the full thickness. If the crack length is a small fraction of the plate width, and if the P/A stress figured on the basis of the net area, $t(2w-2c)$, is less than the yield strength, then the stress intensity factor at the edges of the crack is approximately

$$K_I \cong K_o = \sigma\sqrt{\pi c} = (1.8\sqrt{c})\sigma_g \tag{6.1}$$

where $\sigma = \sigma_g$, is the *gross*-section tensile stress, $P/2wt$ and K_o is the stress intensity factor for a short central crack of length $2c$ in a flat infinite plate of small thickness t (sheet) subjected to the uniform tensile stress σ_g. (Except for the plate with a short central crack, the stress intensity factor K_I will reflect the particular geometry and loading and will thus differ from K_o.) Rapid fracture occurs when K_I becomes equal to K_{Ic}, the fracture toughness value for the material. In this case of a *thin* plate, the plane *stress* value of K_{Ic} would be preferred. Thus, failure occurs when three basic variables reach the following approximate relationship:

$$K_{Ic} = (1.8\sqrt{c})\sigma_g \tag{6.2}$$

For geometries that differ from that of the central crack in a small fraction of the plate width (central crack in an infinite sheet), a *configuration factor, Y*, is introduced that accounts for the particular geometry and loading. For example, with a crack occurring at the edge of a plate, as in Figure 6.2*b*, the preceding equations apply, with

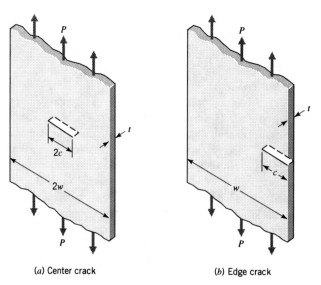

(a) Center crack   (b) Edge crack

FIGURE 6.2

Through-the-thickness cracks in thin plates.

only a small increase in the value of the constant. Thus, the failure criterion for Figure 6.2*b* becomes, approximately,

$$K_{Ic} = K_I = YK_o = \sigma Y\sqrt{\pi c} = (2.0\sqrt{c})\sigma_g \qquad (6.3)$$

SAMPLE PROBLEM 6.1   Determine the Critical Load for a "Thin" Plate with a Central Crack

A plate of width $2w = 6$ in. and thickness $t = 0.06$ in. is made of 7075-T651 aluminum ($S_u = 78$ ksi, $S_y = 70$ ksi). It has a *plane stress* $K_{Ic} = 60$ ksi $\sqrt{\text{in.}}$ It is used in an aircraft component which will be inspected periodically for cracks. Estimate the highest load, P (see Figure 6.2*a*), that can be applied without causing sudden fracture when a central crack grows to a length, $2c$, of 1 in.

SOLUTION

Known: A thin plate is loaded in tension and has a central crack perpendicular to the direction of the applied load (see Figure 6.3).

Find: Estimate the highest load P that the plate will support when the crack is 1 in. long.

Schematic and Given Data:

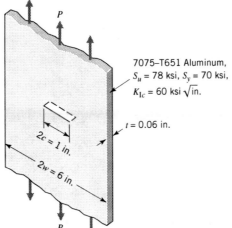

P

7075–T651 Aluminum,
$S_u = 78$ ksi, $S_y = 70$ ksi,
$K_{Ic} = 60$ ksi $\sqrt{\text{in.}}$

$t = 0.06$ in.

$2c = 1$ in.

$2w = 6$ in.

P

FIGURE 6.3
Thin plate with central crack for Sample Problem 6.1.

Assumptions:

1. Yielding has occurred within some small volume of material at the crack tip.

2. Crack propagation to total fracture occurs instantaneously when the limiting value of the stress intensity factor K_I equals or exceeds the fracture toughness K_{Ic} for the material.

3. The crack is a small fraction of the plate width.

4. The tensile stress based on the net area (minus the area of the crack) is less than the yield strength.

Analysis: From Eq. 6.2,

$$\sigma_g = \frac{K_{Ic}}{1.8\sqrt{c}} = \frac{60}{1.8\sqrt{0.5}} = 47.14 \text{ ksi}$$

$$P = \sigma_g(2wt) = 47,140 \text{ psi } (6 \text{ in.} \times 0.06 \text{ in.}) = 16,970 \text{ lb}$$

Comment: The P/A stress based on the net area, $t(2w–2c)$, is 56,567 psi. This value is less than the yield strength ($S_y = 70$ ksi).

6.4.2   Thick Plates

Cracks in thick plates generally begin at the surface, taking a somewhat elliptical form, as shown in Figure 6.4a. If $2w/t > 6$, $a/2c =$ about 0.25, $w/c > 3$, $a/t < 0.5$, and $\sigma_g/S_y < 0.8$, the *stress intensity factor* at the edges of the crack is approximately

$$K_I = K = \frac{\sigma_g\sqrt{a}}{\sqrt{0.39 - 0.053(\sigma_g/S_y)^2}} \tag{6.4}$$

Fracture would be predicted for values of K exceeding K_{Ic}.

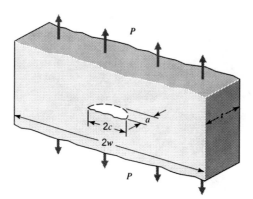

FIGURE 6.4a
Thick plate with central crack starting at one surface.

Table 6.1 gives typical mechanical properties of 1-in.-thick plates made of various structural materials commonly used in aircraft applications. Note particularly (1) the relatively high fracture toughness of the titanium alloy in comparison to its ultimate strength, (2) the room temperature comparison of K_{Ic} for the two steels of nearly equivalent ultimate strengths, and (3) the reduction in K_{Ic} with temperature for the high-toughness D6AC steel.

SAMPLE PROBLEM 6.2   Determine the Critical Crack Depth for a Thick Plate

A Ti-6Al-4V (annealed) titanium plate is loaded as in Figure 6.4b to a gross-area stress σ_g of $0.73S_y$. For dimensions $t = 1$ in., $2w = 6$ in., and $a/2c = 0.25$, estimate the critical crack depth, a_{cr}, at which rapid fracture will occur.

SOLUTION

Known: A **thick** plate is loaded in tension to a known gross-area stress and has a central crack perpendicular to the direction of the applied load.

Find: Determine the critical crack depth.

Schematic and Given Data:

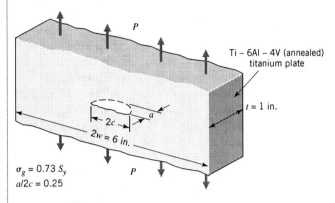

$\sigma_g = 0.73 \, S_y$
$a/2c = 0.25$

FIGURE 6.4b
Thick plate for Sample Problem 6.2.

Assumptions:
1. The temperature is 70°F (room temperature).
2. Fracture occurs when values of the stress intensity factor K exceed K_{Ic}.

Analysis:
1. From Table 6.1 for Ti-6Al-4V (annealed) at room temperature, we have $S_y = 120$ ksi and $K_{Ic} = 65$ ksi $\sqrt{\text{in.}}$
2. From Eq. 6.4, and setting $K = K_{Ic}$ ($a = a_{cr}$),

$$a_{cr} = \left(\frac{K_{Ic} \sqrt{0.39 - 0.053(\sigma_g/S_y)^2}}{\sigma_g} \right)^2$$

$$= \left(\frac{65\sqrt{0.39 - 0.053(0.73)^2}}{(0.73)(120)} \right)^2 = 0.20 \text{ in.}$$

Comments:
1. Equation 6.4 is appropriate if $2w/t > 6$, $a/2c =$ about 0.25, $w/c > 3$, $a/t < 0.5$, and $\sigma_g/S_y < 0.8$. For this problem, $2w/t = 6$, $a/2c = 0.25$, $w/c \geq 7.5$, $a_{cr}/t = 0.20$, and $\sigma_g = 0.73S_y$.
2. An important design requirement of internally pressurized members is that a crack be able to propagate through the full wall thickness (thereby causing a leak that can be readily detected) without becoming unstable and leading to total fracture.

6.4.3 Stress-Intensity Factors[1]

We now wish to evaluate stress intensity factors associated with various geometric configurations and loadings so that the maximum stress intensity factor existing in a part can be determined. In the past, in order to handle other than very simple cases, experimental and analytical methods for determining stress intensity factors were developed and used. The results of many of these studies are available in the form of published graphs, such as those in Figures 6.5a through 6.5h. For geometries that differ from that of a central crack in a small fraction of the plate width (central crack in an infinite sheet), a configuration factor, Y, is introduced that accounts for the particular geometry and loading. The configuration factor, $Y = K_I/K_o$, is plotted versus dimensionless ratios, indicating that only the loading and the shape (for relatively large sizes) of the part influences the configuration factor involved. The figures give values of the stress intensity factor, K_I, at the crack tip (based on linear, elastic, homogenous, and isotropic material). The value of K_o is the stress intensity factor for a short central crack of length $2c$ in an infinite sheet subjected to a uniform uniaxial tensile stress, σ, where $K_o = \sigma\sqrt{\pi c} = (1.8\sqrt{c})\sigma_g$. The stress intensity factor K_I will reflect the particular geometry and loading, and will thus differ from K_o except for a plate with a small central crack. As mentioned before, the value of K_I is compared to the value of K_{Ic} to determine if failure occurs.

Among the most extensive and authoritative compendium of stress intensity factors is that of Rooke and Cartwright [10] which contains a collection of factors

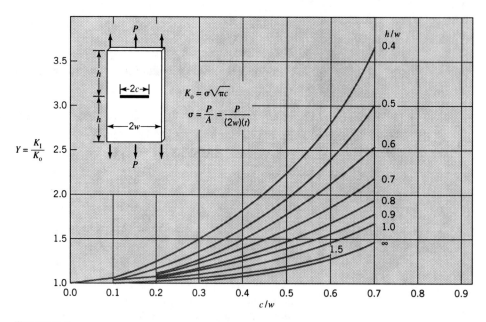

Figure 6.5a

Rectangular sheet with through-the-thickness central crack subjected to a uniform uniaxial tensile load [10].

[1] This section adapted from D. P. Rooke and D. J. Cartwright, *Compendium of Stress intensity factors*, Her Majesty's Stationery Office, London, 1974.

gathered from researchers and presented in a convenient form and grouped by categories: (1) flat sheets, (2) stiffened sheets, (3) discs, tubes, and bars, (4) shapes with three-dimensional cracks and (5) plates and shells. This compendium presents solutions to a multitude of crack problems in a straightforward graphical form. Some classes of problems are excluded, such as those involving thermal cracks and cracks at interfaces between different materials.

We now present eight figures selected from [10] that can be studied to better understand the effect of the proximity of cracks to different geometrical boundaries such as sheet edges, and stress concentrations like holes. Each figure presents curves of stress intensity factor, with an inset for the corresponding geometry.

Figure 6.5a shows a rectangular sheet of width 2w and height 2h, with a central crack of length 2c. A uniform tensile stress acts over the ends of the sheet and is perpendicular to the direction of the crack. Figure 6.5a presents curves of configuration factor, Y, versus c/w for various values of h/w. K_0 is the stress intensity factor for a central crack in an infinite sheet ($h = w = \infty$) and is given by $K_0 = \sigma\sqrt{\pi c}$. Here, $K_I = YK_0$.

Figure 6.5b shows a rectangular sheet of width 2w and height 4w, with two cracks each of equal length, (c-r), at a central circular hole of radius r. The cracks are diametrically opposite and perpendicular to the direction of the uniform load P or uniform uniaxial tensile stress, σ. The crack tips are a distance 2c apart. Figure 6.5b presents curves of configuration factor, Y, versus c/w for various values of r/w. In Figure 6.5b, the height/width ratio is 2, and for the case r/w = 0, the results correspond and agree with those for a central crack in a rectangular sheet (see Figure 6.5a).

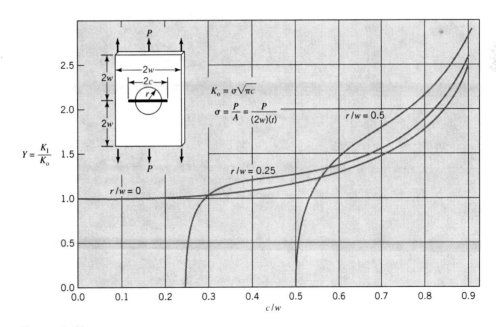

FIGURE 6.5b

Rectangular sheet with a central circular hole and two cracks subjected to a uniform uniaxial tensile load [10].

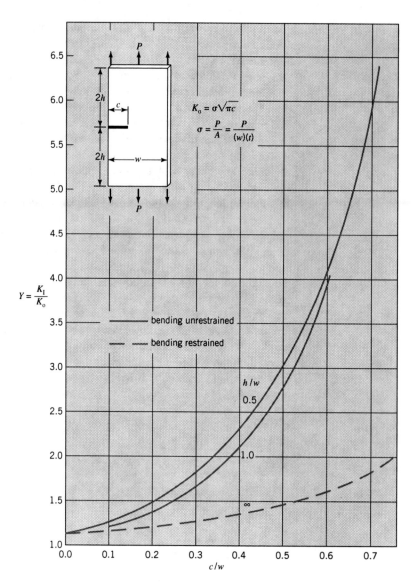

FIGURE 6.5c

Rectangular sheet with an edge crack subjected to a uniform uniaxial tensile load acting perpendicular to the direction of the crack with and without bending constraints [10].

Figure 6.5c shows a flat sheet with width w and height $2h$. The sheet is loaded with a uniform tensile stress σ acting perpendicular to an edge crack of length c. Figure 6.5c presents curves of configuration factor, Y, versus c/w for several values of h/w. Two cases are presented: (i) where the ends are free to rotate—bending unrestrained, and (ii) where the ends are constrained from rotating—bending restrained. As in the previous figures, $K_I = Y K_0$ and $K_0 = \sigma \sqrt{\pi c}$.

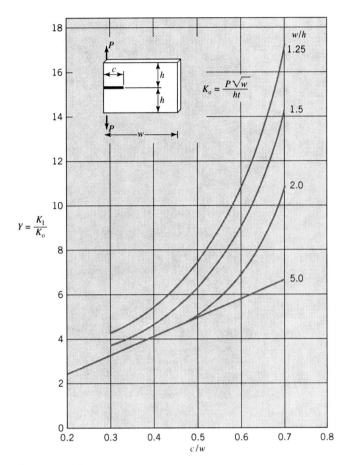

Figure 6.5d

Rectangular sheet with edge crack subjected to splitting forces [10].

Figure 6.5*d* shows a flat sheet of width *w* and height 2*h*. The sheet contains an edge crack in the middle of and perpendicular to one side. A splitting force, *P*, acts symmetrically along the side containing the crack of length *c*. Figure 6.5*d* presents curves of configuration factor, *Y*, versus *c/w* for various values of *w/h*. Here, $K_o = P\sqrt{w}/(ht)$.

Figure 6.5*e* shows a flat sheet with thickness *t*, width *w*, and an edge crack of depth *c*, for both (i) pure bending and (ii) three-point bending for *c/w* ≤ 0.6. Curves of configuration factors, *Y*, versus *c/w* are presented for both cases. Here, $K_I = YK_o$, and $K_o = 6M\sqrt{\pi c}/(w^2 t)$.

Since linear elastic fracture mechanics is being used, stress intensity factors for other types of Mode I components can be obtained by *superposition*. For example, for a flat sheet with an edge crack and loaded with uniform stress and a pure bending moment, the K_I from Figure 6.5*c* and the K_I from Figure 6.5*e* may be added to obtain the K_I for the combined loading.

Figure 6.5*f* shows a tube with inner radius r_i and outer radius r_o. The tube contains a circumferential crack of depth *c* extending radially inward from the outside surface.

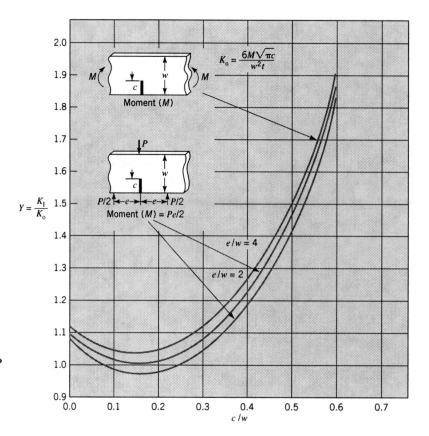

FIGURE 6.5*e*
Finite width sheet with an edge crack perpendicular to one edge subjected to bending loads which open the crack. K_I is for the edge crack [10].

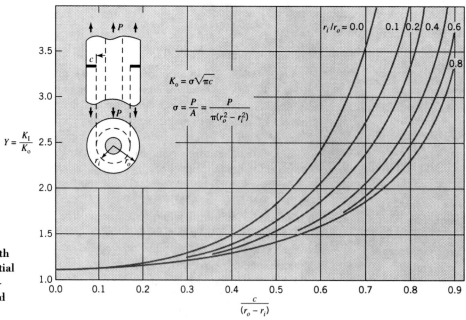

FIGURE 6.5*f*
Long cylindrical tube with an external circumferential crack subjected to a uniform uniaxial tensile load [10].

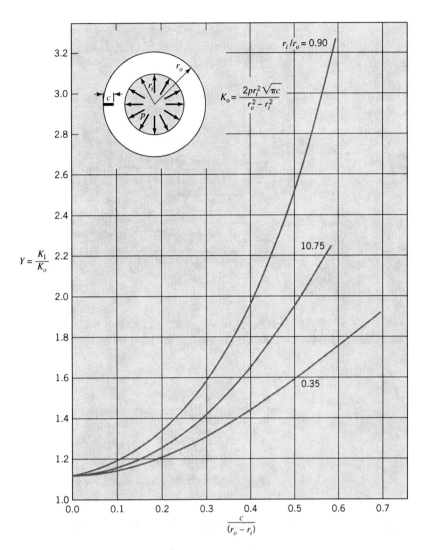

$$Y = \frac{K_I}{K_o}$$

$$K_o = \frac{2pr_i^2\sqrt{\pi c}}{r_o^2 - r_i^2}$$

FIGURE 6.5g

Long cylindrical tube with an external radial edge crack extending from the external boundary subjected to a uniform internal pressure. K_I is for the edge crack [10].

Remote from the crack, a uniform tensile stress σ is applied and acts parallel to the tube axis. Presented are curves of configuration factor, Y, versus $c/(r_o - r_i)$ for values of r_i/r_o for a long tube. Note that in the limiting case of a short circumferential crack in a long tube, the results approach those for a short edge crack in a flat sheet that does not bend (Figure 6.5c).

Figure 6.5g shows the cross section of a tube with inside radius r_i and outer radius r_o. The tube contains a radial crack of length c extending radially inward from the outside cylindrical surface. The tube is subjected to an internal pressure p. Presented are curves of configuration factor, Y, versus $c/(r_o - r_i)$ for various values of r_i/r_o for

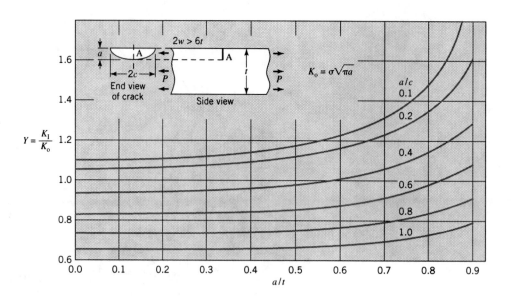

FIGURE 6.5*h*
Slab with a plane semi-elliptical surface crack subjected to a uniform uniaxial tensile load. K_I is for point A on the semi-elliptical edge crack [10].

a long tube. Here, K_o is given by $K_o = \sigma_o \sqrt{\pi c}$, and $K_I = YK_o$. The stress σ_o is equal to the normal tensile stress at the outer surface of the cylinder and is given by

$$\sigma_o = \frac{2pr_i^2}{(r_o^2 - r_i^2)} \tag{a}$$

Figure 6.5*h* pictures a slab of thickness *t*, with a uniform tensile stress σ acting perpendicular to the plane of a semi-elliptical crack. The crack plane is perpendicular to the surface of the slab. The deepest point on the crack front is a distance *a*, the semi-major axis, from the surface. Presented are curves of configuration factor, *Y*, versus *a/t*, for the deepest point of the crack (point A), for various values of *a/c*. Note that in Figure 6.5*h*, K_o is given by $K_o = \sigma \sqrt{\pi a}$ and $K_I = YK_o$.

In summary, for the design and subsequent operation of machine components, fracture mechanics is becoming increasingly important in understanding cracks and crack growth during their service life. Linear elastic fracture mechanics has been used successfully to better understand catastrophic failure, but the procedure requires knowing the stress intensity factor for the configuration and loading being considered.

6.5   The "Theory" of Static Failure Theories

Engineers engaged in the design and development of all kinds of structural and machine components are repeatedly confronted with problems like the one depicted in Figure 6.6: A proposed application has a combination of static loads that produce, at a critical location, stresses of $\sigma_1 = 80$ ksi, $\sigma_2 = -40$ ksi, and $\sigma_3 = 0$. The material

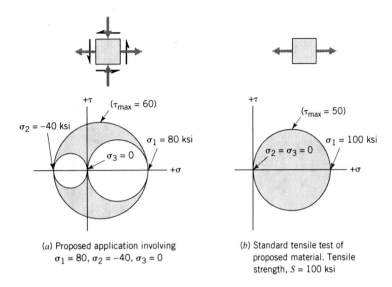

(a) Proposed application involving
$\sigma_1 = 80$, $\sigma_2 = -40$, $\sigma_3 = 0$

(b) Standard tensile test of
proposed material. Tensile
strength, $S = 100$ ksi

FIGURE 6.6
Typical situation requiring a failure theory.

being considered was found to fail on a standard tensile test at a stress of 100 ksi. Will this material fail in the proposed application?

Since it is impractical to test every material and every combination of stresses, σ_1, σ_2, and σ_3, a failure theory is needed for making predictions on the basis of a material's performance on the tensile test, of how strong it will be under any other conditions of static loading. The "theory" behind the various classical failure theories is that *whatever is responsible for failure in the standard tensile test will also be responsible for failure under all other conditions of static loading.* For example, suppose the theory is that failure occurred during the tensile test represented by Figure 6.6*b* simply because the material is unable to withstand a tensile stress above 100 ksi. The theory then predicts that under *any* conditions of loading, the material will fail if, and only if, σ_1 exceeds 100 ksi. Since the proposed application in Figure 6.6*a* has a maximum tensile stress of only 80 ksi, no failure is predicted.

On the other hand, suppose that it is postulated that failure during the tensile test occurred because the material is limited by its inherent capacity to resist *shear* stress, and that, based on the tensile test, the shear stress capacity is 50 ksi. On this basis, failure *would* be predicted in Figure 6.6*a*.

The reader probably recognized the preceding examples as illustrating the *maximum-normal-stress* and *maximum-shear-stress* theories, respectively. Other theories have been advanced that would interpret the information in Figure 6.6*b* as establishing limiting values of other allegedly critical quantities, such as normal strain, shear strain, total energy absorbed, and distortion energy absorbed.

Sometimes one of these theories is modified empirically in order to obtain better agreement with experimental data. It should be emphasized that the failure theories presented in this chapter apply only to situations in which the same type of failure (i.e., ductile or brittle) occurs in the application as in the standard test.

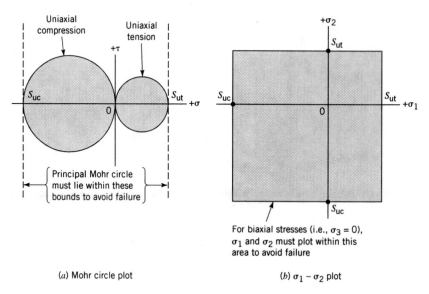

Uniaxial compression   Uniaxial tension

S_{uc} S_{ut} $+\sigma$

Principal Mohr circle must lie within these bounds to avoid failure

$+\tau$

(a) Mohr circle plot

$+\sigma_2$ S_{ut} S_{uc} S_{ut} $+\sigma_1$ S_{uc}

For biaxial stresses (i.e., $\sigma_3 = 0$), σ_1 and σ_2 must plot within this area to avoid failure

(b) $\sigma_1 - \sigma_2$ plot

FIGURE 6.7
Two graphical representations of the maximum-normal-stress theory.

6.6   *Maximum-Normal-Stress Theory*

The theory concerning maximum normal stress, generally credited to the English scientist and educator W. J. M. Rankine (1802–1872), is perhaps the simplest of all failure theories. It contends merely that failure will always occur whenever the greatest tensile stress tends to exceed the uniaxial tensile strength, or whenever the largest compressive stress tends to exceed the uniaxial compressive strength. With respect to the Mohr circle plot in Figure 6.7*a*, failure is predicted for any state of stress for which the principal Mohr circle extends beyond either of the dotted vertical boundaries. On the σ_1–σ_2 plot for biaxial stresses (i.e., $\sigma_3 = 0$) shown in Figure 6.7*b*, failure is predicted for all combinations of σ_1 and σ_2 falling *outside* the shaded area.

This theory has been found to correlate reasonably well with test data for brittle fractures. As might be expected, it is not suited for predicting ductile failures. For this reason, the test points in Figure 6.7 have been marked S_{ut} and S_{uc}, ultimate strengths in tension and compression, respectively, of an assumed brittle material.

6.7   *Maximum-Shear-Stress Theory*

The theory of maximum shear stress is thought to be the oldest failure theory, being originally proposed by the great French scientist C. A. Coulomb (1736–1806), who made major contributions to the field of mechanics as well as to electricity. (The reader is undoubtedly familiar with Coulomb's law of electromagnetic force and the coulomb as the standard unit of quantity of electrical charge.) Tresca wrote an important paper relating to the maximum-shear-stress theory in 1864, and J. J. Guest of England con-

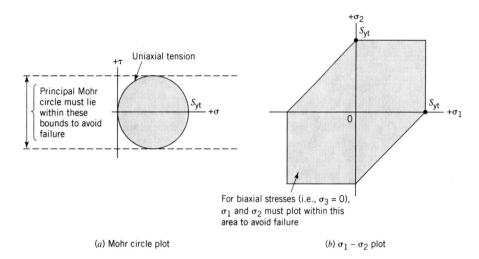

(a) Mohr circle plot   (b) $\sigma_1 - \sigma_2$ plot

FIGURE 6.8

Two graphical representations of the maximum-shear-stress theory.

ducted tests around 1900 that led to wide usage of the theory. For these reasons the maximum-shear-stress theory is sometimes called the Tresca theory or Guest's law.

Regardless of the name, this theory in generalized form states that a material subjected to any combination of loads will fail (by yielding or fracturing) whenever the maximum shear stress exceeds the shear strength (yield or ultimate) of the material. The shear strength, in turn, is usually assumed to be determined from the standard *uniaxial tension* test.

This theory is represented graphically in Figure 6.8. Note carefully in Figure 6.8b that in the first and third quadrants the zero principal stress is involved in the principal Mohr circle, whereas it is not in the second and fourth quadrants. The single test point is marked S_{yt}, yield strength in tension, of an assumed ductile material. A data point in compression or torsion could serve as well, but the tensile test is the most common and the most accurate; hence, it is normally used. Of course, if the material truly behaves in accordance with the maximum-shear-stress theory, all test data would agree on the level of shear stress associated with failure.

This theory correlates reasonably well with the yielding of ductile materials. However, the maximum-distortion-energy theory, discussed in the next section, is recommended because it correlates better with actual test data for the yielding of ductile materials.

6.8 *Maximum-Distortion-Energy Theory (Maximum-Octahedral-Shear-Stress Theory)*

A remarkable thing about the theory of maximum distortion energy is that the equations can be derived from at least five different hypotheses (see [5], pp. 117–122). The two most important pertain to the names given to the theory discussed in Section 6.7. Credit for the theory is often given to M. T. Hueber (Poland), R. von Mises

(Germany and the United States), and H. Hencky (Germany and the United States), who contributed to it in 1904, 1913, and 1925, respectively. More recently, Timoshenko[2] has brought to light the fact that it was proposed in 1856 by James Clerk Maxwell of England who, like Coulomb, is better remembered for his contributions to electrical engineering than for his important contributions to the field of mechanics.

Briefly, the contention of the maximum-distortion-energy theory is that any elastically stressed material undergoes a (slight) change in shape, volume, or both. The energy required to produce this change is stored in the material as elastic energy. It was recognized that engineering materials could withstand enormous hydrostatic pressures (i.e., $\sigma_1 = \sigma_2 = \sigma_3 = $ large compression) without damage. It was therefore postulated that a given material has a definite limited capacity to absorb energy of *distortion* (i.e., energy tending to change shape but not size), and that attempts to subject the material to greater amounts of *distortion* energy result in yielding.

It is convenient, when using this theory to work with an *equivalent stress*, σ_e, defined as the value of uniaxial tensile stress that would produce the same level of distortion energy (hence, according to the theory, the same likelihood of failure) as the actual stresses involved. In terms of the existing principal stresses, the equation for equivalent stress is

$$\sigma_e = \frac{\sqrt{2}}{2}[(\sigma_2 - \sigma_1)^2 + (\sigma_3 - \sigma_1)^2 + (\sigma_3 - \sigma_2)^2]^{1/2} \qquad \textbf{(6.5)}$$

For the case of biaxial stress, where σ_1 and σ_2 are the nonzero principal stresses, this reduces to

$$\sigma_e = (\sigma_1^2 + \sigma_2^2 - \sigma_1\sigma_2)^{1/2} \qquad \textbf{(6.6)}$$

If the direct stresses σ_x, σ_y, and τ_{xy} are more readily obtainable, a convenient form of the equivalent stress equation is

$$\sigma_e = (\sigma_x^2 + \sigma_y^2 - \sigma_x\sigma_y + 3\tau_{xy}^2)^{1/2} \qquad \textbf{(6.7)}$$

If only σ_x and τ_{xy} are present, the equation reduces to

$$\sigma_e = (\sigma_x^2 + 3\tau_{xy}^2)^{1/2} \qquad \textbf{(6.8)}$$

Once the equivalent stress is obtained, this is compared with the yield strength from the standard tensile test. *If σ_e exceeds S_{yt}, yielding is predicted.*

These same equations can readily be derived on the basis of shear stress on an octahedral plane. Figure 6.9 illustrates the relationship of an octahedral plane to the faces of a principal element. There are eight octahedral planes, all of which have the same intensity of normal and shear stress. Then, σ_e can be defined as that value of uniaxial tensile stress that produces the same level of shear stress on the octahedral planes (hence, according to the theory, the same likelihood of failure) as do the actual stresses involved.

Figure 6.10 shows that a σ_1–σ_2 plot for the maximum-distortion-energy theory is an ellipse. This is shown in comparison with corresponding plots for the maximum-shear-stress and maximum-normal-stress theories for a ductile material having $S_{yt} = S_{yc} = 100$ ksi. The distortion energy and the shear stress theories agree fairly

---

[2] Stephen P. Timoshenko, *History of Strength of Materials*, McGraw-Hill, New York, 1953.

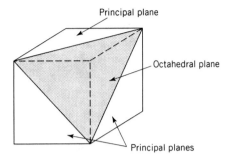

FIGURE 6.9

An octahedral plane, shown with respect to principal planes.

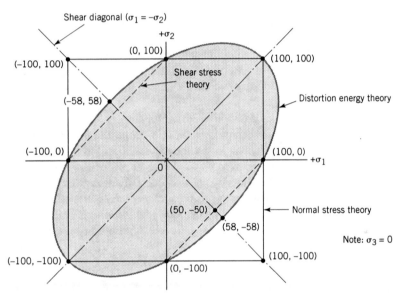

FIGURE 6.10

A $\sigma_1-\sigma_2$ plot of distortion energy theory and other theories for a ductile material of $S_{yt} = S_{yc} = 100$ ksi. (The distortion energy theory predicts failure for all points outside the ellipse.) Note that the point $(58, -58)$ is actually 100 times $(\sqrt{3}/3, -\sqrt{3}/3)$. Distortion energy theory predicts that shear yield strength is $\sqrt{3}/3$, or 0.577 times tensile yield strength, whereas shear stress theory predicts 0.500 times tensile yield, and normal-stress theory predicts 1.0 times tensile yield strength.

well, with the distortion energy theory giving the material credit for 0 to 15 percent more strength, depending on the ratio of σ_1 to σ_2. Also shown on this figure is the *shear diagonal*, or locus of all points, corresponding to pure shear ($\sigma_1 = -\sigma_2$; $\sigma_3 = 0$). It is interesting to note the wide variation in shear strengths predicted by the various theories. As previously noted, actual tests of ductile materials usually agree quite well with the distortion energy theory, which predicts (Eq. 6.8, or Figure 6.10) that the shear yield strength, S_{sy}, is $0.58S_y$.

The complete derivation of the equations for equivalent stress, from both the distortion energy and octahedral-shear-stress points of view, is contained in several references, such as [2].

6.9   *Modified Mohr Theory*

Over the years, various empirical modifications to the basic failure theories have been proposed, one of which is the *Mohr theory* (also known as the Coulomb–Mohr theory), represented in Figure 6.11. This theory was suggested for brittle materials, for which the compressive strength far exceeds the tensile strength. (Although the theory is generally thought of as an empirical modification of the maximum-shear-stress theory, using experimental values for both tensile and compressive strengths, it can be derived analytically on the basis of including the effect of *internal friction*. See [5], pp. 122–127.)

A modification of the Mohr theory, illustrated in Figure 6.12, is recommended for predicting the fracture of brittle materials. It correlates better with most experimental data than do the Mohr or maximum-normal-stress theories, which are also used.

It is well to remember that, at best, a failure theory is a substitute for good test data pertaining to the actual material and the combination of stresses involved. Any additional good test data can be used to improve a theoretical failure theory curve for a given material. For example, suppose that the material involved in Figure 6.10 was known to have an experimentally determined torsional yield strength of 60 ksi (but before accepting this value, one should be well aware of the inherent difficulty of making an accurate experimental determination of S_{sy}). We might then conclude that the material did indeed appear to behave in general accordance with the distortion energy

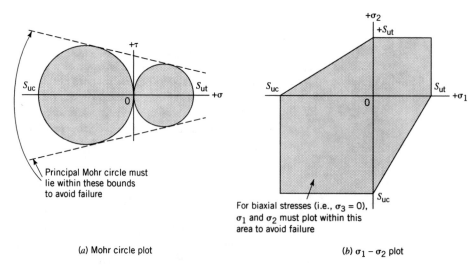

(a) Mohr circle plot   (b) $\sigma_1 - \sigma_2$ plot

FIGURE 6.11

Two graphical representations of the Mohr (or Coulomb–Mohr) theory.

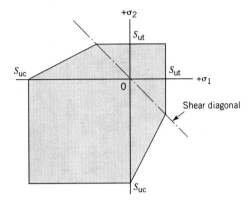

FIGURE 6.12
Graphical representation of the modified
Mohr theory for biaxial stresses ($\sigma_3 = 0$).

theory, but not exactly. By empirically modifying the ellipse just enough that it passes through the experimental point, we would have a presumably better failure theory curve for making predictions in the second and fouth quadrants.

6.10   *Selection and Use of Failure Theories*

In situations in which we can reasonably expect an overloaded part in service to fail in the same manner as the standard tensile test bar made of the same material, it is recommended that (1) the maximum-distortion-energy theory be used to predict ductile yielding and (2) the modified Mohr theory be used to predict brittle fracture.

SAMPLE PROBLEM 6.3   Estimate the Safety Factor of a Steel Part

Strain gage tests have established that the critical location on the surface of a steel part is subjected to principal stresses of $\sigma_1 = 35$ ksi and $\sigma_2 = -25$ ksi. (Because the surface is exposed and unloaded, $\sigma_3 = 0$.) The steel has a yield strength of 100 ksi. Estimate the safety factor with respect to initial yielding, using the preferred theory. As a matter of interest, compare this with results given by other failure theories.

SOLUTION

Known: The constant stress at a point is $\sigma_1 = 35$ ksi, $\sigma_2 = -25$ ksi, $\sigma_3 \cong 0$; and the yield strength is given (see Figure 6.13).

Find: Determine the safety factor based on (a) distortion energy theory, (b) shear stress theory, and (c) normal-stress theory.

Schematic and Given Data:

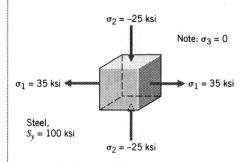

FIGURE 6.13
Stresses on the surface of a part for Sample Problem 6.3.

Analysis: Figure 6.14 depicts a graphical solution. Starting from the "nominal load point," the stresses can be proportionally increased until σ_1 reaches values of 58 ksi, 66 ksi, and 100 ksi, according to the shear stress, distortion energy, and normal-stress theories, respectively. Corresponding safety factor estimates are 58/35 = 1.7, 66/35 = 1.9, and 100/35 = 2.9. (Final answers were given with only two significant figures to emphasize that neither the inherent validity of the theories nor the accuracy of graphical construction justifies an implication of highly precise answers.) It is concluded that

a. The "best" prediction of safety factor is 1.9, based on the distortion energy theory.

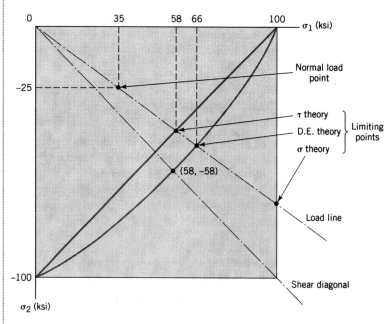

FIGURE 6.14
Graphical solution to Sample Problem 6.3.

b. The shear stress theory is in reasonably good agreement (it is often used by engineers to obtain quick estimates).

c. The normal-stress theory has no validity in this case. (To use it mistakenly would give an answer indicating a degree of safety that does not exist.)

The graphical solution was illustrated because it is quick, it is at least as accurate as the theories themselves, and it gives us a good intuitive feel for what is going on. Analytical solutions are, of course, equally valid, and are as follows.

a. For the distortion energy theory, Eq. 6.6 gives

$$\sigma_e = (\sigma_1^2 + \sigma_2^2 - \sigma_1\sigma_2)^{1/2}$$
$$= [(35)^2 + (-25)^2 - (35)(-25)]^{1/2} = 52.2$$

Thus the given stresses are *equivalent* to a simple tensile stress of 52.2 ksi. The tensile test established that the material can withstand a tensile stress of 100 ksi. The safety factor is therefore 100/52.2, or 1.9.

b. When we use the shear stress theory, the principal stresses define a principal Mohr circle having a diameter of 60 and a radius of 30. Thus the maximum shear stress in the part is 30 ksi. The standard tensile test gave a principal Mohr circle having a *radius* of 50. Thus the material is capable of withstanding a shear stress of 50 ksi. The safety factor is therefore 50/30, or 1.7.

c. When we use the normal-stress theory, the application involves a maximum normal stress of 35 ksi, whereas the standard tensile test established that the material is capable of withstanding a normal stress of 100 ksi. The safety factor (by wishful thinking!) is therefore 100/35, or 2.9.

Comment: In many situations the exposed surface of parts are subjected to atmospheric pressure ($p = 14.7$ psi). Relative to other principal stresses (e.g., in this problem $\sigma_1 = 35$ ksi and $\sigma_2 = -25$ ksi), $\sigma_3 = p = 14.7$ psi is zero stress.

The preceding discussion of failure theories applies to *isotropic* materials. For anisotropic materials subjected to various combinations of stress, the reader is referred to special references, as [6].

6.11 Safety Factors—Concept and Definition

A safety factor was originally a number by which the ultimate tensile strength of a material was divided in order to obtain a value of "working stress" or "design stress." These design stresses, in turn, were often used in highly simplified calculations that made no allowance for such factors as stress concentration, impact, fatigue, differences between properties of the material in the standard test specimen and in the manufactured part, and so on. As a result, one can still find in handbooks safety factor recommendations as high as 20 to 30. Modern engineering design gives a rational accounting for all factors possible, leaving relatively few items of uncertainty to be covered by a safety factor, which is commonly in the range of 1.25 to 4.

Modern engineering practice also bases the safety factor on the *significant strength* of the material—not necessarily the static tensile strength. For example, if failure involves static yielding, the safety factor relates (through the use of an appropriate failure theory) the static stress caused by the anticipated load, called the *significant stress*, to the static yield strength of the material, called the *significant strength*, exactly as illustrated in Sample Problem 6.3. If the significant stresses involve fatigue, then the safety factor is based on the fatigue strength; if brittle fracture is the expected mode of failure, then the factor is based on tensile strength, and so forth. Thus the safety factor *SF* can be defined as

$$SF = \frac{\text{significant strength of the material}}{\text{corresponding significant stress, from normal loads}^3} \qquad \textbf{(6.9)}$$

Safety factor can also be defined in terms of loads:

$$SF = \frac{\text{design overload}}{\text{normal load}^3} \qquad \textbf{(6.10)}$$

where the *design overload* is defined as being just sufficient to cause failure.

In most situations, the two definitions of safety factor are equivalent. For example, if a material has a significant strength of 200 MPa and the significant stress is 100 MPa, the safety factor is 2. Looking at it the other way, the design overload needed to bring the stress up to the limiting value of 200 MPa is twice the normal load, thus giving a safety factor of 2.

Although the distinction between Eqs. 6.9 and 6.10 may seem trivial, it is recommended that the design overload concept and Eq. 6.10 be used. These are always valid, whereas there are instances in which Eq. 6.9 cannot be properly applied. For example, consider the design of a slender column for a safety factor of 2. Figure 6.15 shows how load and stress increase to buckling failure, and where operation with a safety factor of 2 would be calculated both ways. The discrepancy is due to nonlinearity of the load–stress curve. It is clear which interpretation is most conducive to the engineer's peace of mind.

Another example in support of the design overload concept concerns the general case of fatigue loading (treated in Chapter 8), which consists of a combination of mean (or static) and alternating loads. The kind of overload most likely to occur may involve increasing either or both of these load components. The design overload concept permits the safety factor to be computed with respect to whatever kind of overload is of interest.

A word of caution: It follows from the preceding comments that there are instances in which the term "safety factor" is ambiguous. It is therefore necessary to be sure that it is clearly defined in all cases for which there could be ambiguity.

---

[3] This is one of the seemingly inevitable instances in which a word, or letter, has more than one meaning. Here a "normal load" is distinguished from an "abnormal load" or an "overload." From the context it should be clear that the meaning is not "normal load" as distinguished from a "shear load."

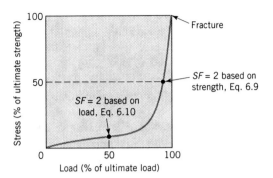

FIGURE 6.15

Two concepts of safety factor for a buckling column.

6.12 *Safety Factors—Selection of a Numerical Value*

After going as far as is practical in determining the significant strength of the actual fabricated part and the details of the loading to which it will be subjected, there always remains some margin of uncertainty that must be covered by a safety factor. The part *must* be designed to withstand a "design overload" somewhat larger than the normally expected load.

In the last analysis, selection of the safety factor comes down to engineering judgment based on experience. Sometimes these selections are formalized into design codes covering specific situations—for example, the ASME Pressure Vessel Codes, the various building codes, and stipulated safety factor values in legal contracts covering the design and development of special machines. Safety factors are often embodied into computer programs or software for the design of specific components. Then the responsibility for making the engineering judgment falls upon the engineer responsible for the code or computer software. But only partly so because the engineer *using* the code or software must be satisfied that this detail of the code or software is indeed appropriate for the particular application.

6.12.1 Factors in the Selection of a Safety Factor

The selection of an appropriate value of safety factor is based primarily on the following five factors.

1. *Degree of uncertainty about loading.* In some situations loads can be determined with virtual certainty. The centrifugal forces in the rotor of an alternating-current motor cannot exceed those calculated for synchronous speed. The loads acting on an engine valve spring are definitely established by the "valve open" and "valve closed" positions (however, in a later chapter we will mention "spring surge," which could introduce a degree of uncertainty). But what loads should be used for the design of automotive suspension components, whose loads can vary tremendously depending on the severity of use and abuse? And

what about a comparable situation in a completely new kind of machine for which there is no previous experience to serve as a guide? The greater the uncertainty, the more conservative the engineer must be in selecting an appropriate design overload or safety factor.

2. *Degree of uncertainty about material strength.* Ideally, the engineer would have available extensive data pertaining to the strength of the material *as fabricated* into the actual (or very similar) parts, and tested at temperatures and in environments similar to those actually encountered. But this is seldom the case. More often, the available material strength data pertain to samples smaller than the actual part, which have not experienced any cold working in part fabrication, and which have been tested at room temperature in ordinary air. Moreover, there is bound to be some variation in strength from one test specimen to another. Sometimes the engineer must work with material test data for which such information as specimen size and degree of data scatter (and the relationship between the reported single value and the total range of scatter) are unknown. Furthermore, the material properties may sometimes change significantly over the service life of the part. The greater the uncertainty about all these factors, the larger the safety factor that must be used.

3. *Uncertainties in relating applied loads to material strength via stress analysis.* At this point the reader is already familiar with a number of possible uncertainties, such as (a) validity of the assumptions involved in the standard equations for calculating nominal stresses, (b) accuracy in determining the effective stress concentration factors, (c) accuracy in estimating residual stresses, if any, introduced in fabricating the part, and (d) suitability of any failure theories and other relationships used to estimate "significant strength" from available laboratory strength test data.

4. *Consequences of failure—human safety and economics.* If the consequences of failure are catastrophic, relatively large safety factors must, of course, be used. In addition, if the failure of some relatively inexpensive part could cause extensive shutdown of a major assembly line, simple economics dictates increasing the cost of this part severalfold (if necessary) in order to virtually eliminate the possibility of its failure.

    An important item is the *nature* of a failure. If failure is caused by ductile yielding, the consequences are likely to be less severe than if caused by brittle fracture. Accordingly, safety factors recommended in handbooks are invariably larger for brittle materials.

5. *Cost of providing a large safety factor.* This cost involves a monetary consideration and may also involve important consumption of resources. In some cases, a safety factor larger than needed may have serious consequences. A dramatic example is a hypothetical aircraft with excessive safety factors making it too heavy to fly! With respect to the design of an automobile, it would be possible to increase safety factors on structural components to the point that a "maniac" driver could hardly cause a failure even when trying. But to do so would penalize "sane" drivers by requiring them to pay for stronger components than they can use. More likely, of course, it would motivate them to buy competitor's cars! Consider this situation. Should an automotive engineer increase the cost per car by $10 in order to avoid 100 failures in a production run of a million cars, where the failures would not involve safety, but would entail a $100 repair? That is, should $10,000,000 be spent to save $10,000 plus some customer inconvenience?

A key point in safety factor selection is *balance*. All parts of a machine or system should have *consistent* safety factors. Components that might possibly cause human injury or entail major costs should have the greatest safety factors; components that are comparable in these respects should generally have about the same safety factor, and so on. In fact, balance is perhaps the key to proper safety factor selection—balance based on good engineering judgment, which is in turn based on all available information and experience. (Now, marvel again at the balance achieved by the deacon in his design of the amazing "One-Hoss Shay"!)

6.12.2 Recommended Values for a Safety Factor

Having read through this much philosophy of safety factor selection, the reader is entitled to have, at least as a guide, some suggestions for "ball park" values of safety factor that have been found useful. For this purpose, the following recommendations of Joseph Vidosic [8] are suggested. These safety factors are based on yield strength.

1. $SF = 1.25$ to 1.5 for exceptionally reliable materials used under controllable conditions and subjected to loads and stresses that can be determined with certainty—used almost invariably where low weight is a particularly important consideration.

2. $SF = 1.5$ to 2 for well-known materials, under reasonably constant environmental conditions, subjected to loads and stresses that can be determined readily.

3. $SF = 2$ to 2.5 for average materials operated in ordinary environments and subjected to loads and stresses that can be determined.

4. $SF = 2.5$ to 3 for less tried materials or for brittle materials under average conditions of environment, load, and stress.

5. $SF = 3$ to 4 for untried materials used under average conditions of environment, load, and stress.

6. $SF = 3$ to 4 should also be used with better-known materials that are to be used in uncertain environments or subjected to uncertain stresses.

7. Repeated loads: the factors established in items 1 to 6 are acceptable but must be applied to the *endurance limit* rather than to the yield strength of the material.

8. Impact forces: the factors given in items 3 to 6 are acceptable, but an *impact factor* should be included.

9. Brittle materials: where the ultimate strength is used as the theoretical maximum, the factors presented in items 1 to 6 should be approximately doubled.

10. Where higher factors might appear desirable, a more thorough analysis of the problem should be undertaken before deciding on their use.

6.13 *Reliability*

A concept closely related to safety factor is *reliability*. If 100 "identical" parts are put into service and two fail, then the parts proved to be 98 percent reliable (which might or might not be good enough). Although the reliability concept finds considerably more application with parts subjected to wear and fatigue loading, we introduce it

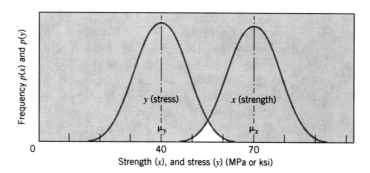

FIGURE 6.16
Distribution curves for significant strength *x* and significant stress *y*.

here in the simpler context of static loading. The usefulness of the reliability approach depends on having adequate information on the statistical distribution of (1) *loading* applied to parts in service, from which can be calculated the significant stress, and (2) the significant *strength* of production runs of manufactured parts.

Figure 6.16 shows hypothetical distribution curves for significant stress and for corresponding significant strength. The mean value of strength is 70 and the mean value of stress 40. This means that if an "average" part from the production run were put into service under "average" conditions of loading, there would be a *margin of safety*[4] of 30. However, the unshaded area of the curve indicates that there is *some* possibility of a weak part (as strength equals 50) being installed in a particularly severe application (as stress equals 60), in which case failure would occur. Thus, even though the margin of safety is, on the average, 30, in a few instances the margin of safety will be negative and failure expected. Figure 6.17 shows a corresponding plot of the distribution of margin of safety. In most instances, interest would be focused on the size of the unshaded area at the left, indicating failures.

In order to obtain quantitative estimates of the percentage of anticipated failures from a study like the preceding, we must look into the nature of the distribution curves for significant stress and strength. We will consider here only the case involving *normal* or *Gaussian* distributions. Although this is only one of the "mathematical models" sometimes found best suited to actual cases, it is probably the most common.

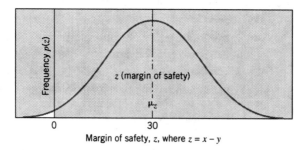

FIGURE 6.17
Distribution curve for margin of safety *z*.

---

[4] In aeronautical design, the term *margin of safety* has a different meaning from that used in this text and in other areas.

6.14   *Normal Distributions*

The normal distribution function is most commonly credited to Gauss but was also discovered independently by two other eighteenth-century mathematicians, Laplace and DeMoivre. Several normal distribution curves are plotted in Figure 6.18. They have the equation

$$p(x) = \frac{1}{\sqrt{2\pi}\,\sigma} \exp\left[-\frac{(x-\mu)^2}{2\sigma^2}\right], \qquad -\infty < x < \infty \qquad (6.11)$$

where $p(x)$ is the probability density function, μ is the mean value of the quantity and σ the standard deviation[5] (more about this a little later).

One limitation of this mathematical model for many applications is the fact that the curve extends asymptotically all the way to plus and minus infinity. Since the probability that any individual value of x will fall between plus and minus infinity is one, the area under each of the curves in Figure 6.18 is unity. Likewise, the probability that the value of x will be between any specific values x_1 and x_2 is equal to the area under the curve between x_1 and x_2, as shown in Figure 6.18.

Varying μ with constant σ merely shifts the curve to the right or left. Varying σ with constant μ changes the shape of the curve, as shown in Figure 6.18. Standard deviation, σ, can be thought of as the standard index of *dispersion* or scatter of the particular quantity. Mathematically, μ and σ are defined as

$$\mu = \text{mean} = \frac{1}{n}\sum_{i=1}^{n} x_i \qquad (6.12)$$

$$\sigma = \text{standard deviation} = \sqrt{\frac{1}{n-1}\sum_{i=1}^{n}(x_i - \mu)^2} \qquad (6.13)$$

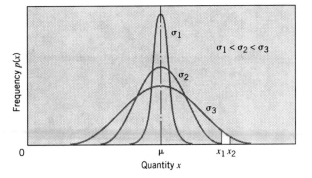

FIGURE 6.18
Normal distribution curves having a common μ and various σ.

---

[5] We apologize for using these letters again, but our ancestors utterly disregarded the needs of future generations of engineers and scientists when they put only 26 and 24 letters in the Roman and Greek alphabets, respectively. But perhaps an engineer who cannot tell a normal stress from a standard deviation has more serious problems anyway!

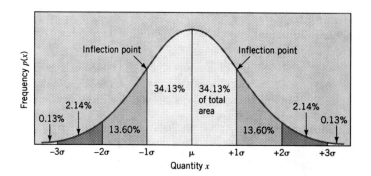

FIGURE 6.19
Properties of all normal distribution curves.

Figure 6.19 illustrates a particularly useful property of *all* normal distribution curves: 68 percent of the population represented fall within the band $\mu \pm 1\sigma$, 95 percent fall within the band $\mu \pm 2\sigma$ and so on. Percentages of the population corresponding to any other portions of the distribution can be determined from Figure 6.20. (Note: It is suggested that the reader not familiar with normal distributions verify the numerical values given in Figure 6.19 by using Figure 6.20.)

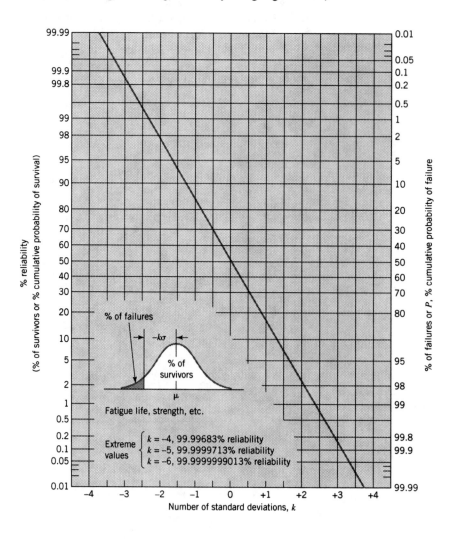

FIGURE 6.20
Generalized normal distribution curve plotted on special probability coordinates.

6.15   *Interference Theory of Reliability Prediction*

The interference theory of reliability prediction has already been illustrated by the "interference" or shaded area of overlap in Figure 6.16, and by Figure 6.17. The margin of safety, z, is given by $z = x - y$. It can be shown that

$$\mu_z = \mu_x - \mu_y \qquad (6.14)$$

and

$$\sigma_z = \sqrt{\sigma_x^2 + \sigma_y^2} \qquad (6.15)$$

By definition, the probability of failure is $p(z < 0)$.

If the strength x and stress y are normally distributed, then it can be shown that the margin of safety z also has a normal distribution.

The following example illustrates a typical application of the interference theory.

SAMPLE PROBLEM 6.4   Application of Interference Theory of Reliability

---

Bolts installed on a production line are tightened with automatic wrenches. They are to be tightened sufficiently to yield the full cross section in order to produce the highest possible initial tension. The limiting condition is twisting off the bolts during assembly. The bolts have a mean twisting-off strength of 20 N·m with a standard deviation of 1 N·m. The automatic wrenches have a standard deviation of 1.5 N·m. What mean value of wrench torque setting would result in an estimated 1 bolt in 500 twisting off during assembly (see Figure 6.21)?

SOLUTION

Known: Bolts have a normal distribution of twist-off strength, and the wrench torque used to tighten the bolts has a standard deviation of 1.5 N·m. One bolt in 500 twists off.

Find: Determine the mean value of wrench torque.

Schematic and Given Data: See Figure 6.21.

Assumption: Both the bolt twist-off strength and the wrench twist-off torque are normal distributions.

Analysis:
a. $\sigma_x = 1$ N·m, $\sigma_y = 1.5$ N·m. From Eq. 6.15, $\sigma_z = 1.80$ N·m.
b. Figure 6.20 shows that a failure percentage of 0.2 corresponds to 2.9 standard deviations below the mean: $\mu_z = k\sigma_z = (2.9)(1.80 \text{ N·m}) = 5.22 \text{ N·m}$. Hence, $\mu_z = 5.22$ N·m.

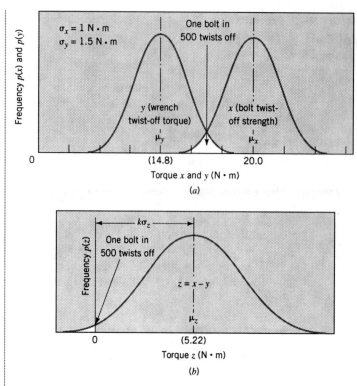

FIGURE 6.21
(a) Distribution curves for *x* and *y* in Sample Problem 6.4.
(b) Distribution curve for *z*.

c. Since $\mu_x = 20$ N·m, we obtain from Eq. 6.14 $\mu_y = 14.78$ N·m. This is the required value of wrench setting.

Comment: Note that the interference theory of reliability prediction does not require or preclude an order in which the bolts are tested. That is, one group of 500 bolts could be tested in one order and a second group of bolts in a different order and still only one bolt would fail.

References

1. Hertzberg, Richard W., *Deformation and Fracture Mechanics of Engineering Materials*, 3rd ed., Wiley, New York, 1989.

2. Juvinall, Robert C., *Engineering Considerations of Stress, Strain, and Strength*, McGraw-Hill, New York, 1967.

3. Lipson, Charles, and R. C. Juvinall, *Handbook of Stress and Strength*, Macmillan, New York, 1963.

4. Lipson, Charles, and J. Sheth, *Statistical Design and Analysis of Engineering Experiments*, McGraw-Hill, New York, 1973.

5. Marin, Joseph, *Mechanical Behavior of Engineering Materials*, Prentice-Hall, Englewood Cliffs, N.J., 1962.

6. Marin, Joseph, "Theories of Strength for Combined Stresses and Nonisotropic Materials," *J. Aeron. Sci.*, **24**(4):265–269 (April 1957).

7. Tipper, C. F., *The Brittle Fracture Story*, Cambridge University Press, New York, 1962.

8. Vidosic, Joseph P., *Machine Design Projects*, Ronald Press, New York, 1957.

9. Wilhem, D. P., "Fracture Mechanics Guidelines for Aircraft Structural Applications," U.S. Air Force Technical Report AFFDL-TR-69-111, Feb., 1970.

10. Rooke, D.P., and D.J. Cartwright, *Compendium of Stress Intensity Factors*, Her Majesty's Stationery Office, London, 1976.

Problems

Sections 6.1–6.4

6.1 A large sheet with a 2-in.-long crack fractures when loaded to 75 ksi. Determine the fracture load for a similar sheet containing a 4-in. crack.

[Ans.: 53 ksi]

6.2 A large rectangular sheet with a 1-in.-long central crack fractures when loaded to 80 ksi. Determine the fracture load for a similar sheet containing a 1.75-in. crack (see Figure P6.2).

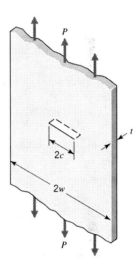

FIGURE P6.2

6.3 A large sheet with a 1.75-in.-long edge crack fractures when loaded to 85 ksi. Determine the fracture load for a similar sheet containing a 2.625-in. crack (see Figure P6.3).

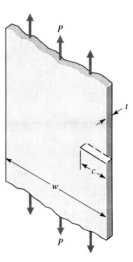

FIGURE P6.3

6.4 A thin plate of width $2w = 6$ in. and thickness $t = 0.035$ in. is made of 7075-T651 aluminum ($S_u = 78$ ksi, $S_y = 70$ ksi). The plate is loaded in tension and has a central crack perpendicular to the direction of the applied load. Estimate the highest load, P (see Figure 6.2a), that can be applied without causing sudden fracture when a central crack grows to a length, $2c$, of 1 in. The plate has a *plane stress* $K_{Ic} = 60$ ksi $\sqrt{\text{in.}}$ and will be used in an aircraft fuselage, which will be inspected periodically for cracks.

6.5 Repeat Sample Problem 6.1 using a material of D6AC steel at −40°F with properties of $S_u = 227$ ksi, $S_y = 197$ ksi, and a plane stress $K_{Ic} = 100$ ksi $\sqrt{\text{in.}}$

6.6 Repeat Sample Problem 6.1 using a material of D6AC steel at room temperature, with properties of $S_u = 220$ ksi, $S_y = 190$ ksi, and a plane stress $K_{Ic} = 115$ ksi $\sqrt{\text{in.}}$

6.7 Repeat Sample Problem 6.1 using a material of 4340 steel at room temperature, with properties of $S_u = 260$ ksi, $S_y = 217$ ksi, and a plane stress $K_{Ic} = 115$ ksi $\sqrt{\text{in.}}$

6.8 Repeat Sample Problem 6.1 using a material of Ti-6Al-4V annealed titanium alloy, with properties of $S_u = 130$ ksi, $S_y = 120$ ksi, and a plane stress $K_{Ic} = 110$ ksi $\sqrt{\text{in.}}$

6.9 A plate of width $2w = 8$ in. and thickness $t = 0.05$ in. is made of leaded beryllium copper ($S_u = 98$ ksi, $S_y = 117$ ksi), and a plate stress $K_{Ic} = 70$ ksi $\sqrt{\text{in.}}$ It is used in a boiler, where periodic inspection for cracks will be made. Estimate the highest load, P (refer to Section 6.4, Figure 6.2a), that can be applied without causing sudden fracture when a central crack grows to a length, $2c$, of 1.5 in.

6.10 Repeat Problem 6.9 using a material of leaded brass, with properties of $S_u = 55$ ksi, $S_y = 42$ ksi, and a plane stress $K_{Ic} = 35$ ksi $\sqrt{\text{in.}}$

6.11 A plate has a width $w = 5$ in., thickness $t = 0.05$ in., and an edge crack of length $c = 0.75$ in. The plate is made of Ti-6A-4V having $S_u = 130$ ksi, $S_y = 120$ ksi and a plane stress $K_{Ic} = 65$ ksi $\sqrt{\text{in.}}$ With a safety factor of 2.5 for failure by sudden fracture, estimate the highest load P that can be applied to the ends of the plate (see Figure P6.3 or Figure 6.2b).

6.12 A 1 in. deep edge crack is found during routine maintenance in a long rectangular bar made from a material whose fracture toughness is 55 ksi $\sqrt{\text{in.}}$ Referring to Figure P6.12, and assuming linear elastic fracture mechanics, is it safe to return the bar to service without repair? Use superposition and calculate the stress intensities for the tensile and bending components separately, then combine them by addition.

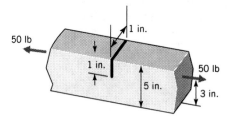

FIGURE P6.12

6.13 Repeat Sample Problem 6.2 using a material of 7075-T651 aluminum.

6.14 Repeat Sample Problem 6.2 using a material of D6AC steel at room temperature.

6.15 Repeat Sample Problem 6.2 using a material of D6AC steel at −40°F.

6.16 Repeat Sample Problem 6.2 using a material of 4340 steel at room temperature.

6.17   A D6AC steel (at room temperature) plate is loaded to a gross-area stress $\sigma_g = 0.50\ S_y$. The dimensions for the thick plate are $t = 1$ in., $2w = 8$ in., $a/2c = 0.25$, and $2c = 1$ in. Calculate the center crack depth, a, and determine if the plate will fail due to the center crack. What is the safety factor (see Figure P6.17)?

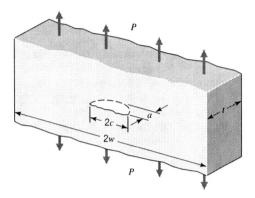

FIGURE P6.17

6.18   Equation 6.4 gives the stress intensity factor at the edges of a central elliptical crack for the geometric and load conditions of $2w/t > 6$, $a/2c =$ about 0.25, $w/c > 3$, $a/t < 0.5$, and $\sigma_g/S_y < 0.8$. For these geometric and load conditions, what conclusions can be drawn from an analysis of Figure 6.5h?

Sections 6.5–6.12

6.19   A machine frame is made of steel having $S_y = 400$ MPa and $S_{sy} = 250$ MPa. When loaded in a test fixture, the stresses were found to vary linearly with load. Two points on the surface were found to be most critical. With a 4-kN test load, stresses at these points were: point a, $\sigma_1 = 200$ MPa, $\sigma_2 = 100$ MPa; point b, $\sigma_1 = 150$ MPa, $\sigma_2 = -100$ MPa. Compute the test load at which the frame will experience initial yielding according to the (a) maximum-normal-stress theory, (b) maximum-shear-stress theory, and (c) maximum-distortion-energy theory. Discuss briefly the relative validity of each theory for this application. Considering all the information available, what is your best judgment of the value of test load at which yielding would actually be expected to begin (see Figure P6.19)?

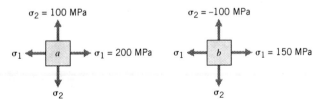

FIGURE P6.19

6.20   A machine component is loaded so that stresses at the critical location are $\sigma_1 = 20$ ksi, $\sigma_2 = -15$ ksi, and $\sigma_3 = 0$. The material is ductile, with yield strengths in tension and compression of 60 ksi. What is the safety factor according to (a) the maximum-normal-stress theory, (b) the maximum-shear-stress theory, and (c) the maximum-distortion-energy theory? Which theory would be expected to agree most closely with an actual test?

[Partial ans.: (a) 3.0, (b) 1.71, (c) 1.97]

6.21   Repeat Problem 6.20 with $\sigma_1 = 25$ ksi, $\sigma_2 = -15$ ksi, and $\sigma_3 = 0$.

[Partial ans.: (a) 2.4, (b) 1.5, (c) 1.71]

6.22   Consider the following states of biaxial stress: (1) $\sigma_1 = 30$, $\sigma_2 = 0$, (2) $\sigma_1 = 30$, $\sigma_2 = -15$, (3) $\sigma_1 = 30$, $\sigma_2 = -30$, (4) $\sigma_1 = 30$, $\sigma_2 = 15$, (5) pure shear, $\tau = 30$. With the aid of a σ_1–σ_2 plot, list these stress states in order of increasing likelihood of causing failure according to (a) the maximum-normal-stress theory, (b) the maximum-shear-stress theory, and (c) the maximum-distortion-energy theory. Assume an arbitrary value of $S_y = 80$ psi for the plot and calculate safety factors for each failure theory and stress state.

6.23   What tensile yield strength must a ductile material have in order to provide a safety factor of 2 with respect to initial yielding at the location(s) investigated in Problems (a) 4.34, (b) 4.37, (c) 4.39, (d) 4.41, (e) 4.43, (f) 4.44, (g) 4.46, (h) 4.50, and (i) 4.54? In each case, determine the answer using both the maximum-shear-stress theory and the maximum-distortion-energy theory.

6.24   What tensile yield strength must a ductile material have in order to provide a safety factor of 1.5 with respect to initial yielding at the location(s) investigated in Problems (a) 4.34, (b) 4.37, (c) 4.39, (d) 4.41, (e) 4.43, (f) 4.44, (g) 4.46, (h) 4.50, and (i) 4.54? In each case, determine the answer using both the maximum-shear-stress theory and the maximum-distortion-energy theory.

6.25   What ultimate tensile strength would be required of a brittle material in order to provide a safety factor of 4 to a member subjected to the same state(s) of stress as those determined in Problems (a) 4.34, (b) 4.37, (c) 4.39, (d) 4.41, (e) 4.43, (f) 4.44, (g) 4.46, (h) 4.50, and (i) 4.54? Use the modified Mohr theory, and assume a compressive ultimate strength of 3.5 times the tensile strength. If overloaded to failure, what would be the orientation of the brittle crack in each case?

6.26   Repeat Problem 6.25, except use a safety factor of 3.5.

6.27   The surface of a steel machine member is subjected to principal stresses of 200 MPa and 100 MPa. What tensile yield strength is required to provide a safety factor of 2 with respect to initial yielding:

(a)   According to the maximum-shear-stress theory?

(b)   According to the maximum-distortion-energy theory?

[Ans.: (a) 400 MPa, (b) 346 MPa]

6.28   A load causes principal stresses of 300 and 100 MPa on the surface of a steel machine member. What tensile yield strength is required to provide a safety factor of 2 with respect to initial yielding:

(a)   According to the maximum-shear-stress theory?

(b)   According to the maximum-distortion-energy theory?

[Ans.: (a) 600 MPa, (b) 530 MPa]

6.29   A round steel rod is subjected to axial tension of 50 MPa with superimposed torsion of 100 MPa. What is your best prediction of the safety factor with respect to initial yielding if the material has a tensile yield strength of 500 MPa (see Figure P6.29)?

[Ans.: 2.77]

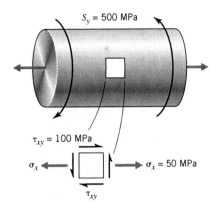

$S_y = 500$ MPa

$\tau_{xy} = 100$ MPa

σ_x $\sigma_x = 50$ MPa

τ_{xy}

FIGURE P6.29

6.30 Repeat Problem 6.29 except use a tensile yield strength of 400 MPa.

[Ans.: 2.22]

6.31 A straight round shaft is subjected to a torque of 5000 lb · in. Determine the required diameter, using steel with a tensile yield strength of 60 ksi and a safety factor of 2 based on initial yielding:

(a) According to the maximum-normal-stress theory.

(b) According to the maximum-shear-stress theory.

(c) According to the maximum-distortion-energy theory.

Discuss briefly the relative validity of the three predictions.

6.32 Repeat Problem 6.31, except use a torque of 6000 lb · in.

6.33 A round steel bar having $S_y = 800$ MPa is subjected to loads producing calculated stresses of $P/A = 70$ MPa, $Tc/J = 200$ MPa, $Mc/I = 300$ MPa, and $4V/3A = 170$ MPa.

(a) Sketch Mohr circles showing the relative locations of maximum normal stress and maximum shear stress.

(b) Determine the safety factor with respect to initial yielding according to the maximum-shear-stress theory and according to the maximum-distortion-energy theory.

6.34 The surface of a steel machine member is subjected to stresses of $\sigma_1 = 100$ MPa, $\sigma_2 = 20$ MPa, and $\sigma_3 = -80$ MPa. What tensile yield strength is required to provide a safety factor of 2.5 with respect to initial yielding:

(a) According to the maximum-shear-stress theory?

(b) According to the maximum-distortion-energy theory?

6.35 A downhold oil tool experiences critical static biaxial stresses of $\sigma_1 = 45,000$ psi and $\sigma_2 = 25,000$ psi. The oil tool is made of normalized 4130 steel that has an ultimate tensile strength of 97,000 psi and a yield strength of 63,300 psi. Determine the factor of safety based on predicting failure by the maximum-normal-stress theory, the maximum-shear-stress theory, and the distortion energy theory.

6.36 A lawn mower component experiences critical static stresses of $\sigma_x = 45,000$ psi, $\sigma_y = 25,000$ psi, and $\tau_{xy} = 15,000$ psi. The component is made of 4130 normalized steel that has an ultimate strength of 97,000 psi and a yield strength of 63,300 psi. Determine the factor of safety based on predicting failure by the maximum-normal-stress theory, the maximum-shear-stress theory, and the distortion energy theory.

6.37   A shaft is subjected to a maximum load of 20 kN. It is designed to withstand a load of 25 kN. If the maximum load encountered is normally distributed with a standard deviation of 3.0 kN, and if shaft strength is normally distributed with a standard deviation of 2.0 kN, what failure percentage would be expected?

6.38   Assume that the failure rate calculated in Problem 6.37 is unacceptable.

    (a) To what value would the standard deviation of shaft strength have to be reduced in order to give a failure rate of 5%, with no other changes?

    (b) To what value would nominal shaft strength have to be increased in order to give a failure rate of only 5%, with no other changes?

6.39   A particular machine part is subjected in service to a maximum load of 10 kN. With the thought of providing a safety factor of 1.5, it is designed to withstand a load of 15 kN. If the maximum load encountered in various applications is normally distributed with a standard deviation of 2 kN, and if part strength is normally distributed with a standard deviation of 1.5 kN, what failure percentage would be expected in service?

    [Ans.: 2.3%]

6.40   Assume that the failure rate calculated in Problem 6.39 is unacceptable.

    (a) To what value would the standard deviation of part strength have to be reduced in order to give a failure rate of only 1%, with no other changes?

    (b) To what value would the nominal part strength have to be increased in order to give a failure rate of only 1%, with no other changes?

6.41   A shaft is subjected to a maximum load of 10 kN. It is designed to withstand a load of 15 kN. If the maximum load encountered is normally distributed with a standard deviation of 2.5 kN, and if shaft strength is normally distributed with a standard deviation of 2.0 kN, what failure percentage would be expected?

    [Ans.: 7.0%]

6.42   Assume that the failure rate calculated in Problem 6.41 is unacceptable.

    (a) To what value would the standard deviation of shaft strength have to be reduced in order to give a failure rate of only 3%, with no other changes?

    (b) To what value would the nominal shaft strength have to be increased in order to give a failure rate of only 3%, with no other changes?

CHAPTER 7

Impact

7.1 Introduction

The previous chapters have dealt almost exclusively with *static* loading. We turn now to the more commonly encountered case of *dynamic* loading. Dynamic loading includes both *impact*, the subject of this chapter, and *fatigue*, which will be introduced in Chapter 8.

Impact loading is also called *shock, sudden,* or *impulsive* loading. The reader has inevitably experienced and observed many examples of impact loading—driving a nail or stake with a hammer, breaking up concrete with an air hammer, automobile collisions (even minor ones such as bumper impacts during careless parking), dropping of cartons by freight handlers, razing of buildings with an impact ball, automobile wheels dropping into potholes, and so on.

Impact loads may be divided into three categories in order of increasing severity: (1) rapidly moving loads of essentially constant magnitude, as produced by a vehicle crossing a bridge, (2) suddenly applied loads, such as those in an explosion, or from combustion in an engine cylinder, and (3) direct-impact loads, as produced by a pile driver, drop forge, or vehicle crash. These are illustrated schematically in Figure 7.1. In Figure 7.1a, mass *m* is held so that it just touches the top of spring *k* and is suddenly released. Dashpot *c* (also called a damper or shock absorber) adds a frictional supporting force that prevents the full gravitational force *mg* from being applied to the spring immediately. In Figure 7.1b there is no dashpot, so the release of

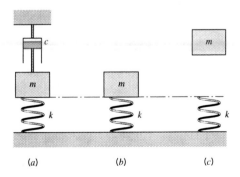

FIGURE 7.1
FIGURE 7.1
Three levels of impact loading produced upon instantaneous release of mass *m*.

(a)   (b)   (c)

mass m results in an instantaneous application of the full force mg. In Figure 7.1c, not only is the force applied instantaneously, but the mass acquires kinetic energy before it strikes the spring.

The significant thing about the dashpot action in Figure 7.1a is that it results in a *gradual* application of the load mg. If the load is applied slowly enough, it can be considered as static. *The usual way of distinguishing between impact and static loading in this situation is to compare the time required for applying the load with the natural period of vibration of the undamped mass on the spring.*

[For the reader not yet acquainted with elementary vibration theory, imagine that the mass in Figure 7.1b is attached to the spring, that it is pushed down and then suddenly released. The mass will then vibrate up and down, with a fixed interval between consecutive times that it is in the "full up" or "full down" position. This time interval is the *natural period of vibration* of the mass on the spring. The relationship between this period (τ, s), the mass (m, kg or lb $\cdot$ s^2/in.), and the spring constant (k, N/m or lb/in.) is

$$\tau = 2\pi\sqrt{\frac{m}{k}} \tag{a}$$

Thus, the *greater* the mass and the *softer* the spring the *longer* the period of vibration (or, the lower the natural frequency of vibration).]

If the time required to apply the load (i.e., to increase it from zero to its full value) is greater than three times the natural period, dynamic effects are negligible and static loading may be assumed. If the time of loading is less than half the natural period, there is definitely an impact. Of course, there is a "gray area" in between—see Table 7.1.

Impact loads can be compressive, tensile, bending, torsional, or a combination of these. The sudden application of a clutch and the striking of an obstruction by the bit of an electric drill are examples of torsional impact.

An important difference between static and impact loading is that statically loaded parts must be designed to *carry loads*, whereas parts subjected to impact must be designed to *absorb energy*.

Material strength properties usually vary with speed of load application. In general, this works out favorably because both the yield and ultimate strengths tend to increase with speed of loading. (Remember, though, that rapid loading tends to promote brittle fracture, as noted in Section 6.2.) Figure 7.2 shows the effect of strain rate on tensile properties of mild steel.

One of the problems in applying a theoretical analysis of impact to actual engineering problems is that often the time rates of load application and of strain development can only be approximated. This sometimes leads to the use of empirically determined stress impact factors, together with the static strength properties of the material. This practice works out well when good empirical data are available that

TABLE 7.1   **Type of Loading**

Load Type	Time Required to Apply Load (s)
Static loading	$t_{\text{applied loading}} > 3\tau$
"Gray area"	$\frac{1}{2}\tau < t_{\text{applied loading}} < 3\tau$
Dynamic loading	$t_{\text{applied loading}} < \frac{1}{2}\tau$

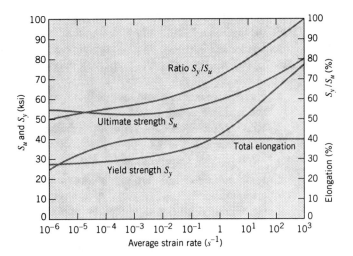

FIGURE 7.2
Effect of strain rate on tensile properties of mild steel at room temperature [2].

apply closely to the part being designed. An example is the use of a stress impact factor of 4 in designing automotive suspension parts. Even when the use of these empirical factors is justified, it is important for the engineer to have a good understanding of the basic fundamentals of impact loading.

7.2 Stress and Deflection Caused by Linear and Bending Impact

Figure 7.3 shows an idealized version of a freely falling mass (of weight *W*) impacting a structure. (The structure is represented by a spring, which is appropriate because *all* structures have *some* elasticity.) To derive from Figure 7.3 the simplified equations

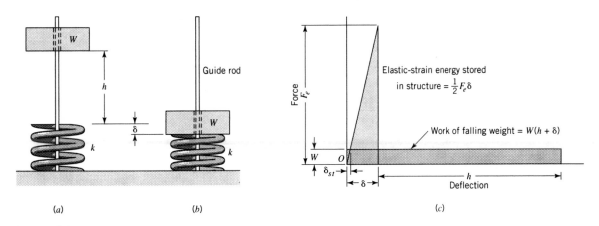

FIGURE 7.3
Impact load applied to elastic structure by falling weight: (*a*) initial position; (*b*) position at instant of maximum deflection; (*c*) force–deflection-energy relationships.

for stress and deflection, the same assumptions are made as when deriving the equation for the natural frequency of a simple spring–mass system: (1) the mass of the structure (spring) is negligible, (2) deflections within the mass itself are negligible, and (3) damping is negligible. These assumptions have some important implications.

1. The first assumption implies that the dynamic deflection curve (i.e., the instantaneous deflections resulting from impact) is identical to that caused by the static application of the same load, multiplied by an *impact factor.* In reality, the dynamic deflection curve inevitably involves points of higher *local* strain (hence, higher local stress) than does the static curve.

2. *Some* deflection must inevitably occur within the impacting mass itself. To the extent that it does, a portion of the energy is absorbed within the mass, thereby causing the stresses and deflections in the structure to be a little *lower* than the calculated values.

3. Any actual case involves some (though perhaps very little) friction damping in the form of windage, rubbing of the mass on the guide rod and end of the spring (in Figure 7.3), and internal friction within the body of the deflecting structure. This damping can cause the actual stresses and deflections to be significantly less than those calculated from the idealized case.

Keeping the above limitations in mind, the following analysis of the idealized case provides an understanding of basic impact phenomena, together with equations that are very helpful as a *guide* in dealing with linear impact.

In Figure 7.3, the falling mass is such that (in the gravitational field involved) it has a weight, W (newtons or pounds). The structure is assumed to respond to the impact elastically, with a spring constant of k (newtons per meter or pounds per inch). The maximum value of deflection that is due to impact is δ (meters or inches). F_e is defined as an *equivalent static force* that would produce the same deflection δ; that is, $F_e = k\delta$. The static deflection that exists after the energy is damped out and the weight comes to rest on the structure is designated by δ_{st}, where $\delta_{st} = W/k$.

Equating the potential energy given up by the falling mass with the elastic energy absorbed by the spring (structure),

$$W(h + \delta) = \tfrac{1}{2} F_e \delta \qquad \textbf{(b)}$$

Note that the factor of $\tfrac{1}{2}$ appears because the spring takes on the load *gradually.*

By definition, since $F_e = k\delta$ and $k = W/\delta_{st}$

$$F_e = (\delta/\delta_{st})\,W \quad \text{or} \quad \delta/\delta_{st} = F_e/W \qquad \textbf{(c)}$$

Substituting Eq. c into Eq. b gives

$$W(h + \delta) = \frac{1}{2}\frac{\delta^2}{\delta_{st}}W \qquad \textbf{(d)}$$

Equation d is a quadratic equation in δ, which is solved routinely to give

$$\delta = \delta_{st}\left(1 + \sqrt{1 + \frac{2h}{\delta_{st}}}\right) \qquad \textbf{(7.1)}$$

Substitution of Eq. c in Eq. 7.1 gives

$$F_e = W\left(1 + \sqrt{1 + \frac{2h}{\delta_{st}}}\right) \tag{7.2}$$

Since the structure (spring) is assumed to respond elastically to the impact, the stress produced is proportional to the load. The term in parentheses in Eqs. 7.1 and 7.2 is called the *impact factor*. It is the factor by which the load, stress, and deflection caused by the dynamically applied weight, W, exceed those caused by a slow, static application of the same weight.

In some cases it is more convenient to express Eqs. 7.1 and 7.2 in terms of velocity at impact v (meters per second or inches per second) instead of height of fall h. For free fall, the relationship between these quantities is

$$v^2 = 2gh \quad \text{or} \quad h = \frac{v^2}{2g} \tag{e}$$

where g is the acceleration of gravity measured in meters per second per second or inches per second per second.

Substitution of Eq. e in Eqs. 7.1 and 7.2 gives

$$\delta = \delta_{st}\left(1 + \sqrt{1 + \frac{v^2}{g\delta_{st}}}\right) \tag{7.1a}$$

and

$$F_e = W\left(1 + \sqrt{1 + \frac{v^2}{g\delta_{st}}}\right) \tag{7.2a}$$

Reducing distance h to zero with v equal to zero gives the special case of a *suddenly applied load*, for which the impact factor—in Eqs. 7.1 and 7.2—is equal to 2. This may have been one basis for designers in the past sometimes doubling safety factors when impact was expected.

In many problems involving impact, the deflection is almost insignificant in comparison to h (see Figure 7.3). For this case, where $h \gg \delta_{st}$, Eqs. 7.1 and 7.2 can be simplified to

$$\delta = \delta_{st}\sqrt{\frac{2h}{\delta_{st}}} = \sqrt{2h\delta_{st}} \tag{7.3}$$

$$F_e = W\sqrt{\frac{2h}{\delta_{st}}} = \sqrt{2Whk} \tag{7.4}$$

Similarly, Eqs. 7.1a and 7.2a simplify to

$$\delta = \delta_{st}\sqrt{\frac{v^2}{g\delta_{st}}} = \sqrt{\frac{\delta_{st}v^2}{g}} \tag{7.3a}$$

$$F_e = W\sqrt{\frac{v^2}{g\delta_{st}}} = \sqrt{\frac{v^2kW}{g}} \tag{7.4a}$$

In the preceding four equations, gravity was considered *only* as the means for developing the velocity of the weight at the point of impact (the further action of gravity after impact being neglected). Hence, Eqs. 7.3a and 7.4a apply also to the case of a *horizontally* moving weight striking a structure, where the impact velocity v is developed by means other than gravity. In this case, δ_{st} is the static deflection that *would* exist *if* the entire system were rotated 90° to allow the weight to act vertically upon the structure. Thus, regardless of the actual orientation,

$$\delta_{st} = W/h \tag{f}$$

It is useful to express the equations for deflection and equivalent static force as functions of the impact kinetic energy U, where, from elementary physics,

$$U = \tfrac{1}{2}mv^2 = Wv^2/2g \tag{g}$$

Substitution of Eqs. f and g into Eqs. 7.3a and 7.4a gives

$$\delta = \sqrt{\frac{2U}{k}} \tag{7.3b}$$

$$F_e = \sqrt{2Uk} \tag{7.4b}$$

Thus, the greater the energy, U, and the stiffer the spring, the greater the equivalent static force.

7.2.1 Linear Impact of Straight Bar in Tension or Compression

An important special case of linear impact is that of a straight rod or bar impacted in compression or in tension. The tensile case is illustrated schematically in Figure 7.4a. The tensile rod sometimes takes the form of a bolt. *If* the impact load is applied concentrically, and *if* stress concentration can be neglected (mighty big "ifs" usually!), then we can substitute into Eq. 7.4b the elementary expressions

$$\sigma = F_e/A \tag{h}$$

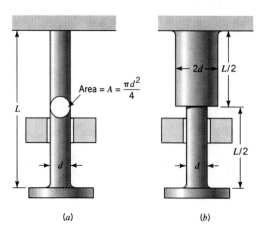

$$\text{Area} = A = \frac{\pi d^2}{4}$$

(a)   (b)

FIGURE 7.4

Tensile impact.

and

$$k = AE/L \tag{i}$$

where A and L are the rod cross-sectional area and length, respectively. The resulting equation is

$$\sigma = \sqrt{\frac{2UE}{AL}} = \sqrt{\frac{2UE}{V}} \tag{7.5}$$

where V is the volume of material in the rod.

Note the important implication of Eq. 7.5—the stress developed in the rod is a function of its *volume* irrespective of whether this volume is made up of a long rod of small area or a short rod of large area.

Solving Eq. 7.5 for U gives

$$U = \frac{\sigma^2 V}{2E} \tag{7.5a}$$

This shows the *impact energy capacity* of a straight rod to be a remarkably simple function of its volume, its modulus of elasticity, and the *square* of the allowable stress.

Despite the importance of this basic relationship, it should be emphasized that Eqs. 7.5 and 7.5a may, in practice, give results that are considerably optimistic—that is, give a calculated stress *lower* than the actual peak stress, and, correspondingly, a calculated energy capacity *greater* than that which actually exists. The main reasons for this are: (1) the stresses are not uniform throughout the member, due to stress concentration and nonuniformity of loading on the impacted surface, and (2) the impacted member has mass. The inertia resulting from the rod mass causes the impacted end of the rod to have a greater *local* deflection (hence, stress) than it would if inertial effects did not prevent the instantaneous distribution of deflection throughout the length of the rod. The effect of stress raisers is considered in Section 7.4. The quantitative effect of the mass of the struck member is left for more advanced works; see [1], [6], and [8].

7.2.2 Sample Problems for Linear and Bending Impact

SAMPLE PROBLEM 7.1 Axial Impact—Importance of Section Uniformity

Figure 7.4 shows two round rods subjected to tensile impact. How do their elastic energy-absorbing capacities compare? (Neglect stress concentration and use S_y as an approximation of the elastic limit.)

SOLUTION

Known: Two round rods of given geometry are subjected to tensile impact.

Find: Compare the elastic energy-absorbing capacities of the two rods.

Schematic and Given Data: See Figure 7.4.

Assumptions:

1. The mass of each rod is negligible.
2. Deflections within each impacting mass itself are negligible.

3. Frictional damping is negligible.

4. Each rod responds to the impact elastically.

5. The impact load is applied concentrically.

6. Stress concentration can be neglected.

Analysis:

1. The elastic capacity for Figure 7.4a is determined directly from Eq. 7.5a, where $\sigma = S_y$:

$$U_a = \frac{S_y^2 V}{2E}$$

2. In Figure 7.4b, the energy absorbed by the upper and lower halves must be determined separately. The smaller lower half is critical; it can be brought to a stress of S_y, and its volume is $V/2$ (where V = volume of the full-length rod in Figure 7.4a). Thus, energy capacity of the lower half is

$$U_{bl} = \frac{S_y^2 V/2}{2E} = \tfrac{1}{2} U_a$$

3. The same force is transmitted through the full length of the rod. The upper half has four times the area of the lower half; hence, it has four times the volume and only $\tfrac{1}{4}$ the stress. Thus the energy capacity of the upper half is

$$U_{bu} = \frac{(S_y/4)^2(2V)}{2E} = \tfrac{1}{8} U_a$$

4. The total energy capacity is the sum of U_{bl} and U_{bu}, which is *only five-eighths the energy capacity of Figure 7.4a.* Since the rod in Figure 7.4b has $2\tfrac{1}{2}$ times the volume and weight of the straight rod, it follows that the *energy capacity per pound* is *four times as great* with the uniform-section rod.

Comment: The stress concentration in the middle of the stepped bar would further reduce its capacity and would tend to promote brittle fracture. This point is treated further in the next section.

SAMPLE PROBLEM 7.2   Relative Energy Absorption Capacity of Various Materials

Figure 7.5 shows a falling weight that impacts on a block of material serving as a bumper. Estimate the relative elastic-energy-absorption capacities of the following bumper materials.

Material	Density (kN/m³)	Elastic Modulus (E)	Elastic Limit (S_e, MPa)
Soft steel	77	207 GPa	207
Hard steel	77	207 GPa	828
Rubber	9.2	1.034 MPa	2.07

SOLUTION

Known: A weight falls on energy-absorbing bumpers of specified materials.

Find: Compare the elastic-impact capacity of the bumper materials.

Schematic and Given Data:

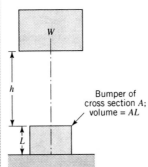

W

h

Bumper of
cross section A;
volume = AL

L

FIGURE 7.5
Impact loading of compression bumper.

Assumptions:

1. The mass of the bumper is negligible.
2. Deflections within the impacting weight itself are negligible.
3. Damping is negligible.
4. The bumper responds elastically.
5. The impact load is applied uniformly.

Analysis:

1. From Figure 7.3, the elastic strain energy absorbed is $\frac{1}{2}F_e\delta$, or the area under the force-deflection curve. At the elastic limit, $F_e = S_eA$, and $\delta = F_eL/AE$. Substitution of these values gives

$$U = \tfrac{1}{2}F_e\delta = \frac{S_e^2AL}{2E} = \frac{S_e^2V}{2E}$$

which, not surprisingly, corresponds exactly with Eq. 7.5a.

2. Substitution of the given material properties in the above equation indicates that on the basis of unit volume, the relative elastic-energy-absorption capacities of the soft steel, hard steel, and rubber are $1:16:20$. On a unit mass or weight basis the relative capacities are $1:16:168$.

Comment: The capacity per unit volume of a material to absorb elastic energy is equal to the area under the elastic portion of the stress–strain diagram and is called the *modulus of resilience* of the material. The *total* energy absorption capacity in tension per unit volume of the material is equal to the total area under the stress–strain curve (extending out to fracture) and is sometimes called the *modulus of toughness* of the material. In the above problem the two steels differed markedly in their moduli of resilience, but their relative toughnesses would likely be comparable.

SAMPLE PROBLEM 7.3   Bending Impact—Effect of Compound Springs

Figure 7.6 shows a wood beam supported on two springs and loaded in bending impact. Estimate the maximum stress and deflection in the beam, based on the assumption that the masses of the beam and spring can be neglected.

SOLUTION

Known: A 100-lb weight falls from a specified height onto a wood beam of known material and specified geometry that is supported by two springs.

Find: Determine the maximum beam stress and deflection.

Schematic and Given Data:

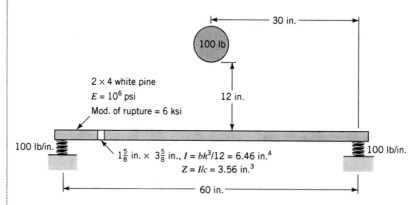

FIGURE 7.6
Bending impact, with compound spring.

Assumptions:

1. As stated in the problem, the masses of the beam and spring can be neglected.
2. The beam and springs respond elastically.
3. The impact load is applied uniformly at the center of the beam.

Analysis:

1. The static deflection for the beam only, supporting springs only, and total system are

$$\delta_{st}(\text{beam}) = \frac{PL^3}{48EI} = \frac{100(60)^3}{48(10^6)(6.46)} = 0.070 \text{ in.}$$

$$\delta_{st}(\text{springs}) = \frac{P}{2k} = \frac{100}{2(100)} = 0.50 \text{ in.}$$

$$\delta_{st}(\text{total}) = 0.070 + 0.50 = 0.57 \text{ in.}$$

2. From Eq. 7.1 or 7.2 the *impact factor* is

$$1 + \sqrt{1 + \frac{2h}{\delta_{st}}} = 1 + \sqrt{1 + \frac{24}{0.57}} = 7.6$$

3. Hence, the total impact deflection is $0.57 \times 7.6 = 4.3$ in., but the deflection of the beam itself is only $0.07 \times 7.6 = 0.53$ in.

4. The extreme-fiber beam stress is estimated from $F_e = 100 \times 7.6 = 760$ lb:

$$\sigma = \frac{M}{Z} = \frac{F_e L}{4Z} = \frac{760(60)}{4(3.56)} = 3200 \text{ psi}$$

Comments:

1. The estimated stress is well within the given *modulus of rupture* of 6000 psi. (The modulus of rupture is the computed value of M/Z at failure in a standard static test.)

2. If the supporting springs are removed, the total static deflection is reduced to 0.07 in., and the impact factor increases to 19.6. This would give a computed maximum beam stress of 8250 psi, which is greater than the modulus of rupture. If the inertial effect of the beam mass does not cause the actual stress to be very much higher than 8250 psi, it is possible that the "dynamic-strengthening effect" shown in Figure 7.2 would be sufficient to prevent failure. Because this effect is usually appreciable for woods, the results of standard beam impact tests are often included in references giving properties of woods.

7.3 Stress and Deflection Caused by Torsional Impact

The analysis of the preceding section could be repeated for the case of torsional systems, and a corresponding set of equations developed. Instead, advantage will be taken of the direct analogy between linear and torsional systems to write the final equations directly. The analogous quantities involved are

Linear	Torsional
δ, deflection (m or in.)	θ, deflection (rad)
F_e, equivalent static force (N or lb)	T_e, equivalent static torque (N · m or lb · in.)
m, mass (kg or lb · s^2/in.)	I, moment of inertia (N · s^2 · m or lb · s^2 · in.)
k, spring rate (N/m or lb/in.)	K, spring rate (N · m/rad or lb · in./rad)
v, impact velocity (m/s or in./s)	ω, impact velocity (rad/s)
U, kinetic energy (N · m or in. · lb)	U, kinetic energy (N · m or in. · lb)

The two following equations have the letter t added to the equation number to designate torsion:

$$\theta = \sqrt{\frac{2U}{K}} \qquad \textbf{(7.3bt)}$$

$$T_e = \sqrt{2UK} \qquad \textbf{(7.4bt)}$$

For the important special case of torsional impact of a solid round bar of diameter d:

1. From Table 5.1,

$$K = \frac{T}{\theta} = \frac{K'G}{L} = \frac{\pi d^4 G}{32L} \tag{i}$$

2. From Eq. 4.4 with T replaced by T_e,

$$\tau = \frac{16T_e}{\pi d^3} \tag{j}$$

3. Volume, $V = \pi d^2 L/4$ (k)

Substitution of Eqs. i, j, and k into Eq. 7.4bt gives

$$\tau = 2\sqrt{\frac{UG}{V}} \tag{7.6}$$

SAMPLE PROBLEM 7.4   Torsional Impact

Figure 7.7a shows the shaft assembly of a grinder, with an abrasive wheel at each end and a belt-driven sheave at the center. When turning at 2400 rpm, the smaller abrasive wheel is accidentally jammed, causing it to stop "instantly." Estimate the resulting maximum torsional stress and deflection of the shaft. Consider the abrasive wheels as solid disks of density $\rho = 2000$ kg/m^3. The shaft is steel ($G = 79$ GPa), and its weight may be neglected.

SOLUTION

Known: The smaller wheel of a grinder turning at 2400 rpm is stopped instantly.

Find: Determine the maximum shaft stress and torsional deflection.

Schematic and Given Data:

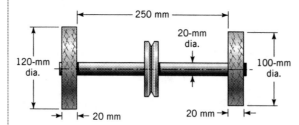

FIGURE 7.7a
Torsional impact of grinder shaft.

Assumptions:

1. The weight of the shaft and pulley may be neglected.
2. The shaft acts as a torsional spring and responds elastically to the impact.
3. Deflections within the abrasive wheels are negligible.

Analysis:

1. It is the energy in the 120-mm wheel that must be absorbed by the shaft. From the torsional equivalent of Eq. g, this is

$$U = \tfrac{1}{2} I \omega^2$$

where

$$I = \tfrac{1}{2} m r^2_{\text{wheel}}$$

and

$$m = \pi r^2_{\text{wheel}} t \rho$$

2. Combining the preceding equations, we have

$$U = \tfrac{1}{4} \pi r^4_{\text{wheel}} t \rho \omega^2$$

3. Substituting numerical values (with units of meters, kilograms, and seconds) gives

$$U = \tfrac{1}{4}\pi(0.060)^4(0.020)(2000)\left(\frac{2400 \times 2\pi}{60}\right)^2$$

$$U = 25.72\,\frac{\text{kg} \cdot \text{m}^2}{s^2} = 25.72\,\text{N} \cdot \text{m}$$

4. From Eq. 7.6

$$\tau = 2\sqrt{\frac{UG}{V}}$$

$$= 2\sqrt{\frac{(25.72)(79 \times 10^9)}{\pi(0.010)^2(0.250)}} = 321.7 \times 10^6\,\text{Pa}$$

or

$$\tau = 322\,\text{MPa}$$

5. The torsional deflection,

$$\theta = \frac{TL}{JG}$$

where $T = \tau J/r$ (i.e., $\tau = Tr/J$); hence,

$$\theta = \frac{\tau L}{rG} = \frac{(321.7 \times 10^6)(0.250)}{(0.010)(79 \times 10^9)} = 0.10\,\text{rad} = 5.7°$$

Comments:

1. The preceding calculations assumed that the stresses are within the elastic range. Note that no provision was made for stress concentration or for any superimposed bending load that would also be present as a result of the jamming. Torque applied to the sheave by the belt was also neglected, but this would likely be negligible because of belt slippage. In addition, it is only because of assumed belt slippage that the inertia of the driving motor is not a factor.

2. The effect of the shaft radius, r, on shaft shear stress, τ, and torsional deflection, θ, can be explored by computing and plotting the shaft stress and torsional deflection for a shaft radius from 5 mm to 15 mm, and for a shear modulus, G, of steel (79 GPa), cast iron (41 GPa) and aluminum (27 GPa)—see Figure 7.7*b*.

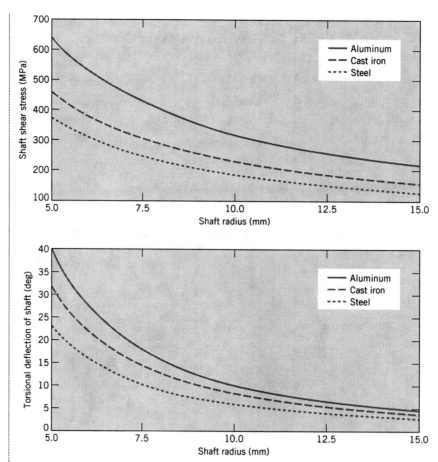

FIGURE 7.7*b*
Shear stress and torsional deflection vs. shaft radius.

3. For a 2024-T4 aluminum alloy shaft with a 10 mm radius, with $S_y = 296$ MPa (Appendix C-2) and with $S_{sy} = 0.58S_y = 172$ MPa, the shear stress is $\tau = 188$ MPa and the shaft rotation is $\theta = .174$ rad $= 10°$. Inspection of the plot of shaft shear stress versus shaft radius shows that shaft radius should be greater than 11 mm to avoid yielding in a 2024-T4 aluminum alloy shaft.

7.4   *Effect of Stress Raisers on Impact Strength*

Figure 7.8 shows the same tensile impact bar as Figure 7.4*a*, except that recognition is given to the fact that stress concentration exists at the ends of the bar. As with static loading it is *possible* that local yielding would redistribute the stresses so as to virtually nullify the effect of the stress raiser. But under impact loading the *time* available for plastic action is likely to be so short that brittle fracture (with an effective stress concentration factor almost as high as the theoretical value, K_t, obtained from a chart

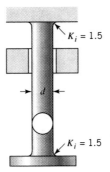

FIGURE 7.8
Plain impact bar.

similar to Figure 4.35*b*) will sometimes occur even in a material that exhibits ductile behavior in the tensile test. In terms of the discussion in Section 6.2, adding a stress raiser and applying an impact load are both factors tending to raise the *transition temperature*—that is, cause brittle fracture without dropping to as low a temperature.

Because of the difficulty in predicting impact notch effects from theoretical considerations, standard notched impact tests are used, such as the *Charpy* and *Izod*. These, too, have their limitations, for notched impact strength varies markedly with size, shape, and nature of impact. Because of this, special laboratory tests that more closely simulate actual conditions are sometimes used.

SAMPLE PROBLEM 7.5　Notched Tensile Impact

Suppose that from special tests it has been determined that the effective stress concentration factor for impact loading, K_i, at the ends of the rod in Figure 7.8 is 1.5, as shown. How much does the stress raiser decrease the energy-absorbing capacity of the rod, as estimated from Eq. 7.5a?

SOLUTION

Known:　A round rod subject to impact loading has a specified stress concentration at each end.

Find:　Determine the effect of a stress raiser on rod energy-absorbing capacity.

Schematic and Given Data:　See Figure 7.8.

Assumption:　Under impact loading, the rod material exhibits brittle behavior.

Analysis:　First, two observations: (a) if the rod is sufficiently long, the volume of material in the region of the end fillets is a very small fraction of the total and (b) the material at the critical fillet location cannot be stressed in excess of the material strength S. This means that *nearly all* the material can be considered as stressed to a uniform level that cannot exceed S/K_i, or, in this instance, $S/1.5$. Thus, a good approximation is that after considering the stress raiser, the same volume of material is involved, but at a stress level reduced by a factor of 1.5. Since the stress is squared in Eq. 7.5a, taking the notch into consideration *reduces the energy capacity by a factor of 1.5^2, or 2.25.*

SAMPLE PROBLEM 7.6   Notched Tensile Impact

Figure 7.9 shows the same impact bar as Figure 7.8, except that a sharp groove, with $K_i = 3$, has been added. Compare the impact-energy capacities of the bars in Figures 7.8 and 7.9.

SOLUTION

Known: A grooved impact bar and a plain impact bar are each subjected to impact loading.

Find: Compare the impact-energy capabilities of both bars.

Schematic and Given Data:

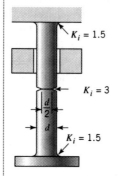

$K_i = 1.5$

$K_i = 3$

$\frac{d}{2}$

d

$K_i = 1.5$

FIGURE 7.9
Grooved impact bar.

Assumption: The rod materials exhibit brittle behavior.

Analysis: In Figure 7.9, the impact capacity is limited to the value that brings the stress at the groove to the material strength S. Since the effective stress concentration factor is 3, the nominal stress level in the section of the groove is $S/3$. Because of the $4:1$ area ratio, the nominal stress in the bulk of material (*not* in the groove plane) is only $S/12$. For a long bar, the percentage of volume near the groove is very small. Thus, with reference to Eq. 7.5a, the only substantial difference made by introducing the groove is to reduce the value of σ from $S/1.5$ to $S/12$. Since σ is squared in the equation, the groove reduces the energy capacity by a factor of 64; that is, the grooved bar has *less than 2 percent* of the energy-absorbing capacity of the ungrooved bar!

From this discussion, it follows that the effective design of an efficient energy-absorbing member comprises two key steps.

1. Minimize stress concentration as much as possible. (Always try to reduce the stress at the point where it is highest.)

2. Having done this, remove all possible "excess material" so that the stress everywhere is as close as possible to the stress at the most critical point. Removing this excess material does not reduce the *load* that the member can carry, and the *deflection* is increased. Since energy absorbed is the integral of force times deflection, energy-absorbing capacity is thereby increased. (Recall the dramatic example of this principle in Sample Problem 7.1.)

SAMPLE PROBLEM 7.7   Modifying a Bolt Design for Greater Impact Strength

Figure 7.10*a* shows a bolt that is subjected to tensile impact loading. Suggest a modified design that would have greater energy-absorbing capacity. How much increase in capacity would the modified design provide?

SOLUTION

Known: A standard bolt of specified geometry is to be modified for tensile impact loading.

Find: Modify the bolt geometry and estimate the increase in energy-absorbing capacity.

Schematic and Given Data:

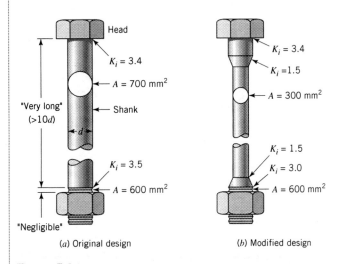

(*a*) Original design   (*b*) Modified design

FIGURE 7.10
Bolt subjected to tensile impact.

Decisions: The following decisions are made in the design analysis.

1. Minimize stress concentration by using a thread with a smooth, generous fillet at the root.

2. Leave a short length of full-diameter shank under the bolt head to serve to center the bolt in the bolt hole.

3. Design for uniform stress throughout the bolt by reducing the diameter in the lesser-stressed portion of the shank.

Assumptions: Material of strength S is used for both bolts. Other assumptions are made as required throughout the design analysis.

Design Analysis:

1. Reduce stress concentration where it is most critical. The highest stress is at the thread ($K_i = 3.5$, acting at an area of only 600 mm²). Assume that by modifying

the thread slightly to provide a smooth, generous fillet at the root, K_i can be reduced to 3.0, as shown in Figure 7.10b. The other point of stress concentration is in the fillet under the bolt head. This fillet must be small in order to provide adequate flat area for contact. Actually, there is no incentive to reduce stress concentration at that point because the stress there will be less than at the thread root, even with the modified thread design.[1]

$$\sigma = \frac{P}{A} K_i; \quad \left(\frac{P}{700} \times 3.4 \right)_{\text{fillet}} < \left(\frac{P}{600} \times 3.0 \right)_{\text{thread root}}$$

2. Leave a short length of full-diameter shank under the bolt head to serve as a pilot to center the bolt in the bolt hole. The diameter in the rest of the shank can be reduced to make the shank stress nearly equal to the stress at the thread root. Figure 7.10b shows a reduced shank diameter that is flared out to the full diameter with a large radius, to give minimal stress concentration. On the basis of a conservative stress concentration estimate of 1.5, the shank area can be reduced to half the effective-stress area at the thread:

$$A = 600 \times \frac{1.5}{3.0} = 300 \text{ mm}^2$$

3. Assume that the bolt is sufficiently long so that the volume of uniformly stressed material in the central portion of the shank is the only volume that need be considered, and that the volumes in the two critical regions are proportional to the areas 700 and 300 mm². From Eq. 7.5a, $U = \sigma^2 V / 2E$. Since E is a constant, the ratio of energy capacities for Figures 7.10b and 7.10a is

$$\frac{U_b}{U_a} = \frac{\sigma_b^2 V_b}{\sigma_a^2 V_a} \tag{m}$$

In Figure 7.10a the stress in the large volume of material in the shank is less than the material strength S because of *both* the stress concentration *and* the difference in area between the thread and shank. Thus, if $\sigma = S$ at the thread root, the shank stress is

$$\sigma_a = \frac{S}{3.5} \left(\frac{600}{700} \right) = 0.245S$$

Let the shank volume in Figure 7.10a be designated as V. In Figure 7.10b, the stress at the thread can again be S. Corresponding shank stress is

$$\sigma_b = \frac{S}{3.0} \left(\frac{600}{300} \right) = 0.667S$$

The shank volume in Figure 7.10b is $V (300/700)$, or $0.429V$. Substituting these values in Eq. m gives

$$\frac{U_b}{U_a} = \frac{(0.667S)^2 (0.429V)}{(0.245S)^2 (V)} = 3.18$$

---

[1] This is usually, but not *always*, the case.

Comments:

1. The redesign has over three times the capacity of the original, as well as being lighter.

2. For a given volume of material, the bolt design with the more nearly uniform stress throughout will have the greater energy-absorbing capacity.

Two other designs of bolts with increased energy-absorbing capacity are illustrated in Figure 7.11. In Figure 7.11*a*, the full-diameter piloting surface has been moved to the center of the shank in order to provide alignment of the two clamped members. Figure 7.11*b* shows a more costly method of removing excess shank material, but it preserves nearly all the original torsional and bending strength of the bolt. The torsional strength is often important, for it influences how much the nut can be tightened without "twisting off" the bolt.

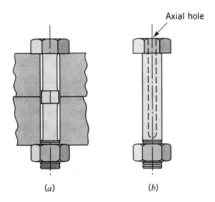

FIGURE 7.11
Bolts designed for energy absorption.

References

1. Juvinall, R. C., *Engineering Considerations of Stress, Strain, and Strength*, McGraw-Hill, New York, 1967.

2. Manjoine, M. J., "Influence of Rate of Strain and Temperature on Yield Stresses of Mild Steel," *J. Appl. Mech.*, **66:** A-221–A-218 (1944).

3. Marin, Joseph, *Mechanical Behavior of Engineering Materials*, Prentice-Hall, Englewood Cliffs, N.J., 1962.

4. Pilkey, W. D., *Formulas for Stress, Strain, and Structural Matrices*, Wiley, New York, 1994.

5. Rinehart, John S., and John Pearson, *Behavior of Metals under Impulsive Loads*, The American Society for Metals, Cleveland, 1954.

6. Timoshenko, S., and J. N. Goodier, *Theory of Elasticity*, 2nd ed., McGraw-Hill, New York, 1951.

7. Vigness, Irwin, and W. P. Welch, "Shock and Impact Considerations in Design," in *ASME Handbook: Metals Engineering—Design*, 2nd ed., Oscar J. Horger (ed.), McGraw-Hill, New York, 1965.

8. Young, W. C., *Roark's Formulas for Stress and Strain*, 6th ed., McGraw-Hill, New York, 1989.

Problems

Section 7.2

7.1   The previous chapters have dealt essentially with considerations of stress, strain, and strength arising from *static* loading. The present chapter deals with impact, and the subsequent chapter treats fatigue—both are cases of dynamic loading. Impact loading is also referred to as *shock*, *sudden*, or *impulsive* loading. Impact loads may be torsional and/or linear in nature. How does *impact* loading differ from *static* loading?

7.2   A tensile impact bar, similar to the one in Figure 7.4a, fractured in service. Because the failure happened to occur near the center, a naive technician makes a new bar exactly like the old one except that the middle third is enlarged to twice the diameter of the ends. Assuming that stress concentration can be neglected (not very realistic), how do the impact capacities of the new and old bars compare?

7.3   A vertical member is subjected to an axial impact by a 100-lb weight dropped from a height of 2 ft (similar to Figure 7.4a). The member is made of steel, with $S_y = 45$ ksi, $E = 30 \times 10^6$ psi. Neglect the effect of member mass and stress concentration. What must be the length of the member in order to avoid yielding if it has a diameter of (a) 1 in., (b) $1\frac{1}{2}$ in., (c) 1 in. for half of its length and $1\frac{1}{2}$ in. for the other half?

[Ans. 90.5 in., 40 in., 125.2 in.]

7.4   A car skidded off an icy road and became stuck in deep snow at the road shoulder. Another car, of 1400-kg mass, attempted to jerk the stuck vehicle back onto the road using a 5-m steel tow cable of stiffness $k = 5000$ N/mm. The traction available to the rescue car prevented it from exerting any significant force on the cable. With the aid of a push from bystanders, the rescue car was able to back against the stuck car and then go forward and reach a speed of 4 km/h at the instant the cable became taut. If the cable is attached rigidly to the masses of cars, estimate the maximum impact force that can be developed in the cable, and the resulting cable elongation (see Figure P7.4).

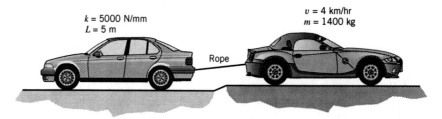

$k = 5000$ N/mm
$L = 5$ m

$v = 4$ km/hr
$m = 1400$ kg

Rope

FIGURE P7.4

7.5   The rescue attempt in Problem 7.4 resulted in only slight movement of the stuck car because the cable force decayed so quickly to zero. Besides, concern was felt about possible damage to the car attachment points because of the high "instantaneous" force developed. One witness to the proceedings brought a 12-m elastic cable of overall stiffness only 2.4 N/mm and suggested that it be tried. Because of the longer length of the elastic cable, its use enabled the rescue car to reach 12 km/h at the point of becoming taut. Estimate the impact force developed and the resulting cable elongation. If the stuck vehicle does not move significantly until the rescue car has just come to a stop, how much energy is stored in the cable? (Think of this in terms of the height from which a 100-kg mass would have to be dropped to represent an equivalent amount of energy, and consider the potential hazard if the cable should break or come loose from either car.) What warnings would you suggest be provided with elastic cables sold for this purpose?

7.6 A tow truck weighing 6000-lb attempts to jerk a wrecked vehicle back onto the roadway using a 15-ft length of steel cable 1 in. in diameter ($E = 12 \times 10^6$ psi for the cable). The truck acquires a speed of 3 mph at the instant the cable slack is taken up, but the wrecked car does not move. (a) Estimate the impact force applied to the wrecked vehicle and the stress produced in the cable. (b) The cable breaks in the middle, and the two 7.5-ft halves are connected in parallel for a second try. Estimate the impact force and cable stress produced if the wrecked vehicle still remains fixed.

[Ans. (a) 60.6 ksi, 47,600 lb]

7.7 Repeat Sample Problem 7.3, except use a 1.0×1.0-in. ($b \times h$) aluminum beam.

7.8 A 5-ton elevator is supported by a standard steel cable of 2.5-in.^{2} cross section and an effective modulus of elasticity of 12×10^6 psi. As the elevator is descending at a constant 400 ft/min, an accident causes the top of the cable, 70 ft above the elevator, to stop suddenly. Estimate the maximum elongation and maximum tensile stress developed in the cable (see Figure P7.8).

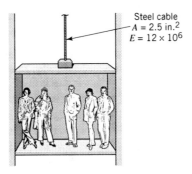

Steel cable
$A = 2.5$ in.^{2}
$E = 12 \times 10^6$

FIGURE P7.8

7.9 A 60-foot long, 950-lb gin pole used to raise sections of a communication tower is suspended by a standard steel cable of 0.110-in.^{2} cross section with an effective modulus of elasticity of 12×10^6 psi. As the gin pole descends at a constant speed of 30 ft/min, an accident causes the top of the cable, 70 ft above the gin pole, to stop suddenly. Estimate the maximum elongation and maximum tensile stress developed in the cable.

Section 7.3

7.10 The vertical drive shaft in Figure P2.18 is 20 mm in diameter, 650 mm long, and made of steel. The motor to which it is attached at the top is equivalent to a steel flywheel 300 mm in diameter and 25 mm thick. When the vertical shaft is rotating at 3000 rpm, the propeller strikes a heavy obstruction, bringing it to a virtually instantaneous stop. Assume that the short horizontal propeller shaft and the bevel gears have negligible flexibility. Calculate the elastic torsional shear stress in the vertical shaft. (Since this stress far exceeds any possible torsional elastic strength, a shear pin or slipping clutch would be used to protect the shaft and associated costly parts.)

7.11 For the tensile impact bar shown in Figure P7.11, estimate the ratio of impact energy that can be absorbed with and without the notch (which reduces the diameter to 24 mm).

[Ans.: 0.06:1]

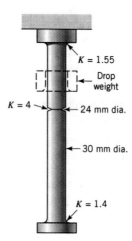

$K = 1.55$

Drop weight

$K = 4$ 24 mm dia.

30 mm dia.

$K = 1.4$

FIGURE P7.11

7.12 A platform is suspended by long steel rods as shown in Figure P7.12*a*. Because heavy items are sometimes dropped on the platform, it is decided to modify the rods as shown in Figure P7.12*b* to obtain greater energy-absorbing capacity. The new design features enlarged ends, blended into the main portion with generous fillets, and special threads giving less stress concentration.

(a) What is the smallest effective threaded section area A (Figure P7.12*b*) that would provide maximum energy-absorbing capability?

(b) Using this value of A (or that of the next larger standard thread size), what increase in energy-absorbing capacity would be provided by the new design?

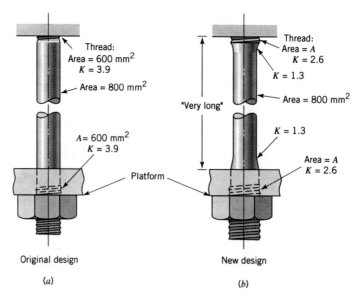

Original design
(a)

New design
(b)

FIGURE P7.12

296

7.13 The initial design of a bolt loaded in tensile impact is shown in Figure P7.13a. The bolt fractures next to the nut, as shown. A proposed redesign, Figure P7.13b involves drilling an axial hole in the unthreaded portion and incorporating a larger fillet radius under the bolt head.

(a) What is the theoretically optimum diameter of the drilled hole?

(b) Using this hole size, by what approximate factor do the modifications increase the energy-absorbing capacity of the bolt?

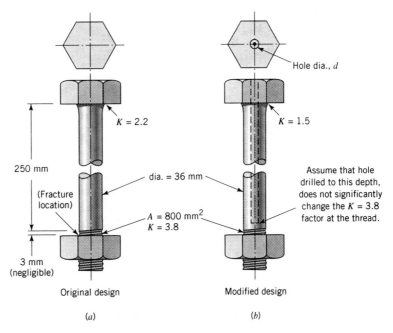

FIGURE P7.13

7.14 Figure P7.14 shows a tensile impact bar with a small transverse hole. By what factor does the hole reduce the impact-energy-absorbing capacity of the bar?

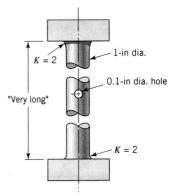

FIGURE P7.14

7.15D Redesign the bolt loaded in tensile impact and shown in Figure P7.13a to *increase* the energy absorbing capacity by a factor of 3 or more.

7.16D Redesign the plain impact bar shown in Figure 7.8 of the text to *reduce* the impact-energy-absorbing capacity of the impact bar by a factor of 2 or more. Assume that the bar has a diameter, $d = 1.0$ in.

CHAPTER 8

Fatigue

8.1 Introduction

Until about the middle of the nineteenth century engineers treated fluctuating or repeated loading the same as static loading, except for the use of larger safety factors. Use of the term *fatigue* in these situations appears to have been introduced by Poncelet of France in a book published in 1839. Modern authorities suggest that the term *progressive fracture* would perhaps have been more appropriate.

"Fatigue" fractures begin with a minute (usually microscopic) crack at a critical area of high local stress. This is almost always at a geometric stress raiser. Additionally, minute material flaws or preexisting cracks are commonly involved (recall from Section 6.3 that the fracture mechanics approach assumes preexisting cracks in *all* materials). An inspection of the surfaces after final fracture (as in Figure 8.1) often reveals where the crack has gradually enlarged from one "beach mark" to the next until the section is sufficiently weakened that final fracture occurs on one final load application. This can happen when the stress exceeds the ultimate strength, with fracture occurring as in a static tensile test. Usually, however, the final fracture is largely "brittle" and takes place in accordance with the fracture mechanics concepts treated in Sections 6.3 and 6.4. (Recall that brittle fracture is promoted by a stress concentration and a rapidly applied load, both of which are normally present when final fatigue fracture occurs.)

In Figure 8.1, the curvature of the beach marks serves to indicate where the failure originates. The beach-marked area is known as the *fatigue zone*. It has a smooth, velvety texture developed by the repeated pressing together and separating of the mating crack surfaces. This contrasts with the relatively rough final fracture. A distinguishing characteristic of fatigue fracture of a ductile material is that little if any macroscopic distortion occurs during the entire process, whereas failure caused by static overload produces gross distortion.

8.2 Basic Concepts

Extensive research over the last century has given us a partial understanding of the basic mechanisms associated with fatigue failures. Reference 3 contains a summary of much of the current knowledge as it applies to engineering practices. The following

Final fracture (usually brittle) zone
(rough surface)

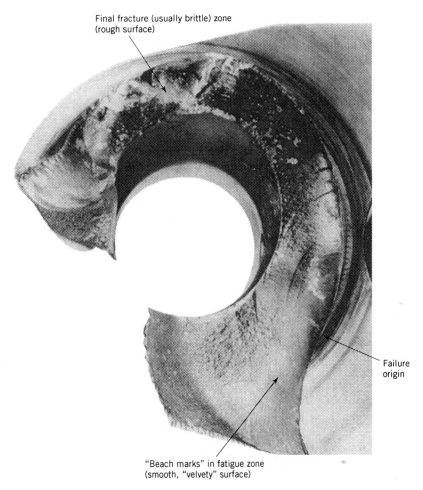

Failure
origin

"Beach marks" in fatigue zone
(smooth, "velvety" surface)

FIGURE 8.1

Fatigue failure originating in the fillet of an aircraft crank-shaft (SAE 4340 steel, 320 Bhn).

are a few fundamental and elementary concepts that are helpful in understanding the patterns of observed fatigue behavior.

1. Fatigue failure results from *repeated plastic deformation*, such as the breaking of a wire by bending it back and forth repeatedly. Without repeated plastic yielding, fatigue failures cannot occur.

2. Whereas a wire can be broken after a few cycles of gross plastic yielding, fatigue failures typically occur after thousands or even millions of cycles of minute yielding that often exists only on a *microscopic level*. Fatigue failure can occur at stress levels far below the conventionally determined yield point or elastic limit.

3. Because highly localized plastic yielding can be the beginning of a fatigue failure, it behooves the engineer to focus attention on all potentially vulnerable locations such as holes, sharp corners, threads, keyways, surface scratches, and

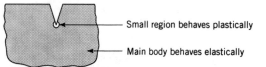

Small region behaves plastically

Main body behaves elastically

FIGURE 8.2

Enlarged view of a notched region.

corrosion. Such a location is shown at the root of a notch in Figure 8.2. *Strengthening these vulnerable locations is often as effective as making the entire part from a stronger material.*

4. If the local yielding is sufficiently minute, the material *may* strain-strengthen, causing the yielding to cease. The part will then have actually benefited from this mild overload. But if the local yielding is any more than this, the repeated load cycling will cause a loss of local ductility (in accordance with concepts discussed in Section 3.3) until the cyclic strain imposed at the vulnerable spot in question can no longer be withstood without fracture.

5. The initial fatigue crack usually results in an increase in local stress concentration. As the crack progresses, the material at the crack root at any particular time is subjected to the destructive localized reversed yielding. As the crack deepens, thereby reducing the section and causing increased stresses, the rate of crack propagation increases until the remaining section is no longer able to support a single load application and final fracture occurs, usually in accordance with the principles of fracture mechanics. (There are situations in which a fatigue crack advances into a region of lower stress, greater material strength, or both, and the crack ceases to propagate, but these situations are unusual.)

Present engineering practice relies heavily on the wealth of empirical data that has accumulated from fatigue tests of numerous materials, in various forms, and subjected to various kinds of loading. The remainder of this chapter is based largely on these data. The next section describes the standardized R. R. Moore fatigue test, which is used to determine the fatigue strength characterstics of materials under a standardized and highly restricted set of conditions. After the pattern of results obtained from this test has been reviewed, succeeding sections deal with the effects of deviating from the standard test in various ways, thus working toward the completely general case of fatigue in an orderly fashion.

The generalizations or patterns of fatigue behavior developed in the remainder of this chapter enable the engineer to estimate the fatigue behavior for combinations of materials, geometry, and loading for which test data are not available. This estimating of fatigue behavior is an extremely important step in modern engineering. The preliminary design of critical parts normally encompasses this procedure. Then prototypes of the preliminary design are built and fatigue-tested. The results provide a basis for refining the preliminary design to arrive at a final design, suitable for production.

8.3   *Standard Fatigue Strengths (S_n') for Rotating Bending*

Figure 8.3 represents a standard R. R. Moore rotating-beam fatigue-testing machine. The reader should verify that the loading imposed by the four symmetrically located bearings causes the center portion of the specimen to be loaded in *pure bending*

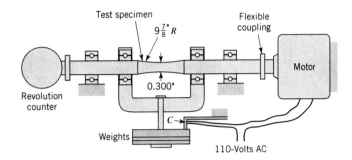

FIGURE 8.3

R. R. Moore rotating-beam fatigue-testing machine.

(i.e., zero transverse shear), and that the stress at any point goes through a cycle of tension-to-compression-to-tension with each shaft rotation. The highest level of stress is at the center, where the diameter is a standard 0.300 in. The large radius of curvature prevents a stress concentration. Various weights are chosen to give the desired stress levels. The motor speed is usually 1750 rpm. When the specimen fails, the weight drops, opening contact points C, which stops the motor. The number of cycles to failure is indicated by the revolution counter.

A series of tests made with various weights and using test specimens carefully made to be as nearly identical as possible gives results that are plotted as *S–N curves.* As illustrated in Figure 8.4, *S–N* curves are plotted either on semilog or on log-log coordinates. Note that the intensity of reversed stress causing failure after a given number of cycles is called the *fatigue strength* corresponding to that number of loading cycles. Numerous tests have established that *ferrous materials* have an *endurance limit,* defined as the highest level of alternating stress that can be withstood indefinitely without failure. The usual symbol for endurance limit is S_n. It is designated as S'_n in Figure 8.4, where the prime indicates the special case of the standard test illustrated in Figure 8.3. Log-log coordinates are particularly convenient for plotting ferrous *S–N* curves because of the straight-line relationship shown.

Figure 8.4c illustrates the "knee" of *S–N* curves for materials that have a clearly defined endurance limit. This knee normally occurs between 10^6 and 10^7 cycles. It is customary to make the conservative assumption that ferrous materials must not be stressed above the endurance limit if a life of 10^6 or more cycles is required. This assumption is illustrated in the generalized *S–N* curve for steel shown in Figure 8.5.

Because fatigue failures originate at *local* points of relative weakness, the results of fatigue tests have considerably more scatter than do those of static tests. For this reason the statistical approach to defining strength (see Sections 6.13 through 6.15) takes on greater importance. Standard deviations of endurance limit values are commonly in the range of 4 to 9 percent of the nominal value. Ideally, the standard deviation is determined experimentally from tests corresponding to the specific application. Often, 8 percent of the nominal endurance limit is used as a conservative estimate of the standard deviation when more specific information is not available.

The data scatter illustrated in Figure 8.4 is typical for carefully controlled tests. The scatter band marked on Figure 8.4c illustrates an interesting point: The scatter in *fatigue strength* corresponding to a given life is small; the scatter in *fatigue life* corresponding to a given stress level is large. Even in carefully controlled tests, these life values can vary over a range of five or ten to one.

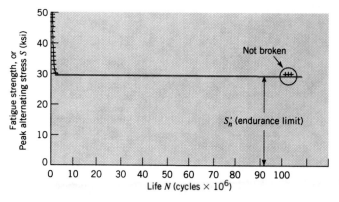

(a) Linear coordinates (not used for obvious reasons)

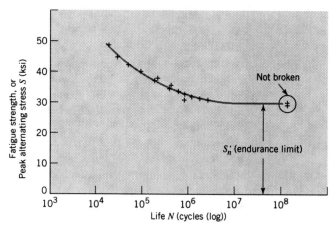

(b) Semilog coordinates

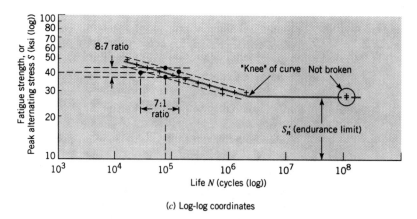

(c) Log-log coordinates

FIGURE 8.4

Three *S–N* plots of representative fatigue data for 120 Bhn steel.

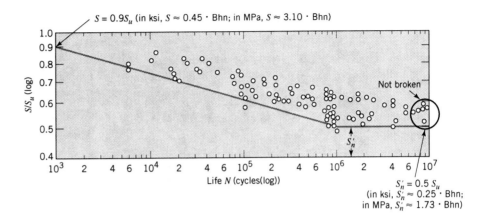

$S = 0.9S_u$ (in ksi, $S \approx 0.45 \cdot$ Bhn; in MPa, $S \approx 3.10 \cdot$ Bhn)

$S'_n = 0.5\,S_u$
(in ksi, $S'_n \approx 0.25 \cdot$ Bhn;
in MPa, $S'_n \approx 1.73 \cdot$ Bhn)

FIGURE 8.5

Generalized *S–N* curve for wrought steel with superimposed data points [7].

A multitude of standard fatigue tests (Figure 8.3) have been conducted over the last few decades, with results tending to conform to certain generalized patterns. The most commonly used of these is shown in Figure 8.5. With a knowledge of only the ultimate tensile strength, a good approximation of the complete *S–N* curve for steel can quickly be made. Furthermore, tensile strength can be estimated from a nondestructive hardness test. For steels, the tensile strength in psi is about 500 times the Brinell hardness (see Chapter 3); hence, a conservative estimate of endurance limit is about 250 H_B. *The latter relationship can be counted on only up to Brinell hardness values of about 400.* The endurance limit may or may not continue to increase for greater hardnesses, depending on the composition of the steel. This is illustrated in Figure 8.6.

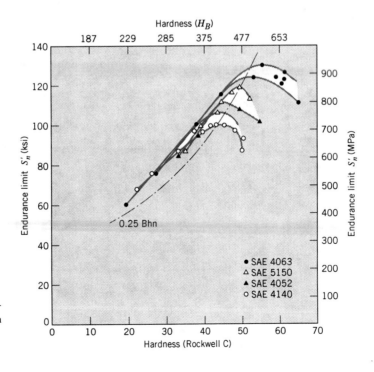

FIGURE 8.6

Endurance limit versus hardness for four alloy steels. (From M. F. Garwood, H. H. Zurburg, and M. A. Erickson, *Interpretation of Tests and Correlation with Service*, American Society for Metals, 1951, p. 13.)

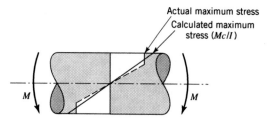

FIGURE 8.7
**Representation of maximum bending stress at low
fatigue life (at 1000 cycles). (Note: *Calculated*
maximum stress is used in *S–N* plots.)**

Although the 10^3-cycle fatigue strength in Figure 8.5 is computed as being about
90 percent of the ultimate strength, the *actual* stress is not that high. The reason is that
fatigue strength values corresponding to the test points in Figure 8.4 are *computed*
according to the elastic formula, $\sigma = Mc/I$. Loads large enough to cause failure in
1000 cycles usually cause significant yielding, resulting in *actual* stresses that are
lower than calculated values. This point is illustrated in Figure 8.7.

The fatigue strength characteristics of cast iron are similar to those of steel, with
the exception that the endurance limit corresponds to about 0.4 (rather than 0.5) times
the ultimate strength.

Representative *S–N* curves for various aluminum alloys are shown in Figure 8.8.
Note the absence of a sharply defined "knee" and true endurance limit. This is typical of nonferrous metals. In the absence of an endurance limit, the fatigue strength at
10^8 or 5×10^8 cycles is often used. (To give a "feel" for the time required to accumulate this many cycles, an automobile would typically travel nearly 400,000 miles

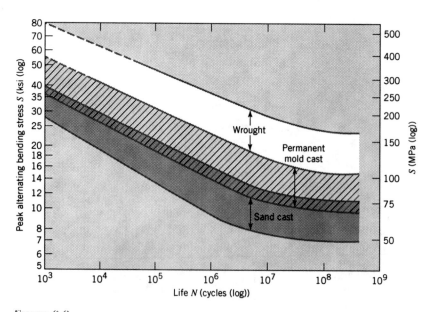

FIGURE 8.8
***S–N* bands for representative aluminum alloys, excluding wrought alloys with
$S_u < 38$ ksi.**

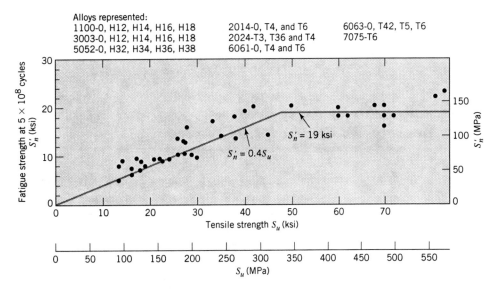

Alloys represented:
1100-0, H12, H14, H16, H18   2014-0, T4, and T6   6063-0, T42, T5, T6
3003-0, H12, H14, H16, H18   2024-T3, T36 and T4   7075-T6
5052-0, H32, H34, H36, H38   6061-0, T4 and T6

FIGURE 8.9

Fatigue strength at 5×10^8 cycles, common wrought-aluminum alloys.

before any one of its cylinders fired 5×10^8 times.) For typical wrought-aluminum alloys, the 5×10^8-cycle fatigue strength is related to the static tensile strength as indicated in Figure 8.9.

Typical *S–N* curves for magnesium alloys are shown in Figure 8.10. The 10^8-cycle fatigue strength is about 0.35 times tensile strength for most wrought and cast alloys.

For most copper alloys (including brasses, bronzes, cupronickels, etc.), the ratio of 10^8-cycle fatigue strength to static tensile strength ranges between 0.25 and 0.5. For nickel alloys, the ratio of these strengths is usually between 0.35 and 0.5.

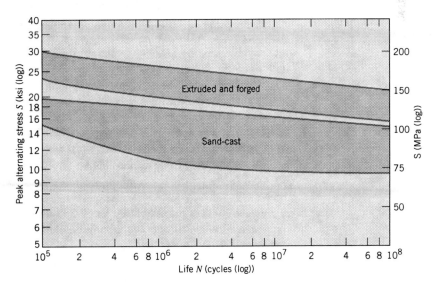

FIGURE 8.10

General range of *S–N* curves for magnesium alloys.

Titanium and its alloys behave like steel in that they tend to exhibit a true endurance limit in the range of 10^6 to 10^7 cycles, with the endurance limit being between 0.45 and 0.65 times the tensile strength.

8.4 *Fatigue Strengths for Reversed Bending and Reversed Axial Loading*

If a test specimen, similar to the one used in the R. R. Moore testing machine, is not rotated but mounted horizontally with one end fixed and the other pushed alternately up and down, *reversed* bending stresses are produced. These differ from stresses caused by *rotating* bending only in that the maximum stresses are limited to the top and bottom, whereas rotating bending produces maximum stresses all around the circumference. In rotating bending, a fatigue failure will originate from the weakest point on the surface; in reversed bending there is an excellent statistical probability that the weakest point will not be at exactly the top or bottom. This means that the fatigue strength in reversed bending is usually slightly greater than in rotating bending. The difference is small and usually neglected. Thus, for problems involving reversed bending, a small error on the conservative side is deliberately introduced.

Similar reasoning indicates that a reversed *axial* loading—which subjects the *entire cross section* to the maximum stress—should give *lower* fatigue strengths than rotating bending. This is indeed the case, and this difference should be taken into account. Axial or "push–pull" tests give endurance limits about 10 percent lower than rotating bending. Furthermore, if the supposedly axial load is just a *little* off-center (as with nonprecision parts having as-cast or as-forged surfaces), slight bending is introduced which causes the stresses on one side to be a little higher than P/A. Ideally, one would determine the load eccentricity and calculate the peak alternating stress as $P/A + Mc/I$, but the magnitude of the unwanted eccentricity is often not known. In such cases it is customary to take this into account by using only the P/A stress, and reducing the rotating bending endurance limit by a little *more* than 10 percent (perhaps by 20 to 30 percent).

Since this reduction of 10 percent or more in the endurance limit for rotating bending is associated with *differences in stress gradient*, we will take this into account by multiplying the basic endurance limit, S_n', by a *gradient factor* or *gradient constant*, C_G, where, $C_G = 0.9$ for pure axial loading of precision parts and C_G ranges from perhaps 0.7 to 0.9 for axial loading of nonprecision parts.

Stress gradient is also responsible for the 10^3-cycle fatigue strength being lower for axial loading than for bending loads. Recall, from Figure 8.7, that the $0.9S_u$ strength for rotating bending was in most cases an artificial calculated value that neglected the effect of yielding at the surface. Yielding cannot reduce the surface stress in the case of axial loading. Accordingly, tests indicate that the 10^3-cycle strength for this loading is only about $0.75S_u$.

The preceding points are illustrated in Figure 8.11. The top two curves in Figure 8.11 show comparative estimated *S–N* curves for bending and axial loading. The bottom curve in Figure 8.11 shows a comparative estimated *S–N* curve for torsion loading.

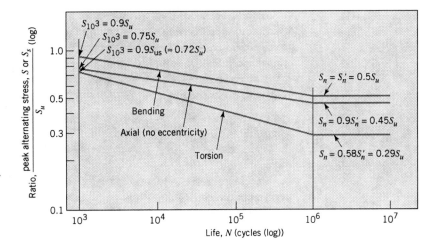

FIGURE 8.11
Generalized *S–N* curves for polished 0.3-in.-diameter steel specimens (based on calculated elastic stresses, ignoring possible yielding).

8.5 *Fatigue Strength for Reversed Torsional Loading*

Since fatigue failures are associated with highly localized yielding, and since yielding of ductile materials has been found to correlate well with the distortion energy theory, it is perhaps not surprising that this theory has been found useful in predicting the endurance limit of ductile materials under various combinations of reversed biaxial loading, including torsion. This is illustrated in Figure 8.12. *Thus, for ductile metals, the endurance limit (or long-life endurance strength) in reversed torsion is about 58 percent of endurance limit (or long-life endurance strength) in reversed bending.* This is taken into account by multiplying the basic endurance limit S'_n by a *load factor* C_L of 0.58.

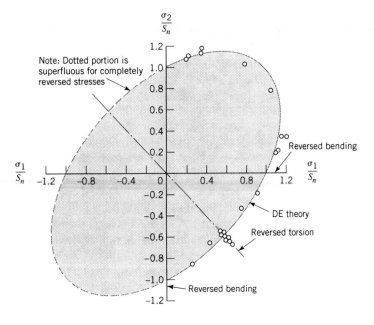

FIGURE 8.12
A σ_1–σ_2 plot for completely reversed loading, ductile materials. [Data from Walter Sawert, Germany, 1943, for annealed mild steel; and H. J. Gough, "Engineering Steels under Combined Cyclic and Static Stresses," *J. Appl. Mech.*, **72**: 113–125 (March 1950).]

Since torsional stresses involve stress gradients similar to bending, it is not surprising that, as in bending, the 10^3-cycle fatigue strength is generally about 0.9 times the *appropriate* ultimate strength. Thus, for reversed torsion the 10^3-cycle strength is approximately 0.9 times the ultimate *shear* strength. Experimental values for ultimate torsional shear strength should be used if they are available. If not, they may be *roughly* approximated as

$$S_{us} = 0.8S_u \quad \text{(for steel)}$$
$$= 0.7S_u \quad \text{(for other ductile metals)}n$$

The bottom curve of Figure 8.11 shows an estimated torsional *S–N* curve for steel based on the preceding relationships.

There are fewer data available to support a generalized procedure for estimating torsional *S–N* curves for *brittle* materials, and this makes it all the more desirable to obtain actual experimental fatigue data for the specific material and loading condition in the problem at hand. In the absence of such data, torsional *S–N* curves for brittle materials are sometimes *estimated* on the basis of (1) assuming an endurance limit at 10^6 cycles of 0.8 times the standard reversed bending endurance limit (this correlates somewhat with using the Mohr theory of failure to relate bending and torsion in the same way that the distortion energy theory is used for ductile materials) and (2) assuming a 10^3-cycle strength of $0.9S_{us}$, the same as for ductile materials.

8.6 Fatigue Strength for Reversed Biaxial Loading

Figure 8.12 illustrates the good general agreement of the distortion energy theory with the endurance limit (or long-life fatigue strength) of ductile materials subjected to all combinations of reversed biaxial loading. For shorter-life fatigue strengths of ductile materials, and for brittle materials, we are not in a very good position to make fatigue strength predictions without the benefit of directly applicable experimental data. With this reservation in mind, the following procedure is tentatively recommended.

1. For *ductile* materials, use the *distortion energy* theory (usually Eq. 6.8) to convert from the actual load stresses to an equivalent stress that is regarded as a reversed *bending* stress. Then proceed to relate this stress to the fatigue properties of the material (i.e., the *S–N* curve) in reversed bending.

2. For *brittle* materials, use the *Mohr* theory to obtain an equivalent reversed stress that is regarded as a reversed *bending* stress, and relate this to the bending fatigue properties (i.e., *S–N* curve) of the material. (A convenient graphical procedure for determining the equivalent bending stress is to draw a σ_1–σ_2 plot like that in Figure 6.11*b* for the material, and then plot the point corresponding to the actual reversed stresses. Next, draw a line through this point and parallel to the failure line. The intersection of this line with the σ_1 axis gives the desired equivalent bending stress.)

8.7 *Influence of Surface and Size on Fatigue Strength*

Up to this point, all discussions of fatigue strength have assumed the surface to have a special "mirror polish" finish. This requires a costly laboratory procedure but serves to minimize (1) surface scratches and other geometric irregularities acting as points of stress concentration, (2) any differences in the metallurgical character of the surface layer of material and the interior, and (3) any residual stresses produced by the surface finishing procedure. Normal commercial surface finishes usually have localized points of greater fatigue vulnerability: hence the commercially finished parts have lower fatigue strengths. The amount of "surface damage" caused by the commercial processes depends not only on the process but also on the susceptibility of the material to damage. Figure 8.13 gives estimated values of surface factor, C_S, for various finishes applied to steels of various hardnesses. In all cases the endurance limit for the laboratory polished surface is multiplied by C_S to obtain the corresponding endurance limit for the commercial finish. It is standard practice *not* to make any surface correction for the 10^3-cycle strength—the reason being that this is close to the strength for static loads and that the static strength of ductile parts is not significantly influenced by surface finish.

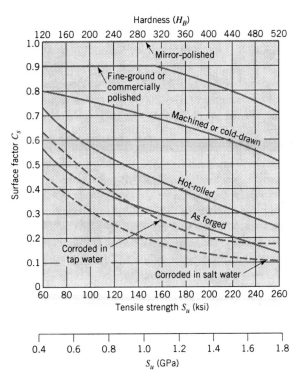

FIGURE 8.13

Reduction in endurance limit owing to surface finish—steel parts.

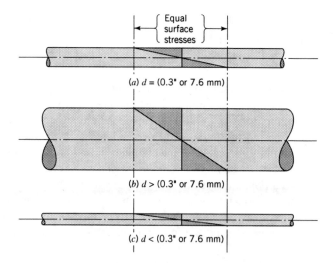

Stress gradients versus diameter for bending and torsion.

The surface factor for ordinary gray cast iron is approximately 1. The reason for this is that even the mirror-polished samples have surface discontinuities because of the graphite flakes in the cast-iron matrix, and that adding even rather severe surface scratches does not make the situation much worse, if any. Unfortunately, there is little published information on surface factors for other materials. For critical parts, actual fatigue tests of the material and surface in question must be conducted.

In Section 8.4 it was pointed out that the endurance limit for reversed axial load is about 10 percent lower than for reversed bending because of *stress gradient*. For the 0.3-in.-diameter bending specimen, the rapid drop in stress level below the surface is somehow beneficial. The 0.3-in.-diameter *axial* specimen does not enjoy this benefit. A comparison of stress gradients in Figures 8.14a and 8.14b shows that large specimens in bending or torsion do not have the same favorable gradients as the standard 0.3-in. specimen. Experiments show that if the diameter is increased to much more than 0.4 in., most of the beneficial gradient effect is lost. *Hence, parts that are more than 0.4 in. (or 10 mm) in diameter and that are subjected to reversed bending or torsion should carry a gradient factor C_G of 0.9, the same as parts subjected to axial loading.* Figure 8.14c shows that very small parts have an even more favorable gradient than the standard R. R. Moore specimen. Thus, we might expect the endurance limit for such parts to be *greater* than for 0.3-in.-diameter parts. *Sometimes* this has been found to be the case—but unless specific data are available to substantiate this increase, it is best to use a gradient factor of unity for these small parts.

Consider the question of what gradient factor to use with the bending of a rectangular section, say 6 mm × 12 mm. If the bending is about the neutral axis that places the tension and compression surfaces 6 mm apart, use $C_G = 1$; if the tension and compression surfaces are 12 mm apart, use $C_G = 0.9$. Thus, the gradient factor is determined on the basis of an equivalent round section having the same stress gradient as the actual part.

Recall that a gradient factor of 0.9 (or lower) was specified (Section 8.4) for *all* axially loaded parts because the stress gradient is unfavorable, regardless of size.

Parts with sections larger than about 50-mm equivalent diameter are usually found to have lower endurance limits than those computed using the gradient factors recommended previously. This is due in part to metallurgical factors such as hardenability, for the interior of large-section parts is usually metallurgically different from the surface metal. The extent to which the endurance limit of very large parts is reduced varies substantially, and generalizations are hardly warranted. If the part in question is critical, there is no substitute for pertinent test data. A *very rough guide* for the values sometimes used is given in Table 8.1.

TABLE 8.1   Generalized Fatigue Strength Factors for Ductile Materials (S–N curves)

a. 10^6-cycle strength (endurance limit)[a]

Bending loads: $S_n = S'_n C_L C_G C_S C_T C_R$

Axial loads: $S_n = S'_n C_L C_G C_S C_T C_R$

Torsional loads: $S_n = S'_n C_L C_G C_S C_T C_R$

where S'_n is the R.R. Moore, endurance limit,[b] and

		Bending	Axial	Torsion
C_L	(load factor)	1.0	1.0	0.58
C_G	(gradient factor): diameter < (0.4 in. or 10 mm)	1.0	0.7 to 0.9	1.0
	(0.4 in. or 10 mm) < diameter < (2 in. or 50 mm)[c]	0.9	0.7 to 0.9	0.9
C_S	(surface factor)	see Figure 8.13		
C_T	(temperature factor)	Values are only for steel		
	T ≤ 840 °F	1.0	1.0	1.0
	840 °F < T ≤ 1020 °F	1 - (0.0032T − 2.688)		
C_R	(reliability factor):[d]			
	50% reliability	1.000	"	"
	90% "	0.897	"	"
	95% "	0.868	"	"
	99% "	0.814	"	"
	99.9% "	0.753	"	"

b. 10^3-cycle strength[e, f, g]

Bending loads: $S_f = 0.9 S_u C_T$

Axial loads: $S_f = 0.75 S_u C_T$

Torsional loads: $S_f = 0.9 S_{us} C_T$

where S_u is the ultimate tensile strength and S_{us} is the ultimate shear strength.

[a] For materials not having the endurance limit, apply the factors to the 10^8 or 5×10^8-cycle strength.
[b] $S'_n = 0.5 S_u$ for steel, lacking better data.
[c] For (2 in. or 50 mm) < diameter < (4 in. or 100 mm) reduce these factors by about 0.1. For (4 in. or 100 mm) < diameter < (6 in. or 150 mm), reduce these factors by about 0.2.
[d] The factor, C_R, corresponds to an 8 percent standard deviation of the endurance limit. For example, for 99% reliability we shift −2.326 standard deviations, and $C_R = 1-2.326(0.08) = 0.814$.
[e] No corrections for gradient or surface are normally made, but the experimental value of S_u or S_{us} should pertain to sizes reasonably close to those involved.
[f] No correction is usually made for reliability at 10^3 cycle strength.
[g] $S_{us} \approx 0.8 S_u$ for steel; $S_{us} \approx 0.7 S_u$ for other ductile metals.

The foregoing recommended consideration of specimen size focused on the effect of size on stress gradient. It should be noted that a more extensive treatment of this subject would consider other facets. For example, the larger the specimen, the greater the statistical probability that a flaw of given severity (from which fatigue failure could originate) will exist somewhere near the surface (with bending or torsional loads) or somewhere within the entire body of material (with axial loads). In addition, the effect of processing on metallurgical factors is often more favorable for smaller parts, even in the size range below 50-mm equivalent diameter.

8.8 Summary of Estimated Fatigue Strengths for Completely Reversed Loading

The foregoing sections have emphasized the desirability of obtaining actual fatigue test data that pertain as closely as possible to the application. Generalized empirical factors were given for use when such data are not available. These factors can be applied with greatest confidence to steel parts because most of the data on which they are based came from testing steel specimens.

Five of these factors are involved in the estimate for endurance limit:

$$S_n = S_n' C_L C_G C_S C_T C_R \tag{8.1}$$

The temperature factor, C_T, accounts for the fact that the strength of a material decreases with increased temperature, and the reliability factor, C_R, acknowledges that a more reliable (above 50%) estimate of endurance limit requires using a lower value of endurance limit.

Table 8.1 gives a summary of all factors used for estimating the fatigue strength of ductile materials (when subjected to completely reversed loading). It serves as a convenient reference for solving problems.

8.9 Effect of Mean Stress on Fatigue Strength

Machine and structural parts seldom encounter completely reversed stresses; rather, they typically encounter a *fluctuating* stress that is a combination of static plus completely reversed stress. A fluctuating stress is usually characterized by its *mean* and *alternating* components. However, the terms *maximum* stress and *minimum* stress are also used. All four of these quantities are defined in Figure 8.15. Note that if any two of them are known, the others are readily computed. This text uses primarily mean and alternating stress components, as in Figure 8.16. The same information can be portrayed graphically with *any* combination of two of the stress components shown in Figure 8.15. For example, σ_m–σ_{max} coordinates are often found in the literature. For convenience, some graphs use all four quantities, as in Figures 8.17 through 8.19.

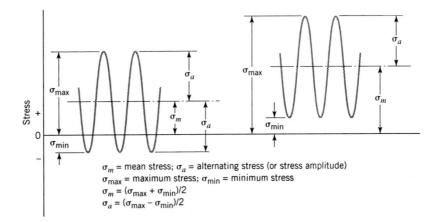

FIGURE 8.15

Fluctuating stress notation illustrated with two examples.

σ_m = mean stress; σ_a = alternating stress (or stress amplitude)
σ_{max} = maximum stress; σ_{min} = minimum stress
$\sigma_m = (\sigma_{max} + \sigma_{min})/2$
$\sigma_a = (\sigma_{max} - \sigma_{min})/2$

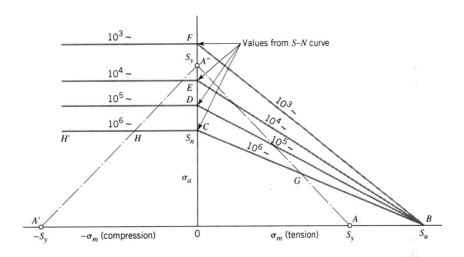

FIGURE 8.16

Constant-life fatigue diagram—ductile materials.

Bending loads: Construct diagram as shown; take points C, D, and so on from S–N curve for reversed bending.

Axial loads: Construct diagram as shown; take points C, and so on from S–N curve for reversed axial loads.

Torsional loads: Omit left half of diagram (*any torsional mean stress is considered positive*); take points C and so on from S–N curve for reversed torsion; use S_{sy} and S_{us} instead of S_y and S_u. (For steel, $S_{us} \approx 0.8S_u$, $S_{sy} \approx 0.58S_y$.)

General biaxial loads: Construct the diagram as for *bending* loads, and use it with *equivalent* load stresses, computed as follows. (Note that these equations apply to the generally encountered situation where σ_a and σ_m exist in one direction only. Corresponding equations for the more elaborate general case are also tentatively applicable.)

1. Equivalent alternating bending stress, σ_{ea}, is calculated from the *distortion energy theory* as being *equivalent* to the combination of existing *alternating* stresses:

$$\sigma_{ea} = \sqrt{\sigma_a^2 + 3\tau_a^2} \tag{a}$$

2. Equivalent *mean* bending stress σ_{em}, is taken as the *maximum principal stress* resulting from the superposition of all existing static (mean) stresses. Use Mohr circle, or

$$\sigma_{em} = \frac{\sigma_m}{2} + \sqrt{\tau_m^2 + \left(\frac{\sigma_m}{2}\right)^2} \tag{b}$$

[For more complex loading, various other suggested equations for σ_{ea} and σ_{em} are found in the literature.]

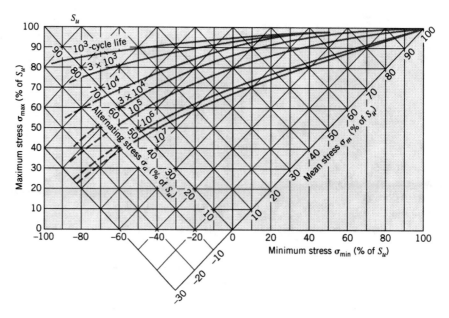

FIGURE 8.17
Fatigue strength diagram for alloy steel, S_u = 125 to 180 ksi, axial loading. Average of test data for polished specimens of AISI 4340 steel (also applicable to other alloy steels, such as AISI 2330, 4130, 8630). (Courtesy Grumman Aerospace Corporation.)

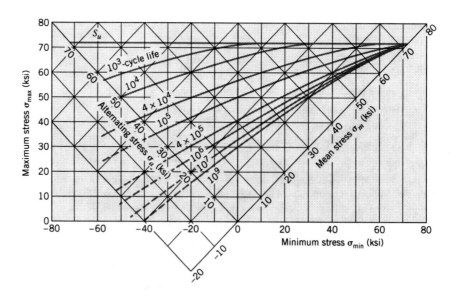

FIGURE 8.18
Fatigue strength diagram for 2024-T3, 2024-T4, and 2014-T6 aluminum alloys axial loading. Average of test data for polished specimens (unclad) from rolled and drawn sheet and bar. Static properties for 2024: S_u = 72 ksi, S_y = 52 ksi; for 2014: S_u = 72 ksi, S_y = 63 ksi. (Courtesy Grumman Aerospace Corporation.)

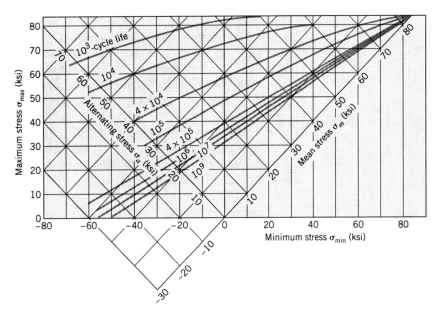

Minimum stress σ_{min} (ksi)

FIGURE 8.19

Fatigue strength diagram for 7075-T6 aluminum alloy, axial loading. Average of test data for polished specimens (unclad) from rolled and drawn sheet and bar. Static properties: S_u = 82 ksi, S_y = 75 ksi. (Courtesy Grumman Aerospace Corporation.)

The existence of a static tensile stress reduces the amplitude of reversed stress that can be superimposed. Figure 8.20 illustrates this concept. Fluctuation *a* is a completely reversed stress corresponding to the endurance limit—the mean stress is zero and the alternating stress S_n. Fluctuation *b* involves a tensile mean stress. In order to have an equal (in this case, "infinite") fatigue life, the alternating stress must be less than S_n. In going from *b* to *c*, *d*, *e*, and *f*, the mean stress continually increases; hence, the alternating stress must correspondingly decrease. Note that in each case the stress

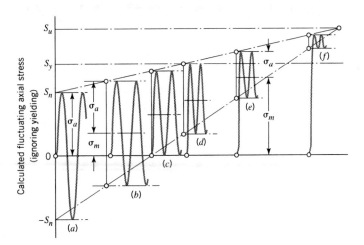

FIGURE 8.20

Various fluctuating uniaxial stresses, all of which correspond to equal fatigue life.

fluctuation is shown as starting from zero, and that the stresses are *computed P/A* values. Microscopic yielding occurs even at *a*, as has previously been noted. Upon reaching *d*, macroscopic yielding begins. Although load fluctuations *e* and *f* give "infinite" life, the part is yielded on the first load application.

Figure 8.16 gives a convenient graphical representation of various combinations of mean and alternating stress in relation to criteria both for yielding and for various fatigue lives. It is often called a *constant-life fatigue diagram* because it has lines corresponding to a constant 10^6-cycle (or "infinite") life, constant 10^5-cycle life, and so forth.

To begin the construction of this diagram, put on it first the information that is already known. The horizontal axis ($\sigma_a = 0$) corresponds to static loading. Yield and ultimate strengths are plotted at points *A* and *B*. For ductile materials, the compressive yield strength is $-S_y$, and this is plotted at point *A'*. If the mean stress is zero and the alternating stress is equal to S_y (point *A''*), the stress fluctuates between $+S_y$ and $-S_y$. All points along the line *AA''* correspond to fluctuations having a tensile peak of S_y; all points on *A'A''* correspond to compressive peaks equal to $-S_y$. All combinations of σ_m and σ_a causing no (macroscopic) yielding are contained within triangle *AA'A''*.

All *S–N* curves considered in this chapter correspond to $\sigma_m = 0$. Hence, we can read from these curves points like *C, D, E,* and *F* for any fatigue life of interest. Connecting these points with *B* gives estimated lines of constant life. This empirical procedure for obtaining constant-life lines is credited to Goodman; hence the lines are commonly called *Goodman lines*.

Laboratory tests have consistently indicated that compressive mean stresses do *not* reduce the amplitude of allowable alternating stress; if anything, they slightly *increase* it. Figure 8.16 is thus conservative in showing the constant-life lines as horizontal to the left of points *C, D,* and so on. (The lines apparently extend indefinitely as far as *fatigue* is concerned, the limitation being only static compression failure.)

Detailed modifications of the diagram for various types of loading are given in Figure 8.16. Let us observe the significance of various areas on the diagram.

1. If a life of at least 10^6 cycles is required *and no* yielding is permitted (even at extreme fibers in bending or torsion, where a little yielding might be difficult to detect), we must stay inside area *A'HCGA*.

2. If *no* yielding but less than 10^6 cycles of life are required, we can also work within some or all of area *HCGA''H*.

3. If 10^6 cycles of life are required but yielding is acceptable, area *AGB* (and area to the left of *A'H*) may be used, in addition to area *A'HCGA*.

4. Area above *A''GB* (and above *A''HH'*) corresponds to yielding on the first application of load *and* fatigue fracture prior to 10^6 cycles of loading.

The procedure for general biaxial loads given in Figure 8.16 should be recognized as a substantial simplification of a very complex situation. It applies best to situations involving long life, where the loads are all in phase, where the principal axes for mean and alternating stresses are the same, and where these axes are fixed with time. For an illustration in which these conditions would be fulfilled, consider the example in Figure 4.25 with the shaft stationary, and with the 2000-lb static load changed to a load that fluctuates between 1500 and 2500 lb. The *static* stresses on element *A* would be unchanged, but *alternating* stresses would be added. The alternating bending and the alternating torsion would obviously be in phase, the principal planes for mean and alternating stresses would be the same, and these planes would remain the same as the load fluctuated.

Figures 8.17 through 8.19 give constant-life fatigue strengths for certain steel and aluminum materials. They differ from Figure 8.16 in the following respects.

1. Figures 8.17 through 8.19 represent actual experimental data for the materials involved, whereas Figure 8.16 shows conservative empirical relationships that are generally applicable.

2. Figures 8.17 through 8.19 are "turned 45°," with scales added to show σ_{max} and σ_{min} as well as σ_m and σ_a.

3. Yield data are not shown on these figures.

4. The experimental constant-life lines shown have some curvature, indicating that Figure 8.16 errs a little on the conservative side in both the straight Goodman lines and in the horizontal lines for compressive mean stress. This conservatism usually exists for ductile but not for brittle materials. Experimental points for brittle materials are usually on or slightly below the Goodman line.

When experimental data like those given in Figures 8.17 through 8.19 are available, these are to be preferred over the estimated constant-life fatigue curves constructed in Figure 8.16.

The reader will find that Figure 8.16 and Table 8.1 provide helpful summaries of information pertaining to the solution of a large variety of fatigue problems.

SAMPLE PROBLEM 8.1   **Estimation of *S–N* and Constant-Life Curves from Tensile Test Data**

Using the empirical relationships given in this section, estimate the *S–N* curve and a family of constant-life fatigue curves pertaining to the axial loading of precision steel parts having $S_u = 150$ ksi, $S_y = 120$ ksi, and commercially polished surfaces. All cross-section dimensions are to be under 2 in.

SOLUTION

Known: A commercially polished steel part having a known size and made of a material with specified yield and ultimate strengths is axially loaded (see Figure 8.21).

Find: Estimate the *S–N* curve and construct constant-life fatigue curves.

Schematic and Given Data:

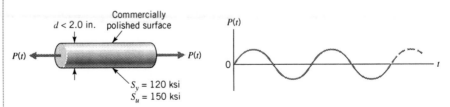

FIGURE 8.21
Axial loading of precision steel part.

Assumptions:

1. Actual fatigue data is not available for this material.

2. The estimated S–N curve constructed using Table 8.1 and the constant-life fatigue curves constructed according to Figure 8.16 are adequate.

3. The gradient factor, $C_G = 0.9$. The temperature factor, $C_T = 1.0$, and the reliability factor, $C_R = 1.0$.

Analysis:

1. From Table 8.1, the 10^3-cycle peak alternating strength for axially loaded ductile material is $S = 0.75S_u = 0.75(150) = 112$ ksi.

2. Also from Table 8.1, the 10^6-cycle peak alternating strength for axially loaded ductile material is $S_n = S_n' C_L C_G C_S C_T C_R$ where $S_n' = (0.5)(150) = 75$ ksi, $C_L = 1.0$, $C_G = 0.9$, $C_T = 1.0$, $C_R = 1.0$ and from Figure 8.13, $C_S = 0.9$; then $S_n = 61$ ksi.

3. The estimated S–N curve is given in Figure 8.22.

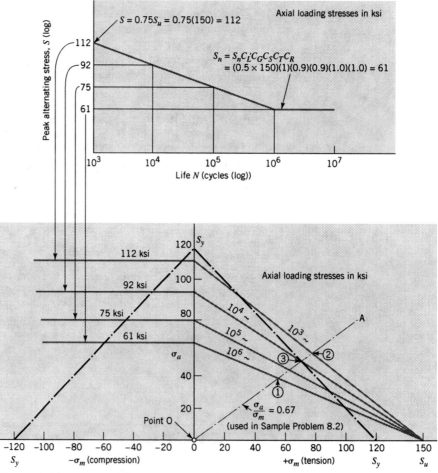

FIGURE 8.22

Sample Problem 8.1—estimate S–N and σ_m–σ_a curves for steel, $S_u = 150$ ksi, axial loading, commercially polished surfaces.

4. From the estimated *S–N* curve we determine that the peak alternating strengths at 10^4 and 10^5 cycles are, respectively, 92 and 75 ksi.

5. The estimated σ_m–σ_a curves for 10^3, 10^4, 10^5, and 10^6 cycles of life are given in Figure 8.22.

Comment: If the steel part design is critical, pertinent test data should be used rather than the preceding rough approximation.

SAMPLE PROBLEM 8.2   Determine the Required Size of a Tensile Link Subjected to Fluctuating Loading

A round tensile link with negligible stress concentration is subjected to a load fluctuating between 1000 and 5000 lb. It is to be a precision member (so that use of $C_G = 0.9$ is justified) with commercially polished surfaces. The material is to be steel, with $S_u = 150$ ksi, $S_y = 120$ ksi. A safety factor of 2 is to be used, applied to all loads.

a. What diameter is required if infinite life is needed?

b. What diameter is required if only 10^3 cycles of life are needed?

SOLUTION

Known: A round steel link with given material properties and a commercially polished surface is to have a safety factor of 2 applied to all loads and is axially loaded with a known fluctuating load.

Find: (a) Determine the required diameter for infinite life. (b) Determine the required diameter for 10^3 cycles of life.

Schematic and Given Data: Figure 8.22 used in Sample Problem 8.1 is applicable.

Assumptions:

1. The diameter is less than 2 in.

2. The gradient factor $C_G = 0.9$.

3. Gross yielding cannot be permitted.

Analysis:

1. The fatigue strength properties of the material conform to those represented in Figure 8.22, *provided* the diameter comes out to be under 2 in.

2. At the *design overload*: $\sigma_m = SF(F_m/A) = 2(3000)/A = 6000/A$, $\sigma_a = SF(F_a/A) = 2(2000)/A = 4000/A$. Thus, regardless of the area, $\sigma_a/\sigma_m = 0.67$. This is represented by line OA on Figure 8.22. Note the interpretation of this line. If area A is infinite, both σ_m and σ_a are zero, and the stresses are represented by the origin, point O. Moving out along line OA corresponds to progressively decreasing values of A. For part a of the problem we need to determine the area corresponding to the intersection of OA with the infinite-life line (same as 10^6 cycles, in this case), which is labeled ①. At this point, $\sigma_a = 38$ ksi; from $\sigma_a = 4000/A$, A is determined as 0.106 in.^{2} From

$A = \pi d^2/4$, $d = 0.367$ in. This is indeed well within the size range for the value of $C_G = 0.9$, which had to be assumed when the diagram was constructed. In many cases, the final answer might be rounded off to $d = \frac{3}{8}$ in.

3. For part b, with only 10^3 cycles of life required, we can move out along line OA of Figure 8.22, seemingly to point ②, where the line intersects the 10^3-cycle life line. However, if point ③ is crossed, the peak design overload of 10,000 lb imposes stresses in excess of the yield strength. In a notch-free tensile bar the stresses are uniform so that gross yielding of the entire link would occur. Assuming that this could not be permitted, we must choose a diameter based on point ③, not point ②. Here, $\sigma_a = 48$ ksi, from which $A = 0.083$ in.², and $d = 0.326$ in., perhaps rounded off to $d = \frac{11}{32}$ in. This diameter corresponds to an estimated life greater than required, but to make it any smaller than 0.326 in. would cause general yielding on the first overload application.

Probably the most common use of fatigue strength relationships is in connection with designing parts for infinite (or 5×10^8 cycle) life or in analyzing parts intended for infinite fatigue life. In these situations no S–N curve is required. Only the estimated endurance limit need be calculated and the infinite-life Goodman line plotted.

8.10   Effect of Stress Concentration with Completely Reversed Fatigue Loading

Figure 8.23 shows typical S–N curves for (1) unnotched specimens and (2) otherwise identical specimens except for a stress raiser. Unlike other S–N curves we will use, the stresses plotted are *nominal* stresses; that is, stress concentration is not taken into account. The specimen dimensions in the section where fatigue fractures occur are the same for both Figures 8.23a and b. Hence, any given *load* causes the same *calculated stress* in both cases. As shown in the figure, the ratio of the unnotched to notched endurance limit is the *fatigue stress concentration factor*, designated as K_f. Theoretically, we might expect K_f to be equal to the theoretical or geometric factor K_t, discussed in Section 4.12. Fortunately, tests show that K_f is often less than K_t. This is

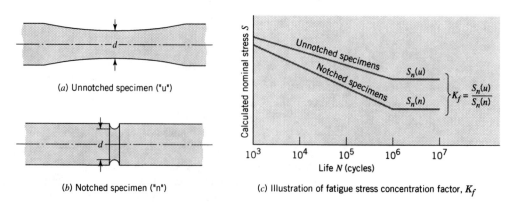

(a) Unnotched specimen ("u")

(b) Notched specimen ("n")

(c) Illustration of fatigue stress concentration factor, K_f

FIGURE 8.23
Reversed-load fatigue tests, notched versus unnotched specimens.

apparently due to internal irregularities in the structure of the material. An "ideal" material would have internal stresses in exact accordance with elastic theory; actual materials have internal irregularities causing local points to have higher stresses. Thus, even unnotched samples suffer from these internal "notches." Adding an external geometric notch (groove, thread, hole, etc.) to this material may not do as much *additional* damage as it would were the material itself "perfect." An extreme case in point is ordinary (not "high-strength") gray cast iron. The internal stress raisers caused by graphite flakes in the matrix are such that the addition of a geometric stress raiser has little or no effect. This means that if the material in Figure 8.23 were one of the lower grades of gray cast iron, the two S–N curves would nearly coincide. A material with a uniform fine-grained matrix is *highly sensitive* to notches (i.e., $K_f \approx K_t$); cast iron is insensitive to notches (i.e., $K_f \approx 1$).

The preceding situation is commonly dealt with by using a *notch sensitivity factor, q*, defined by the equation

$$K_f = 1 + (K_t - 1)q \tag{8.2}$$

where q ranges between zero (giving $K_f = 1$) and unity (giving $K_f = K_t$). Thus, to determine fatigue stress concentration factors from corresponding theoretical (or geometric) factors, we need to know the notch sensitivity of the material.

The situation is a little more complicated than it appears because notch sensitivity depends not only on the material but also on the relative radius of the geometric notch and the dimensions of characteristic internal imperfections. Notch radii so small that they approach the imperfection size give zero notch sensitivity. This is indeed fortunate; otherwise even minute scratches (which give extremely high values of K_t) on what would generally be called a smooth, polished surface would disastrously weaken the fatigue strength. Figure 8.24 is a plot of notch sensitivity versus notch

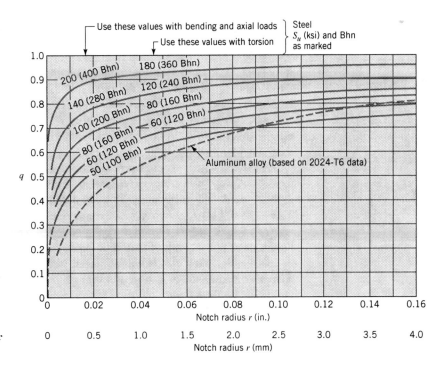

FIGURE 8.24

Notch sensitivity curves (after [9]). Note: (1) Here *r* is the radius at the point where the potential fatigue crack originates. (2) For *r* > 0.16 in., extrapolate or use *q* ≈ 1.

radius for some common materials. Note that in all cases the notch sensitivity approaches zero as the notch radius approaches zero. Also note that the data for steels illustrate the fundamental tendency for the harder and stronger materials to be more notch-sensitive. This means that changing from a soft to a harder and stronger steel normally increases part fatigue strength, but the increase is not as great as might be expected because of the increased notch sensitivity. Finally, Figure 8.24 shows that a given steel is a little more notch-sensitive for torsional loading than for bending and axial loading. For example, a 0.04-in.-radius notch in a 160-Bhn steel part has a notch sensitivity of about 0.71 if the loading is bending or axial and about 0.76 if the load is torsional.

Figure 8.23 shows that the influence of the notch at 10^3 cycles is considerably less than at 10^6 cycles. Some references advise neglecting the influence of the stress raiser at 10^3 cycles. Although certain data support this recommendation, a closer study indicates that this is valid only for a relatively soft metal (steel, aluminum, magnesium, and probably others); but for relatively hard and strong alloys of these same metals, the effect of the notch at 10^3 cycles can be nearly as great as at 10^6 (see [6], Figure 13.26).

There is a fundamental difficulty in analyzing notch effects at the low-cycle end of curves like that in Figure 8.23c. This is so because the *calculated nominal stress* used in the plot does not relate very closely with the *actual loading conditions* imposed upon the local region at the root of the notch where a fatigue crack starts. Figure 8.2 shows an enlarged view of the notch region of a notched specimen, as in Figure 8.23b. Under reversed loading sufficient to cause fatigue failure after, say 10^3 cycles, plastic yielding will occur throughout some small region at the base of the notch. This region contributes little to the rigidity of the total part; thus, the *strains* within this zone are determined almost entirely by the stable elastic resistance of the great bulk of material outside this zone. This means that during a fatigue test with constant maximum load, the maximum *strain* within the "vulnerable" zone will stay constant from cycle to cycle. The *actual stress* within the zone may vary widely with time, depending on the strain-hardening or strain-softening characteristics of the material. Hence, a meaningful study of low-cycle fatigue must deal with actual local strain rather than calculated nominal local stress. This "strain cycling" approach is beyond the scope of this book. (See references such as [3].) For our purposes, it is recommended that the full fatigue stress concentration factor K_f be used in all cases. For relatively short-life situations, this may be overly conservative (i.e., the effect of the stress concentration may be substantially less than K_f).

Another question should be considered here. Is it better to treat K_f as a stress concentration factor or as a strength reduction factor? Authorities differ on this point, but in this book K_f will be regarded as a *stress concentration factor.* Looking at Figure 8.23, we could easily regard K_f as a strength reduction factor and calculate a "notched endurance limit" as equal to $S'_n C_L C_G C_S C_T C_R / K_f$. This would be correct, but it has the disadvantage of implying that the *material itself* is weakened by the notch. It is not, of course—the notch merely caused higher local stresses. In addition, when we use K_f as a stress multiplier (instead of a strength reducer), S–N curves and constant-life fatigue strength curves are independent of notch geometry, and the same curves can be used repeatedly for members with various stress raisers. Finally, for considering residual stresses caused by peak loads (as in Figure 4.43), it is necessary that K_f be regarded as a stress concentration factor.

8.11 *Effect of Stress Concentration with Mean Plus Alternating Loads*

It was shown in Sections 4.14 and 4.15 that peak loads, causing calculated elastic stresses to exceed the yield strength, produce yielding and resultant residual stresses. Furthermore, the residual stresses always serve to lower the *actual* stresses when the same peak load is applied again. To illustrate the effect of residual stresses on fatigue life where mean, as well as alternating, stresses are involved, consider the examples developed in Figure 4.43.

Suppose this notched tensile bar is made of steel, with $S_u = 450$ MPa, $S_y = 300$ MPa, and that its size and surface are such that the estimated constant-life fatigue curves are as shown at the bottom of Figure 8.25. The top of Figure 8.25 shows

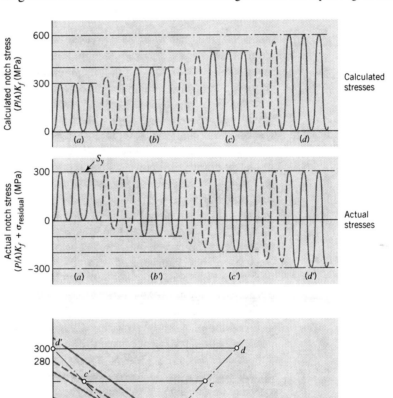

FIGURE 8.25
Estimation of fatigue life for repeated application of stresses shown in Figure 4.43; with steel, $S_u = 450$ MPa, $S_y = 300$ MPa.

a fluctuation of the notch stress calculated without taking yielding into account. The first three cycles correspond to the loading and unloading involved in Figure 4.43*a*. The next two (dotted) cycles represent progressively increasing the load to that involved in Figure 4.43*b*. Note that these dotted cycles show an elastically computed stress at the notch root of about $\frac{7}{6} S_y$. Correspondingly, the three cycles drawn with solid lines at *b* in Figure 8.25 show calculated stresses fluctuating between zero (when the load is removed) and 400 MPa, which is $\frac{4}{3} S_y$. This procedure continues along the top of Figure 8.25 until the condition shown in Figure 4.43*d* is reached. Here, the calculated stress is zero when the load is off, and $2S_y$ when it is on.

Just below this in Figure 8.25 is a corresponding plot of *actual* stresses at the notch root. It is based on the assumption that the ductile material used can be approximated (within the limited strain range involved) by a "flat-top" idealized stress–strain curve, like the one drawn in Figure 4.42*e*. No yielding occurs during the first three cycles at *a*, but yielding *does* occur at the notch root when the calculated stress exceeds 300 MPa during the first dotted cycle. A little more yielding takes place during each cycle that the load goes higher than it had been previously. When the load is "on" during one of the cycles at *b*, the stress distribution corresponds to the solid line in the left drawing of Figure 4.43. When the load is "off," the stresses are not zero but correspond to the residual stress pattern in the right-hand drawing of Figure 4.43. At the notch, these stresses range from S_y when the load is on to the residual stress of $-S_y/3$ when the load is off. This procedure continues along the "actual notch stress" plot of Figure 8.25 until the condition shown in Figure 4.43*d* is reached. Here, the actual notch root stress is S_y when the load is applied and a residual stress of $-S_y$ when the load is off.

At the bottom of Figure 8.25, stresses resulting from "on and off" application of the Figure 4.43 loads are represented in comparison to the fatigue strength characteristics of the material. Points *a*, *b*, *c*, and *d* correspond to the *calculated* notch root stresses (which, because of the yielding and residual stress, have little significance). Points *a′*, *b′*, *c′*, and *d′* correspond to *actual* stresses (based on an ideal stress–strain curve) and are fairly realistic. Note that in every case, yielding has reduced the *mean* stress; it does *not* change the *alternating* stress.

On the basis of the plot in Figure 8.25, the estimated fatigue lives corresponding to repeated application of the various levels of tensile loading would be 10^5 cycles for loading point *a*, perhaps $1\frac{1}{2}$ or 2 times 10^4 cycles for loading *b*, about 6×10^3 cycles for *c*, and about $2\frac{1}{2} \times 10^3$ cycles for *d*. These estimates represent rough visual interpolations between adjacent constant-life lines. The dotted line through point *c′* illustrates a better procedure. This line is a Goodman line corresponding to some unknown life. All points on the line correspond to the *same* life; in particular, point *c′* corresponds to the same life as a completely reversed stress of 280 MPa. Now we can go to the *S–N* curve (not shown) and take from it the life corresponding to 280 MPa. To keep the matter of life predictions in proper perspective, remember that such predictions are inherently very rough, except on a statistical basis—as was illustrated by the scatter band of the *S–N* curve in Figure 8.4*c*. Also, do not forget the previously mentioned limitations of the procedure for making predictions in the low-cycle range.

In this example the stress concentration factor of 2, originally used in Figure 4.43, was taken as a *fatigue* stress concentration factor in Figure 8.25. Assuming that the material has a notch sensitivity *q* of something less than unity, the theoretical stress concentration factor K_t would be greater than 2.

Such life predictions can be made conveniently from fatigue strength diagrams in the form of Figures 8.17 through 8.19. On these diagrams, points *a*, *b*, *c*, and *d* would lie on the vertical axis (i.e., $\sigma_{\min} = 0$), and points b', c', and d' would lie on the horizontal line, $\sigma_{\max} = S_y$.

At first, we may be inclined to become a little alarmed with the appearance of points like b, c, and d on the σ_m–σ_a plot. Even point c—let alone point d—shows a peak stress in excess of the ultimate strength! We must remember that these are fictitious calculated stresses, and that the extent of yielding they represent is usually very small. With the tensile bar in this example, there is no way that *very much* yielding can occur at the notch root without yielding the entire cross section—and this is only on the verge of happening at point d.

In summary, the procedure recommended here for fatigue life prediction of notched parts subjected to combinations of mean and alternating stress is

> *All stresses (both mean and alternating) are multiplied by the fatigue stress concentration factor K_f, and correction is made for yielding and resultant residual stresses if the calculated peak stress exceeds the material yield strength.*

This procedure is sometimes called the *residual stress method* because of the recognition it gives to the development of residual stresses.

An alternative procedure sometimes used is to apply the stress concentration factor to the alternating stress *only*, and *not* take residual stresses into account. We can see that in *some* cases this reduction in mean stress from not multiplying it by K_f might be about the same as the reduction in mean stress achieved with the residual stress method by taking yielding and residual stress into account. Because the mean stress is not multiplied by a stress concentration factor, this alternative procedure is sometimes called the *nominal mean stress method*. Only the residual stress method is recommended here for fatigue life prediction.

SAMPLE PROBLEM 8.3   Determine the Required Diameter of a Shaft Subjected to Mean and Alternating Torsion

A shaft must transmit a torque of 1000 N · m, with superimposed torsional vibration causing an alternating torque of 250 N · m. A safety factor of 2 is to be applied to both loads. A heat-treated alloy steel is to be used, having $S_u = 1.2$ GPa, and $S_y = 1.0$ GPa (unfortunately, test data are not available for S_{us} or S_{ys}). It is required that the shaft have a shoulder, with $D/d = 1.2$ and $r/d = 0.05$ (as shown in Figure 4.35). A good-quality commercial ground finish is to be specified. What diameter is required for infinite fatigue life?

SOLUTION

Known: A commercial ground shaft made from steel with known yield and ultimate strengths and having a shoulder with known D/d and r/d ratios transmits a given steady and superimposed alternating torque with a safety factor of 2 applied to both torques (see Figure 8.26).

Find: Estimate the shaft diameter d required for infinite life.

Schematic and Given Data:

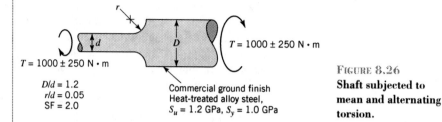

FIGURE 8.26
Shaft subjected to mean and alternating torsion.

Assumptions/Decisions:

1. The shaft is manufactured as specified with regard to the critical fillet and the shaft surface finish.

2. The shaft diameter will be between 10 and 50 mm.

Analysis:

1. Construct the fatigue strength diagram shown in Figure 8.27. (Since infinite life is required, there is no need for an *S–N* curve.) In computing an estimated value for S_n, we assumed that the diameter will be between 10 and 50 mm. If it is not, the solution will have to be repeated with a more appropriate value of C_G.

2. The *calculated* notch root stresses (i.e., not yet taking any possible yielding into account) are

$$\tau_m = (16T_m/\pi d^3)K_f$$

$$\tau_a = (16T_a/\pi d^3)K_f$$

In order to find K_f from Eq. 8.2, we must first determine K_t and q. We find K_t from Figure 4.35*c* as 1.57, but the determination of q from Figure 8.24 again requires an assumption of the final diameter. This presents little difficulty, however, as the curve for torsional loading of steel of this strength ($S_u = 1.2$ GPa = 174 ksi, or

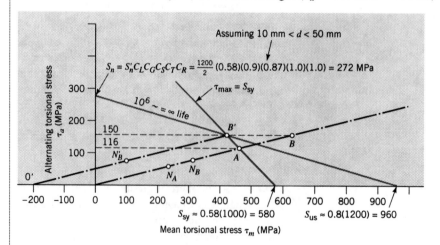

FIGURE 8.27
Fatigue strength diagram for Sample Problem 8.3.

very close to the top curve of the figure) gives $q \approx 0.95$ for $r \geq 1.5$ mm, which in this case corresponds to $d \geq 30$ mm. With the given loading, intuition (or subsequent calculation) tells us that the shaft will have to be at least this large. Substitution of these values, together with the given values for design overload (nominal load times safety factor), gives

$$K_f = 1 + (K_t - 1)q = 1 + (1.57 - 1)0.95 = 1.54$$

$$\tau_m = [(16 \times 2 \times 1000 \text{ N} \cdot \text{m})/\pi d^3]1.54 = 15{,}685/d^3$$

$$\tau_a = [(16 \times 2 \times 250 \text{ N} \cdot \text{m})/\pi d^3]1.54 = 3922/d^3$$

and $\tau_a/\tau_m = 0.25$.

3. Starting at the origin of Figure 8.27 (which corresponds to making the diameter infinite) and moving to the right along the line of slope = 0.25, we tentatively stop at point *A*. If no yielding is to be permitted, the stresses can go no higher than this. At *A*, $\tau_a = 116$ MPa or 0.116 GPa. Thus, $3922/d^3 = 0.116$ or $d = 32.2$ mm.

4. In most situations, perhaps a little yielding in the localized zone of the fillet under "design overload" conditions could be permitted. If so, the diameter can be further reduced until the *calculated* stresses reach point *B* on Figure 8.27, because yielding and residual stresses bring the *actual* stresses back to point *B'*, which is right on the infinite life line. Yielding did not affect the alternating stress magnitude, so the equation for alternating stress can be equated to 150 MPa, giving $d = 29.7$ mm.

5. Before accepting either the $d = 32.3$ mm or the $d = 29.7$ mm answer, it is important to go back and see whether the values for C_G and q are consistent with the diameter finally chosen. In this case they are.

Comments:

1. Before even beginning to solve a problem like this, an engineer should carefully review the design with regard to the critical fillet. Is it really necessary that the radius be so small? If so, is the quality control in the production and inspection departments such that the part will not be made with merely a "sharp corner"? And what about the control of surface finish? As far as shaft fatigue strength is concerned, a high-quality finish *in the fillet* is very important. Will the production and inspection departments be aware of this? The other 99.9 percent of the shaft surface is of little consequence unless a high-quality finish is needed for other reasons (as to provide a good bearing surface or close-tolerance fit). If the quality finish is not needed on these other portions of the shaft, cost might be lowered by changing to an ordinary machined surface.

2. Before we leave this example, it is interesting to note in Figure 8.27 the operating stresses for *normal* operation (i.e., $T_m = 1000$ N · m, $T_a = 250$ N · m). If point *A* is selected as the required overload point, then normal operation involves operating at point N_A (midpoint between 0 and *A*). If *B'* is the selected overload point, normal operation would be at N_B, the midpoint between 0 and *B*. But if the machine is operated at the design overload and *subsequently* operated normally, a residual stress, represented by 0′, is involved. With this residual stress present, stresses are at 0′ when the load is off, at N'_B when the load is normal, and at *B'* with the design overload.

SAMPLE PROBLEM 8.4   Estimate the Safety Factor of a Disk Sander Shaft

Figure 8.28 pertains to the shaft of a disk sander that is made of steel having $S_u = 900$ MPa, and $S_y = 750$ MPa. The most severe loading occurs when an object is held near the periphery of the disk (100-mm radius) with sufficient force to develop a friction torque of 12 N·m (which approaches the stall torque of the motor). Assume a coefficient of friction of 0.6 between the object and the disk. What is the safety factor with respect to eventual fatigue failure of the shaft?

SOLUTION

Known: A shaft with given geometry and loading is made of steel having known ultimate and yield strengths.

Find: Determine the safety factor for eventual failure by fatigue.

Schematic and Given Data:

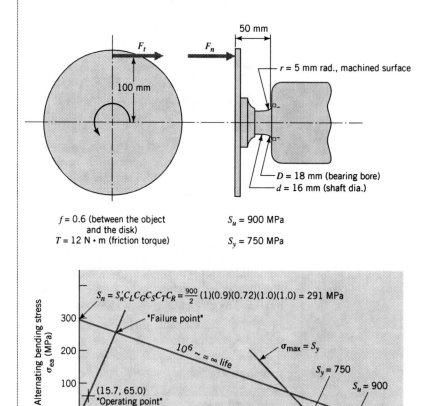

FIGURE 8.28
Sample Problem 8.4—disk sander.

Assumption: The 50-mm disk shaft overhang is necessary.

Analysis:

1. The 12 N·m torque specification requires that the tangential force F_t be 120 N. With a coefficient of friction of 0.6, this requires a normal force F_n of 200 N.

2. These two force components produce the following loading at the shaft fillet:

   Torque: $T = 12\,\text{N·m} = 12{,}000\,\text{N·mm}$

   Axial load: $P = 200\,\text{N}$

   Bending: In the horizontal plane, $M_h = 120\,\text{N} \times 50\,\text{mm}$
   In the vertical plane, $M_v = 200\,\text{N} \times 100\,\text{mm}$
   The resultant is $M = \sqrt{M_h^2 + M_v^2} = 20{,}900\,\text{N·mm}$

3. From Figure 4.35, geometric stress concentration factors for torsion, axial, and bending loads are about

   $$K_{t(t)} = 1.10, \qquad K_{t(a)} = 1.28, \qquad K_{t(b)} = 1.28$$

   From Figure 8.24, estimated notch sensitivities q are 0.93 for torsion and 0.91 for bending and axial loads. From Eq. 8.2, values of K_f are estimated as 1.09, 1.25, and 1.25 for torsional, axial, and bending loads, respectively.

4. The three stress components at the fillet are

   $$\tau = \frac{16T}{\pi d^3} K_{f(t)} = \frac{16(12{,}000)}{\pi (16)^3}(1.09) = 16.3\,\text{MPa}$$

   $$\sigma_{(a)} = \frac{P}{A} K_{f(a)} = \frac{-200(4)}{\pi (16)^2}(1.25) = -1.24\,\text{MPa}$$

   $$\sigma_{(b)} = \frac{32M}{\pi d^3} K_{f(b)} = \frac{32(20{,}900)}{\pi (16)^3}(1.25) = 65.0\,\text{MPa}$$

5. Applying the procedure specified for "general biaxial loads" in Figure 8.16, we construct in Figure 8.28 an estimated infinite-life Goodman line for *bending* loads. Next, an "operating point" that corresponds to the *equivalent* mean and alternating bending stresses is placed on the diagram. Of the three stress components determined, torsional and axial stresses are constant for steady-state operating conditions; the bending stress is completely reversed (the bending stress at any point on the fillet goes from tension-to-compression-to-tension during each shaft revolution). Using the recommended procedure to determine the equivalent mean and alternating stresses, we have

   $$\sigma_{em} = \frac{\sigma_m}{2} + \sqrt{\tau^2 + \left(\frac{\sigma_m}{2}\right)^2}$$

   $$= \frac{-1.24}{2} + \sqrt{(16.3)^2 + \left(\frac{-1.24}{2}\right)^2} = 15.7\,\text{MPa}$$

   $$\sigma_{ea} = \sqrt{\sigma_a^2 + 3\tau_a^2} + \sqrt{(65.0)^2 + 0} = 65.0\,\text{MPa}$$

6. By drawing a line through the origin and the "operating point," we see that all stresses would have to be increased by a factor of about 4 to reach the estimated "failure point" where conditions would be on the verge of causing eventual fatigue failure. Hence, the estimated safety factor is 4.

Comment: With regard to design details relating to shaft fatigue, the relatively large 5-mm radius is excellent for minimizing stress concentration at this necessary step in the shaft. It would be desirable to reduce the 50-mm disk overhang, but we have assumed that for this particular application the overhang is necessary.

8.12 *Fatigue Life Prediction with Randomly Varying Loads*

Predicting the life of parts stressed above the endurance limit is at best a rough procedure. This point is illustrated by the typical scatter band of 7 : 1 life ratio shown in Figure 8.4c. For the large percentage of mechanical and structural parts subjected to randomly varying stress cycle intensity (e.g., automotive suspension and aircraft structural components), the prediction of fatigue life is further complicated. The procedure given here for dealing with this situation was proposed by Palmgren of Sweden in 1924 and, independently, by Miner of the United States in 1945. The procedure is often called the *linear cumulative-damage rule*, with the names of Miner, Palmgren, or both attached.

Palmgren and Miner very logically proposed the simple concept that if a part is cyclically loaded at a stress level causing failure in 10^5 cycles, each cycle of this loading consumes one part in 10^5 of the life of the part. If other stress cycles are interposed corresponding to a life of 10^4 cycles, each of these consumes one part in 10^4 of the life, and so on. When, on this basis, 100 percent of the life has been consumed, fatigue failure is predicted.

The Palmgren or Miner rule is expressed by the following equation in which n_1, n_2, . . . , n_k represent the number of cycles at specific overstress levels, and N_1, N_2, . . . , N_k represent the life (in cycles) at these overstress levels, as taken from the appropriate *S–N* curve. Fatigue failure is predicted when

$$\frac{n_1}{N_1} + \frac{n_2}{N_2} + \cdots + \frac{n_k}{N_k} = 1 \quad \text{or} \quad \sum_{j=1}^{j=k} \frac{n_j}{N_j} = 1 \tag{8.3}$$

Use of the linear cumulative-damage rule is illustrated in the following sample problems.

SAMPLE PROBLEM 8.5   Fatigue Life Prediction with Randomly Varying, Completely Reversed Stresses

Stresses (including stress concentration factor K_f) at the critical notch of a part fluctuate randomly as indicated in Figure 8.29a. The stresses could be bending, torsional, or axial—or even equivalent bending stresses resulting from general biaxial loading. The plot shown represents what is believed to be a typical 20 seconds of operation. The material is steel, and the appropriate *S–N* curve is given in Figure 8.29b. This curve is corrected for load, gradient, and surface. Estimate the fatigue life of the part.

SOLUTION

Known: A stress-versus-time history corrected for stress concentration, load, gradient, and surface is given for a 20-second test of a steel part.

Find: Determine the fatigue life of the part.

Schematic and Given Data:

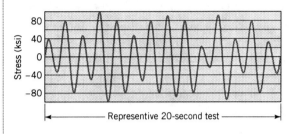

(*a*)
Stress-time plot

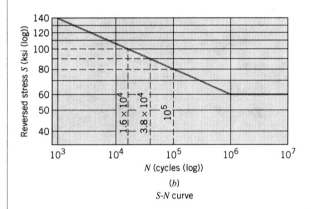

(*b*)
S–N curve

FIGURE 8.29
Sample Problem 8.5—fatigue life prediction, reversed stresses.

Assumptions:

1. The representative 20-second test result for stress will repeat until the part fails by eventual fatigue.
2. The linear cumulative-damage rule applies.

Analysis: In Figure 8.29*a* there are eight stress cycles above the endurance limit of 60 ksi: five at 80 ksi, two at 90 ksi, and one at 100 ksi. The *S–N* curve shows that each 80-ksi cycle uses one part in 10^5 of the life, each at 90 ksi uses one part in 3.8×10^4, and the one at 100 ksi uses one part in 1.6×10^4. Adding these fractions of life used gives

$$\frac{n_1}{N_1} + \frac{n_2}{N_2} + \frac{n_3}{N_3} = \frac{5}{10^5} + \frac{2}{3.8 \times 10^4} + \frac{1}{1.6 \times 10^4} = 0.0001651$$

For the fraction of life consumed to be unity, the 20-second test time must be multiplied by 1/0.0001651 = 6059. This corresponds to 2019 minutes, or about *30 to 35 hours.*

Comment: The linear cumulative damage rule can easily be extended to problems involving mean as well as alternating stresses. The next sample problem illustrates this for the case of fluctuating bending stresses.

SAMPLE PROBLEM 8.6   Fatigue Life Prediction—Randomly Varying Fluctuating Bending Stresses

Figure 8.30a represents the stress fluctuation at the critical notch location of a part during what is believed to be a typical 6 seconds of operation. The bending stresses plotted include the effect of stress concentration. The part (Figure 8.30d) is made of

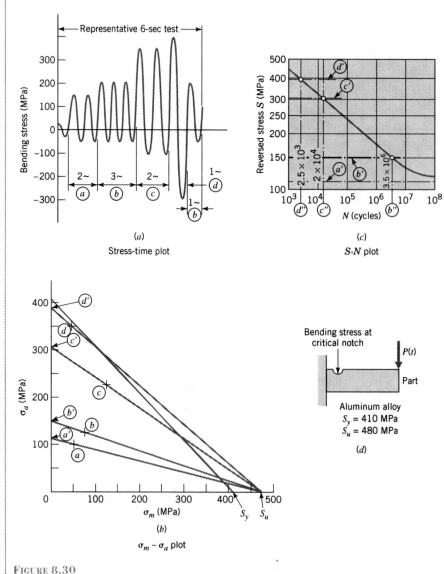

FIGURE 8.30
Fatigue life prediction, randomly varying stresses (Sample Problem 8.6).

an aluminum alloy having S_u = 480 MPa and S_y = 410 MPa. The S–N curve for bending is given in Figure 8.30c. This curve is corrected for stress gradient and surface. Estimate the life of the part.

SOLUTION

Known: A representative 6-s stress-versus-time history corrected for stress concentration for an aluminum alloy part and the S–N curve for bending strength corrected for stress gradient and surface are given.

Find: Determine the life of the part.

Schematic and Given Data: See Figure 8.30.

Assumptions:

1. The Miner rule is applicable.

2. The 6-s of operation is so typical of operation that the stress–time history will repeat until the part fails.

Analysis:

1. The 6-s test period includes, in order, two cycles of fluctuation *a*, three cycles of fluctuation *b*, two cycles of *c*, one cycle of *d*, and one of *b*. Each of these fluctuations corresponds to a combination of mean and alternating stress plotted as a point in Figure 8.30b. For example, *a* consists of σ_m = 50 MPa, σ_a = 100 MPa.

2. Points *a* through *d* on Figure 8.30b are connected by straight lines to the point $\sigma_m = S_u$ on the horizontal axis. This gives a family of four Goodman lines, each corresponding to some constant (but as yet unknown) life.

3. The four Goodman lines intercept the vertical axis at points *a′* through *d′*. According to the Goodman concept, points *a* through *d* correspond to exactly the same fatigue lives as points *a′* through *d′*. These lives are determined from the S–N curve in Figure 8.30c. Note that the life corresponding to conditions *a* and *a′* can be considered infinite.

4. Adding up the portions of life consumed by overload cycles, *b*, *c*, and *d* gives

$$\frac{n_b}{N_b} + \frac{n_c}{N_c} + \frac{n_d}{N_d} = \frac{4}{3.5 \times 10^6} + \frac{2}{2 \times 10^4} + \frac{1}{2.5 \times 10^3} = 0.0005011$$

This means that the estimated life corresponds to 1/0.0005011 or 1996 periods of 6-s duration. This is equivalent to 199.6 minutes, or about $3\frac{1}{3}$ hours.

Comment: The procedure would be the same for a fluctuating *equivalent* bending stress, computed in accordance with the instructions for "general biaxial loads" on Figure 8.16, and illustrated in Sample Problem 8.4.

8.13   *Effect of Surface Treatments on the Fatigue Strength of a Part*

Since fatigue failures originate from localized areas of relative weakness that are usually on the surface, the local condition of the surface is of particular importance. We have already dealt with the surface constant C_S for various categories of *finishing* operations. This and the following two sections are concerned with various surface *treatments*, giving specific regard to their influence on (1) surface strength, in comparison with the strength of the subsurface material, and (2) surface residual stress. All three surface considerations—geometry (smoothness), strength, and residual stress—are somewhat interrelated. For example, the low values of C_S shown in Figure 8.13 for hot-rolled and as-forged surfaces are due partly to surface geometry and partly to decarburization (hence, weakening) of the surface layer.

The influence of surface strengthening and the creation of a favorable (compressive) residual surface stress are illustrated in Figure 8.31. Curve *a* shows the stress gradient in the vicinity of a notch, owing to a tensile load. Curve *b* shows a desirable residual stress gradient, giving compression in the groove surface. Curve *c* shows total stress, the sum of curves *a* and *b*. Curve *d* shows a desirable *strength* gradient,

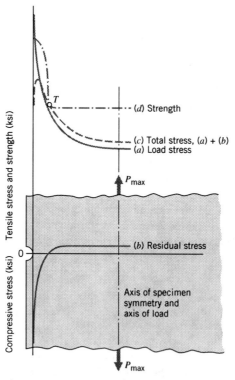

FIGURE 8.31

Stress and strength gradients, surface-strengthened notched part subjected to axial load.

resulting from a treatment causing surface strengthening. Note that (1) the surface strengthening and compressive residual stresses have substantially increased the load that can be carried and (2) the point of potential failure origin has been moved under the surface to point T, where curves c and d are tangent. This means that the surface of the groove could deteriorate somewhat in service (as by corrosion, surface scratches, etc.) without reducing the load-carrying capacity of the part. A further benefit to fatigue strength that is not evident in Figure 8.31 is that compressive residual stresses shift the "operating point" on the mean stress-alternating stress diagram (like points a through d in Figure 8.30b) to the left, which increases fatigue life.

The concept of comparing strength gradients with total stress gradients provides ready explanation of the fact that parts having steep load stress gradients and poor surfaces (low values of C_S) benefit most from surface treatment. Unnotched parts with axial loading benefit very little unless they have poor initial surface finishes. Severely notched parts loaded in bending or torsion benefit most. Since practically all parts have critical areas with stress concentration, surface strengthening treatments are usually quite effective. For example, Figure 8.31 illustrates about a 60 percent increase in allowable load stress caused by the combination of surface strengthening plus residual stress. For applications involving bending or torsional loads, it is not uncommon for the fatigue load capacity to be more than doubled.

The next two sections discuss processes for strengthening surfaces. It is also important to be aware of processes causing a surface to *weaken*. Grinding, for example, if not performed carefully and with slow or moderate feed rates can cause harmful surface residual tensile stresses and even minute surface cracks. Chrome and nickel plating, even though good for the surface in providing corrosion protection, can substantially reduce the endurance limit of steel parts by causing hydrogen gas to be adsorbed. This is known as *hydrogen embrittlement*. This damage can be minimized by taking special care, as in using low plating current densities and baking the parts (usually in the range of 600° to 900°F) after plating. Properly performed, electroplating steel parts with soft metals like copper, cadmium, zinc, lead, and tin causes little if any fatigue weakening. Relatively little information is available on the effect of electroplating and anodizing nonferrous metals. Both beneficial and harmful effects have been reported in specific instances. Welding and flame-cutting operations tend to produce harmful surface residual tensile stresses, unless special precautions are taken, such as subsequent thermal stress-relieving.

The following list of a few basic principles may help to place the subject of fatigue-strengthening surface treatments in proper perspective.

The engineer concerned with the design and development of machine and structural components subjected to dynamic loads should

1. Seek to identify all local areas of stress concentration where fatigue failures could conceivably start.
2. Review possibilities for modifying the design to reduce stress concentration; e.g., move the stress raiser to an area of lower nominal stress.
3. Pay particular attention to the surface finish (C_S) *in these areas.*
4. Consider what can be done in the manufacture of the part to strengthen the surface layer and provide a compressive residual stress at potentially critical stress raisers.

8.14 Mechanical Surface Treatments— Shot Peening and Others

Mechanical surface treatments cold-work the surface material, causing compressive residual stresses and, depending on the properties of the material, often strengthening the surface against strain. The geometry of the surface, its smoothness, is altered—usually for the better unless the surface was initially polished or fine-ground.

The most common and versatile of the cold-working treatments is *shot peening*. It is widely used with springs, gears, shafts, connecting rods, and many other machine and structural components. In shot peening, the surface is bombarded with high-velocity iron or steel shot discharged from a rotating wheel or pneumatic nozzle. The resulting lightly hammered or *peened* effect tends to reduce the thickness and therefore increase the area of the exposed skin. Since the area is resisted by subsurface material, the skin is placed in residual compression. The thickness of the compressive layer is usually less than a millimeter. The highest compressive stresses occur slightly below the surface and are commonly of the order of half the yield strength. Sometimes greater compressive residual stresses are obtained by loading the part in tension while it is being peened. This is called *strain peening*.

With steel parts, shot peening is more effective with harder steel because the yield strength is a greater percentage of the ultimate strength. This means that the resulting residual stresses are less easily "wiped out" by subsequent load stresses that cause the total (load plus residual) stress to exceed the yield strength. With reference to the relationship illustrated in Figure 8.6, endurance strength increases with hardness up to substantially higher values with shot peening. Machine parts made of very high strength steels (tensile strengths above about 1400 MPa or 200 ksi) are particularly benefited.

A related mechanical surface treatment is *cold rolling*. The part is usually rotated while suitable contoured rollers are pressed against the surface to be strengthened, such as a shaft fillet or groove. This can create compressive residual stresses to a depth of a centimeter or more. Cold rolling has been applied to parts of all sizes, including large railway crankpins and axles of diameters up to 400 mm. Cold rolling is particularly effective for fatigue-strengthening shafts used with pressed-fit hubs (this helps to compensate for the high stress concentration in the shaft at the edge of the hub).

The fatigue-strengthening advantages of cold rolling are sometimes obtained as a by-product of a roll-forming operation. Under enough pressure, and with a suitable material, screw threads, shaft splines, and even fine gear teeth can be formed by cold rolling. The properties of the material then reflect the severe cold working. In addition, residual compressive stresses are usually created.

Coining is another cold-forming operation that increases fatigue strength. An example is the pressing of a cone or oversize ball into the surface at the end of a hole, leaving a residual compressive stress at the vulnerable intersection of the hole and surface. Another example is cold-pressing round grooves into a shaft on both sides of a transverse hole.

In the absence of specific data, *it is usually conservative to account for the effects of shot peening or other cold-working treatments by using a surface factor C_S of unity, regardless of the prior surface finish.*

8.15 *Thermal and Chemical Surface-Hardening Treatments (Induction Hardening, Carburizing, and Others)*

The purpose of thermal and chemical surface-hardening treatments is usually to provide surfaces with increased resistance to wear; however, they also serve to increase fatigue strength, and for this reason are considered here.

The strictly thermal processes of flame and induction hardening of steel parts containing sufficient carbon produce surface residual compressive stresses (owing to a phase transformation tending to slightly increase the *volume* of the surface layer) as well as surface hardening. As expected, maximum benefits are obtained with notched parts having steep applied stress gradients. In such situations fatigue strengths can often be more than doubled.

Carburizing and nitriding are examples of chemical–thermal processes that add carbon or nitrogen to the surface layer, together with appropriate heat treatment. The resulting hardened skin (or "case"), together with surface residual compressive stresses, can be very effective in increasing fatigue strength. In fact, nitriding has been found capable of rendering parts nearly immune to weakening by ordinary stress raisers. This point is illustrated by the following table given by Floe (Part 2, Section 8.6 of [5]).

	Endurance Limit (ksi)	
Geometry	**Nitride**	**Not Nitrided**
Without notch	90	45
Half-circle notch	87	25
V notch	80	24

8.16 *Fatigue Crack Growth*

In Chapter 6, we introduced basic concepts of fracture mechanics and defined failure as whenever the stress intensity factor, K, exceeds the critical stress intensity factor, K_c (e.g., for tensile loading, Mode I, failure occurs whenever K_I exceeds K_{Ic}).

We will now consider the fatigue progress where the crack grows under alternating loads. Figure 8.32 plots the process of crack growth from an initial crack length of c_1 to a critical crack length of c_{cr}. We know that as the crack grows with an increase in the number of cycles, N, the tendency for failure increases. For a small, identifiable crack (e.g., 0.004 in.), a typical crack growth history for a cyclical tensile load of constant amplitude would begin with growth in a stable, controlled manner until a critical crack size was reached, i.e., where the crack growth rate increases in an uncontrolled manner and catastrophe looms.

Figures 8.33*a* and 8.33*b* show the proportional relationship between range of stress intensity, $\Delta K = K_{max} - K_{min}$, and range of stress, $\Delta \sigma = \sigma_{max} - \sigma_{min}$, respectively.

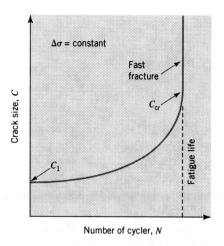

FIGURE 8.32
Crack size versus number of cycles for $\Delta\sigma$ constant.

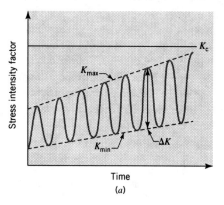

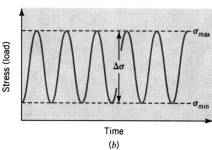

FIGURE 8.33
(a) Stress intensity versus time for constant fluctuating stress, $\Delta\sigma$ where $K_{min} = \sigma_{min} Y\sqrt{\pi c}$, $K_{max} = \sigma_{max} Y\sqrt{\pi c}$, and $\Delta K = \Delta\sigma Y\sqrt{\pi c}$. Note that all K parameters increase with crack size. (b) Stress (load) versus time for fluctuating stress.

Here, $K_{min} = \sigma_{min} Y\sqrt{\pi c}$, $K_{max} = \sigma_{max} Y\sqrt{\pi c}$, and $\Delta K = \Delta\sigma Y\sqrt{\pi c}$. Recall that fatigue life is largely dependent on the mean and alternating component of stress, i.e., the range and magnitude of the stress, which is proportional to the range of stress intensity. For an initial existing crack of size c_1 and for a given material, the slope dc/dN depends upon the range of the stress intensity factor, $\Delta K = K_{max} - K_{min}$. Again, $K_I = \sigma Y\sqrt{\pi c}$.

Figure 8.34 shows a plot of crack propagation rate (crack growth) versus ΔK. The crack propagation rate or crack growth rate increases with cycles of alternating load and is denoted by dc/dN, where N is the number of cycles and c is the crack size. For a particular material, the stress intensity range, ΔK, is related to dc/dN as shown with a sigmoidal curve comprised of three stages. Stage I, *initiation*, shows that growth

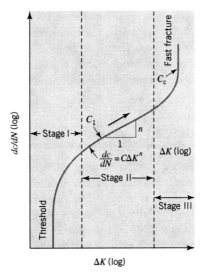

FIGURE 8.34

Three stages of crack growth on dc/dN (log) versus ΔK (log) for $\Delta\sigma$ constant.

of a crack requires that the stress intensity range exceed a threshold value. One mechanism for initial growth relates to cleavage along grain boundaries. Stage II, *stable propagation*, shows that crack growth rate versus intensity range is approximately log-log linear. This important stage is for cracks that grow in a stable manner. The curve for Stage II can be described by the Paris equation

$$dc/dN = C\,\Delta K^n \tag{8.4}$$

where dc/dN is the crack growth rate, and C and the index n are constant material properties, values of which appear in the literature. In stage II, for a certain crack growth rate, $(dc/dN)_o$, there is a corresponding stress intensity range ΔK_o, such that the constant $C = (dc/dN)_o/\Delta K_o^n$.

Stage III, *instability*, begins as the critical crack size is approached, and exists for a small portion of a component's life. The instability is catastrophic in that it takes place suddenly after the start of stage III.

Stages II and III can both be represented by an empirical modification of Eq. 8.4, that is,

$$dc/dN = C\,\Delta K^n/\{1 - (K_{max}/K_c)^n\} \tag{8.5}$$

Note in Eq. 8.5 that if $K_{max} \ll K_c$, then the term $\{1 - (K_{max}/K_c)^n\}$ approaches 1, and Eq. 8.5 represents stage II. If K_{max} approaches K_c, then dc/dN tends to infinity and represents stage III.

Integration of Eq. 8.5 yields the component life, ΔN_{12} cycles, that elapses during crack growth from c_1 to c_2. In normalized form, where $\alpha = c/w$, we have

$$\{(\Delta N_{12}/w)(dc/dN)_o\}\{\Delta\sigma\sqrt{(\pi w)}/\Delta K_o\}^n$$
$$= \int_1^2 (Y\sqrt{\alpha})^{-n}\,d\alpha - (Y_{cr}\sqrt{\alpha_{cr}})^{-n}(\alpha_2 - \alpha_1) \tag{8.6}$$

where α_{cr} is the normalized critical crack size corresponding to K_c, and $\alpha_2 \leq \alpha_{cr}$. For plane strain conditions, $K_c = K_{Ic}$.

Eq. 8.6 can be integrated and then solved for the component life that elapsed during crack growth. The configuration factor is required as a function of crack size; i.e., $Y = Y(\alpha)$. With normalized crack size limits of α_1 and α_2, the integral of Eq. 8.6, may be evaluated numerically noting that a value of w is required and that each term in { } is dimensionless. In practice, closed form integration is usually impossible, and graphical methods may be used.

SAMPLE PROBLEM 8.7   Cycle Life for Fatigue Crack Growth

A long strip with an edge crack is axially stressed as shown in Figure 8.35 and made of material that follows the Paris equation with an index $n = 4$. The strip has a crack growth rate $(dc/dN)_o$ of 1 mm/10^6 cycles that corresponds to a stress intensity range DK_o of 5 MPa$\sqrt{\text{m}}$. The width w of the strip is 30 mm. The configuration factor may be approximated by $Y = Y_o/(1 - a) = 0.85/(1 - a)$, where $a = c/w$. Determine the number of cycles required for a 6 mm crack to grow to 15 mm, if the component is subjected to a cyclically varying uniaxial tensile stress of (**a**) 0 MPa to 40 MPa, and (**b**) 80 MPa to 100 MPa.

SOLUTION

Known: A long strip of known geometry and material properties has an edge crack that grows from 6 mm to 15 mm while the strip is subjected to a cyclically varying uniaxial tensile stress.

Find: Determine the number of cycles for the crack to grow from 5 mm to 15 mm.

Schematic and Given Data:

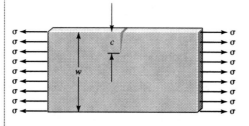

FIGURE 8.35
Sample Problem 8.7—cycle life prediction for cyclically varying stress—long strip, edge crack, tensile stress.

Assumptions:

1. The strip is loaded by a background stress, σ, normal to the crack.
2. The configuration factor, Y, is accurate for the range of α values.
3. The stress intensity is less than the fracture toughness of the material.
4. The crack grows in a stable manner.

Analysis:

1. Equation 8.6 can be integrated and then solved for the component life that elapsed during crack growth. Equation 8.6 is

$$[(\Delta N_{12}/w)(dc/dN)_o][\Delta\sigma\sqrt{(\pi w)}/\Delta K_o]^n$$

$$= \int_1^2 (Y\sqrt{\alpha})^{-n}\, d\alpha - (Y_{cr}\sqrt{\alpha_{cr}})^{-n}(\alpha_2 - \alpha_1) \qquad (8.6)$$

2. The configuration factor, Y, is a function of crack size since $Y = Y(\alpha) = Y_o/(1 - \alpha) = 0.85/(1 - \alpha)$. Note that $Y_o = 0.85$, is a constant.

3. Let the integral in Equation 8.6 be defined by I, i.e.,

$$I \equiv \int_1^2 (Y\sqrt{\alpha})^{-n} \, d\alpha$$

4. Substituting for Y and integrating gives

$$I = \int_1^2 \left(\frac{1-\alpha}{Y_o} \frac{1}{\sqrt{\alpha}}\right)^4 d\alpha$$

$$= \frac{1}{Y_o^4} \int_1^2 \frac{1 - 4\alpha + 6\alpha^2 - 4\alpha^3 + \alpha^4}{\alpha^2} \, d\alpha$$

$$= \frac{1}{Y_o^4} \int \left[\frac{1}{\alpha^2} - \frac{4}{\alpha} + 6 - 4\alpha + \alpha^2\right] d\alpha$$

$$= \frac{1}{Y_o^4} \left[-\frac{1}{\alpha} - 4\ln\alpha + 6\alpha - 2\alpha^2 + \frac{1}{3}\alpha^3\right]_1^2$$

5. With limits of integration $\alpha_1 = 6/30 = 1/5 = 0.20$, and $\alpha_2 = 15/30 = 1/2 = 0.50$,

$$I = \frac{1}{(0.85)^4}\left[\frac{1}{0.20} - \frac{1}{0.50} - 4(\ln 0.5 - \ln 0.2) + 6\left(\frac{3}{10}\right) - 2\left(\frac{1}{4} - \frac{1}{25}\right)\right.$$
$$\left. + \frac{1}{3}\left(\frac{1}{8} - \frac{1}{125}\right)\right]$$

$$I = 1.444$$

6. Recall that

$w = 30 \text{ mm} = 0.03 \text{ m}$ (width of strip)

$(dc/dN)_o = 1 \text{ mm}/10^6$ cycles (crack growth rate at point o)

$\Delta K_o = 5 \text{ MPa}\sqrt{m}$ (stress intensity range at point o)

$\Delta\sigma = (40 \text{ MPa} - 0 \text{ MPa}) = 40 \text{ MPa} = $ [stress amplitude for part (a)]

$n = 4$ (Paris equation index)

7. Inserting $I = 1.444$ and the above values into Eq. (8.6), with the last term negligible gives

$$[(\Delta N_{12}/w)(dc/dN)_o][\Delta\sigma\sqrt{\pi w}/\Delta K_o]^n$$

$$= \left(\frac{\Delta N_{12}}{30 \text{ mm}}\right)\left(\frac{1 \text{ mm}}{10^6 \text{ cycles}}\right)\left(\frac{40 \text{ MPa}\sqrt{\pi 0.03 \text{ m}}}{5 \text{ MPa}\sqrt{m}}\right)^4 = I = 1.444$$

8. Solving for ΔN_{12} gives $\Delta N_{12} = 1.191 \times 10^6$ cycles.

9. In part (b), $\Delta\sigma = 100 - 80 = 20 \text{ MPa}$. Since $\Delta\sigma$ is halved from 40 MPa in part (a) to 20 MPa in part (b), we have $\Delta N_{12} = (1.191 \times 10^6 \text{ cycles})(2^4) = 19.05 \times 10^6$ cycles.

Comments:

1. Although closed form integration of the integral in Eq. (8.6) was possible, usually this is not the case.

2. Ordinarily an integration cannot be performed directly, since Y varies with the crack length. Consequently, cyclic life is estimated by numerical integration procedures by using different values of Y held constant over a small number of small crack length increments or by using graphical techniques.

3. The critical crack length can be calculated by solving $K_{Ic} = \sigma_{max} Y \sqrt{\pi c_{critical}}$. Indeed for $K_{Ic} = 60 \, \text{MPa}\sqrt{\text{m}}$, $\alpha_{crit} = 0.840$.

8.17   *General Approach for Fatigue Design*

8.17.1   Brief Review of Failure Criterion for Simpler Cases

Before presenting a general approach for high cycle fatigue design for the case of combined loading involving both mean and alternating stresses, and applicable to a multitude of fatigue problems, let us briefly review the failure criteria applying to the simpler special cases:

1. For *static loads*, to predict the yielding of ductile materials, the maximum-distortion energy theory was found to be generally satisfactory. For static loading, $\sigma_m \neq 0$ and $\sigma_a = 0$. This condition is a special case of fluctuating stress where $\sigma_a = 0$. The safety factor for yielding will be $SF = S_y/\sigma_m$.

2. For *alternating loads*, to predict the fatigue failure of ductile materials, the maximum-distortion energy theory was found to apply. For fully reversed loading conditions, the *S–N* diagram represents the fatigue strength versus load cycles. This condition is a special case of fluctuating stress where $\sigma_m = 0$. For fully reverse loading, $\sigma_a \neq 0$ and $\sigma_m = 0$. The safety factor for failure by fatigue will be $SF = S_n/\sigma_a$.

3. For *combined alternating plus mean loading*, for predicting fatigue failure of ductile materials, the constant life fatigue diagram represents the component's strength. The distortion-energy theory is applied to calculate an equivalent alternating stress, σ_{ea}, and an equivalent mean bending stress, σ_{em}, to be taken as the highest algebraic principal stress caused by the mean-load components acting alone.

    Note that the distortion energy theory should not be applied to calculate an equivalent stress, σ_{em}, because a mean compressive stress does not decrease the allowable alternating axial stress, whereas a mean tensile stress does. The distortion energy (equivalent stress) is the same for tension and compression. Therefore, using the distortion energy theory to calculate a single equivalent mean stress is not a recommended procedure because it does not correctly account for the influence of the mean stress.

4. For *crack growth in Mode I*, the safety factor for failure by rapid fatigue crack growth (fracture) will be $SF = K_{Ic}/K_I$. The critical crack length can be calculated by solving $K_{Ic} = \sigma_{max} Y\sqrt{\pi c_{critical}}$. Equation 8.6 can be integrated and then solved for the component life that elapsed during crack growth.

8.17.2 Overview of Fatigue Analysis Procedure

In elementary form, the reader should recognize that a fatigue analysis involves three principal steps:

1. Representing the fatigue *strength* of the part or material,
2. Representing the *stresses* involved, and
3. Noting the *relationship* between strength and stress to determine safety factor, estimated life, etc.

The *strength* of the member should be represented by a conventional constant-life-fatigue strength diagram (σ_m–σ_a curve) for *bending* loads. The diagram should be appropriate to the material, size, surface, temperature, reliability, and fatigue life involved.

The *stress* should be represented by (1) an equivalent alternating bending stress determined from the totality of applied alternating loads using the distortion energy theory, and (2) an equivalent mean bending stress to be taken as the highest algebraic principal stress caused by the mean-load components acting alone.

The factor K_f should be applied as a stress concentration factor with each component of the alternating stress and each component of the mean stress multiplied by its own appropriate value of K_f.

The *relationship* between strength and stress for *combined alternating plus mean loading*, for predicting fatigue failure of ductile materials is implemented by utilizing an experimentally verified empirical approach that relates the *strength*, represented by the constant life fatigue diagram (Goodman line), with the *stress* state, determined by calculating separately the equivalent alternating stress and the equivalent mean stress components.

8.17.3 Overview of Fracture Mechanics Procedure

The reader should recall that in elementary form an application of fracture mechanics theory involves three principal steps:

1. Representing the fracture toughness (*strength*) of the part or material,
2. Representing the stress intensity (*stresses*) involved, and
3. Noting the *relationship* between fracture toughness and stress intensity to determine safety factor, estimated remaining life, crack growth rate, etc.

The fracture toughness should be appropriate to the material, size, surface, temperature, reliability, and life involved. The stress intensity factor should be appropriate for the part load and geometry. Recall that for crack growth in Mode I, the safety factor for failure by rapid fatigue crack growth (fracture) will be $SF = K_{Ic}/K_I$. With known geometry and material properties, the cycle life for fatigue crack growth can be calculated from Eq. 8.6.

The operational life of a part is often limited by the initiation and subsequent growth of cracks. Since an existing crack can suddenly open under certain circumstances and/or conditions at stress levels lower than the yield strength, fracture mechanics should be used for predicting failure when known cracks will be present or are present due to sudden crack propagation. If a crack is of sufficient size, then the part can fail at much lower stresses than those causing yielding in the part.

Fracture mechanics should be used in designing parts and components to predict sudden failure caused by crack propagation. As previously discussed, to predict sudden failure, the stress intensity for the part can be calculated and compared to the fracture toughness for the material. That is, the stress intensity factor, $K_I = Y\sigma\sqrt{\pi c}$, is compared to the fracture toughness, K_{Ic}, of the material to determine if there is a danger of crack propagation failure.

Fracture mechanics should also be used to estimate the current safety factor for the part if macroscopic cracks are present or actual cracks are discovered. Regular field inspections should be conducted to detect cracks as they occur, especially if previous experience indicates that cracking is a problem.

Retirement of critical parts before a crack reaches a critical length is essential.

An important part of a failure prevention program is a refined nondestructive evaluation technique to detect small flaws. Obviously, the limitations of crack size detection possible during inspection must be appreciated. No amount of inspection of a part will prevent failure if a crack in the part remains undetected by the process being used. A fail-safe approach acknowledges that cracks exist in components but requires that the part will not fail prior to the time that the defect is discovered and repaired or replaced.

A crack of critical size discovered in a critically important component means that inspection took place just in time and that the component should be replaced or repaired immediately. If no defect of significant dimensions is found, the part is returned to service with a fracture mechanics calculation used to determine the next inspection interval. A fail-safe approach requires periodic inspection of critical components. Sufficient flaw detection resolution is required.

8.17.4   Brief Comparison of Fatigue Analysis with Fracture Mechanics Methods

A fatigue analysis for a component is conducted to avoid a part failure. For completely reversed stresses, the analysis typically considers notch sensitivity, stress concentration and uses a *S–N* diagram to design for finite or infinite cycle life. Fatigue analysis can calculate safety factor, cycle life, stress, part geometry, and required strength.

Fracture mechanics theory also is used to avoid part failure by understanding the crack growth process. A fracture mechanics analysis includes factors that affect crack growth so that crack length can be measured and mathematically related to the remaining life. Also, the critical crack length where rapid advance of the fatigue crack takes place can be determined. Fracture mechanics can predict part safety, remaining part life, crack growth rate, and critical crack size.

At the present level of development, fracture mechanics analysis is less precise than conventional stress-strength-safety analysis. Fracture mechanics constants are typically less available for part material and mode of loading than are constants used in traditional fatigue analysis. Consequentially, the predictions of (1) crack growth rate, (2) component fatigue life that remains, and (3) degree of safety, cannot therefore be viewed with quite the same confidence provided by conventional fatigue analysis safety factors.

8.17.5 General Fatigue Analysis Procedure

The general fatigue analysis procedure presented in this chapter provides the solution to a large variety of real world fatigue problems. Consistent with the sample problems presented in this chapter, the three principal steps useful in a general approach dealing with mean and alternating stresses for high cycle fatigue design for uniaxial or biaxial load/stress fluctuation are:

1. Construct a constant life fatigue diagram (Goodman line) for the desired cycle life and for the correct fatigue strength (see Figure 8.16).

2a. Calculate the mean and alternating stress components at the critical point(s), applying the appropriate stress concentration factors to the corresponding stress components. The stress concentration factors for the different loading (e.g., axial versus bending) can be applied to the appropriate stress component prior to incorporating them into the distortion energy stress calculation.

2b. Calculate the equivalent alternating bending stress and the equivalent mean bending stress from Eqs. (a) and (b) in Figure 8.16. The distortion energy theory is used to transform biaxial alternating stresses into an equivalent (pseudo-uniaxial) alternating tensile stress. The Mohr circle is used to calculate the equivalent mean bending stress, i.e., the maximum principal stress from the superposition of all existing static (mean) stresses.

3. Plot the equivalent alternating and equivalent mean bending (tensile) stresses on the constant life fatigue diagram to establish the operating point and then calculate the safety factor (e.g., see Sample Problem 8.4).

For brittle materials, the authors of this book recommend the same procedure except that the equivalent alternating stress is not estimated from the distortion energy theory but from the appropriate σ_1–σ_2 diagram for alternating (completely reversed) fatigue strength where the reversed torsional strength, unless known, is 80% of the reversed bending fatigue strength.

For critical mean and alternating pure shear stresses (torsional stress with no bending or axial stresses) in a component, the authors of this book recommend the approach discussed in Sample Problem 8.3.

For those cases involving multiaxial fatigue with multidimensional mean and alternating stresses with proportional and nonproportional loading under complex stress states with elastic and plastic deformation there exists no universal and accepted procedure. Experimental work and/or research is required.

8.17.6 Safety Factors for Fatigue Failure

Figure 8.36 pictures the tension side and the compression side of the constant life fatigue diagram and illustrates how the diagram is used to determine safety factors. Point N, the operating point, identifies the combination of equivalent mean and equivalent alternating stresses representing the critical point in a part subjected to combined stresses. For the stress state represented by point N the safety factor depends on how the stress state (defined by the equivalent mean and alternating stress components) changes as the loading would increase to cause failure in service.

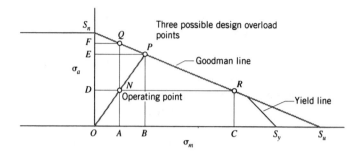

FIGURE 8.36
Three interpretations of safety factor involving mean and alternating stresses.

Figure 8.36 pictures three interpretations that can be applied to the term safety factor in the case of combined mean and alternating stresses. Three possible design *overload* points are shown. The operating-load point corresponds to the combination of mean and alternating stresses caused by the operating loads.

1. If alternating and mean stresses increase by the same percentage during overload, point *P* would be the design-overload point, and the safety factor would be given by

$$SF = OP/ON = OE/OD = OB/OA$$

2. If only the alternating component of stress increases during overload, point *Q* would be the design-overload point, and the safety factor would be

$$SF = OF/OD$$

3. If only the mean component of stress increases during overload, point *R* would be the design-overload point, and the safety factor would be

$$SF = OC/OA$$

Without knowledge regarding the nature of overloading, interpretation 1 would normally be applied. In Figure 8.36, interpretation 1 gives a safety factor of $SF = OP/ON \approx 2.0$. This could also be interpreted to mean that if all the material strengths (S_n, S_y, and S_u) were divided by 2.0 (and the operating loads left unchanged), operation would be on the Goodman line.

The equations for *SF* give the safety factor for infinite fatigue life since the corrected endurance limit, S_n, is inherent in the equations for *SF*. For finite life, the corrected fatigue strength, S_f, at a finite number of cycles should replace S_n in Figure 8.36. The safety factors can be estimated from the constant life fatigue diagram drawn to scale or analytical equations for *SF* may be written.

A graphical or analytical approach to calculate the safety factor can also be used for cases where the equivalent mean stress is compressive (i.e., for the left half of the constant life fatigue diagram) where a load line σ_a/σ_m would have a negative slope.

References

1. American Society for Testing and Materials, *Achievement of High Fatigue Resistance in Metals and Alloys* (Symposium), American Society for Testing Materials, Philadelphia, 1970.

2. Boyer, H. E. (ed.), *Metals Handbook No. 10: Failure Analysis and Prevention*, 8th ed., American Society for Metals, Metals Park, Ohio, 1975.

3. Fuchs, H. O., and R. I. Stephens, *Metal Fatigue in Engineering*, 2nd ed., Wiley, New York, 2000.

4. Rice, R. C. (ed.), *Fatigue Design Handbook*, 3rd ed., Society of Automotive Engineers, Inc., New York, 1997.

5. Horger, O. J. (ed.), *ASME Handbook: Metals Engineering—Design*, 2nd ed., McGraw-Hill, New York, 1965.

6. Juvinall, R. C., *Engineering Considerations of Stress, Strain, and Strength*, McGraw-Hill, New York, 1967.

7. Lipson, C., and R. C. Juvinall, *Handbook of Stress and Strength*, Macmillan, New York, 1963.

8. Madayag, A. F. *Metal Fatigue: Theory and Design*, Wiley, New York, 1969.

9. Sines, G., and J. L. Waisman (eds.), *Metal Fatigue*, McGraw-Hill, New York, 1959.

10. Anderson, T. L., *Fracture Mechanics: Fundamentals and Applications*, 2nd ed., CRC Press, Boca Raton, 1995.

11. Miannay, D. P., *Fracture Mechanics*, Springer-Verlag, New York, 1998.

12. Frost, N.E., K.J. Marsh, and L. P. Pook, *Metal Fatigue*, Dover, New York, 2000.

Problems

Section 8.3

8.1D Select a wrought-titanium alloy from Appendix C-16 having a rotating bending endurance limit for the standard R. R. Moore test specimens above 28 ksi and yield strength above 50 ksi.

8.2D From Appendix C-3a, select a gray cast iron having a rotating bending endurance limit for the standard R. R. Moore test specimens between 95 and 110 MPa.

8.3D Select a steel from Appendix C-4a having a rotating bending endurance limit for the standard R. R. Moore test specimens above 72 ksi.

8.4D Select a steel having a 10^3-cycle fatigue strength for rotating bending for R. R. Moore test specimens above 130 ksi.

8.5 Estimate the rotating bending endurance limit and also the 10^3-cycle fatigue strength for standard R. R. Moore test specimens made of steels having Brinell hardnesses of 100, 300, and 500.

8.6 Estimate the long-life fatigue strength for rotating bending (state whether it is for 10^8 or 5×10^8 cycles) of standard R. R. Moore specimens made of (a) wrought aluminum, $S_u = 250$ MPa, (b) wrought aluminum, $S_u = 450$ MPa, (c) average-grade cast aluminum, and (d) average-grade forged magnesium.

8.7 Three R. R. Moore test specimens are made of steels having ultimate tensile strengths of 95, 185, and 240 ksi. Estimate the 10^3-cycle fatigue strength for rotating bending and also the bending endurance limit for each steel.

8.8 Standard R. R. Moore specimens are made of (a) wrought aluminum, $S_u = 29$ ksi, (b) wrought aluminum, $S_u = 73$ ksi, (c) high-grade cast aluminum, and (d) high-grade forged magnesium. Estimate the long-life fatigue strength for rotating bending (state whether it is for 10^8 or 5×10^8 cycles) of each material.

8.9 Estimate the rotating bending endurance limit and also the 10^3-cycle fatigue strength for standard R. R. Moore steel test specimens having hardnesses of 200, 350, and 500.

8.10   Estimate the 10^3-cycle fatigue strength for rotating bending and also the bending endurance limit for R. R. Moore test specimens made of 1040, 4140, and 9255 steels having ultimate tensile strengths of 100, 160, and 280 ksi, respectively.

Section 8.4

8.11   How would the answers to Problems 8.5 and 8.6 change if the loading is reversed bending rather than rotating bending?

8.12   How would the answers to Problems 8.5 and 8.6 change if the loading is reversed axial loading rather than rotating bending?

8.13   How would the answers to Problems 8.7 and 8.8 change if the loading is reversed bending rather than rotating bending?

8.14   How would the answers to Problems 8.7 and 8.8 change if the loading is reversed axial loading rather than rotating bending?

Section 8.5

8.15   Repeat Problem 8.5 for reversed torsional loading.

8.16   Repeat Problem 8.6 for reversed torsional loading.

8.17   Repeat Problem 8.7 for reversed torsional loading.

8.18   Repeat Problem 8.8 for reversed torsional loading.

Sections 8.7 and 8.8

8.19   Estimate the 2×10^5 fatigue strength for a 25-mm-diameter reversed axially loaded steel bar having $S_u = 950$ MPa, $S_y = 600$ MPa, and a hot-rolled surface.

8.20   Consider a 3.5-in.-diameter steel bar having $S_u = 97$ ksi and $S_y = 68$ ksi and machined surfaces. Estimate the fatigue strength for (1) 10^6 or more cycles and (2) 5×10^4 cycles for (a) bending, (b) axial, and (c) torsional loading.

8.21   A 10-mm-diameter steel bar having $S_u = 1200$ MPa and $S_y = 950$ MPa has a fine-ground surface. Estimate the bending fatigue strength for (1) 10^6 or more cycles and (2) 2×10^5 cycles.

8.22   Estimate the bending fatigue strength for 2×10^5 cycles for a 0.5-in.-diameter steel shaft having a Brinell hardness of 375 and machined surfaces.

8.23   Plot on log-log coordinates estimated *S–N* curves for (a) bending, (b) axial, and (c) torsional loading of a 1-in.-diameter steel bar having $S_u = 110$ ksi, $S_y = 77$ ksi, and machined surfaces. For each of the three types of loading, what is the fatigue strength corresponding to (1) 10^6 or more cycles, and (2) 6×10^4 cycles?
             [Partial ans.: For bending 36.6 ksi, 55 ksi]

8.24   Repeat Problem 8.23 for a 20-mm-diameter steel bar having $S_u = 1100$ MPa, and $S_y = 715$ MPa, for (a) fine ground and (b) machined surfaces.

Section 8.9

8.25   Repeat the determination of the six fatigue strengths in Problem 8.23 for the case of zero-to-maximum (rather than completely reversed) load fluctuation.
             [Partial ans.: For bending, 0 to 56 ksi, 0 to 74 ksi]

8.26   Repeat the determination of the six fatigue strengths in Problem 8.24 for the case of zero-to-maximum (rather than completely reversed) load fluctuation.

Section 8.10

8.27   When in use, the shaft shown in Figure P8.27 experiences completely reversed torsion. It is machined from steel having a hardness of 150 Bhn. With a safety factor of 2, estimate the value of reversed torque that can be applied without causing eventual fatigue failure.

[Ans.: 55.8 N · m]

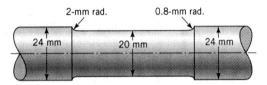

FIGURE P8.27

8.28   Figure P8.28 shows (1) an unnotched bar and (2) a notched bar of the same minimum cross section. Both bars were machined from AISI 1050 normalized steel. For each bar, estimate (a) the value of static tensile load *P* causing fracture and (b) the value of alternating axial load ±*P* that would be just on the verge of producing eventual fatigue fracture (after perhaps 1 to 5 million cycles).

[Ans.: (a) 670 kN for both, (b) 199 kN, 87 kN]

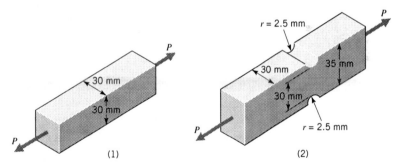

FIGURE P8.28

8.29   A stepped shaft, as illustrated in Figure 4.38, has dimensions of $D = 2$ in., $d = 1$ in., and $r = 0.05$ in. It was machined from steel having tensile properties of $S_u = 90$ ksi and $S_y = 75$ ksi.

(a) Estimate the torque *T* required to produce static yielding. (Note: For static loading of a ductile material, assume that the very first yielding at the notch root is not significant; hence, ignore stress concentration.)

(b) Estimate the value of reversed torque, ±*T*, required to produce eventual fatigue failure.

[Ans.: 8540 lb · in.; 2280 lb · in.]

8.30   The shaft illustrated in Figure P8.30 rotates at high speed while the imposed loads remain static. The shaft is machined from AISI 1040 steel, oil-quenched and tempered at 1000°F. If the loading is sufficiently great to produce a fatigue failure (after perhaps 10^6 cycles), where would the failure most likely occur? (Show all necessary computations and reasoning, but do not do unnecessary computations.)

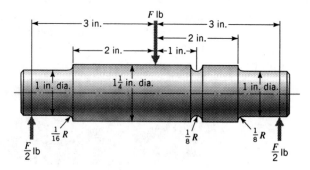

FIGURE P8.30

Section 8.11

8.31D   Design a steel shaft that will transmit a reversed torque of 18.62 N · m for infinite fatigue life.

8.32   A grooved shaft like the one shown in Figure 4.39 is machined from steel of 180 Bhn and $S_y = 65$ ksi. Dimensions are $D = 1.1$ in., $d = 1.0$ in., and $r = 0.05$ in. A commercial polish is given only to the surface of the groove. With a safety factor of 2, estimate the maximum value of torque T that can be applied for infinite life when the fluctuating torsional load consists of (a) completely reversed torsion, with the torque varying between $+T$ and $-T$, (b) a steady torque of T with superimposed alternating torque of $2T$.

[Ans.: 1320 lb · in., 590 lb · in.]

8.33   Figure P8.33 shows a cantilever beam serving as a spring for a latching mechanism. When assembled, the free end is deflected 0.075 in., which corresponds to a force F of 8.65 lb. When the latch operates, the end deflects an additional 0.15 in. Would you expect eventual fatigue failure?

[Ans.: It is marginal.]

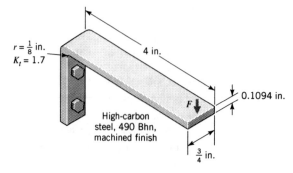

FIGURE P8.33

8.34 Estimate the maximum completely reversed bending moment that can be applied to the ends of the plate shown in Figure 4.40 if the plate is machined from AISI 4320 steel having $S_u = 140$ ksi and $S_y = 90$ ksi. The rectangular plate is 0.5 in. thick, 3 in. wide, and has a central hole 0.5 in. in diameter. An infinite life with 90% reliability and a safety factor of 2 are required.

8.35 A cold-drawn steel shaft of 155 Bhn is 12 in. long, 1.25 in. in diameter, and has a 0.25-in.-diameter transverse hole (as in Figure 4.37). Surfaces have a machined finish. Estimate the safety factor with respect to infinite fatigue life for (a) a torque fluctuation between 0 and 60 lb·ft, (b) a completely reversed torque of 30 lb·ft, and (c) a mean torque of 35 lb·ft plus a superimposed alternating torque of 25 lb·ft.

8.36 A cold-drawn rectangular steel bar of 140 Bhn is 10 mm thick, 60 mm wide, and has a central hole 12 mm in diameter (as in Figure 4.40). Estimate the maximum tensile force that can be applied to the ends and have infinite life with 90% reliability and a safety factor of 1.3: (a) if the force is completely reversed and (b) if the force varies between zero and a maximum value.

[Ans.: 22 kN, 34 kN]

8.37 A 20-mm-diameter shaft with a 6-mm-diameter transverse hole is made of cold-drawn steel having $S_u = 550$ MPa and $S_y = 462$ MPa. Surfaces in the vicinity of the hole have a machined finish. Estimate the safety factor with respect to infinite fatigue life for (a) torque fluctuations between 0 and 100 N·m, (b) a completely reversed torque of 50 N·m, and (c) a mean torque of 60 N·m plus a superimposed alternating torque of 40 N·m.

[Ans.: 1.5, 1.9, 1.7]

8.38 For the shaft and loading involved in Problem 8.37, estimate the safety factors with respect to *static* yielding. (Note: For these calculations stress concentration is usually neglected. Why?)

[Ans.: 3.1, 6.3, 3.1]

8.39 Figure P8.39 shows a $\frac{1}{2}$-in. pitch roller chain plate, as used on a bicycle chain. It is made of carbon steel, heat-treated to give $S_u = 140$ ksi and $S_y = 110$ ksi. All surfaces are comparable to the "machined" category. Since a roller chain cannot transmit compression, the link is loaded in repeated axial tension (load fluctuates between 0 and a maximum force as the link goes from the slack side to the tight side of the chain) by pins that go through the two holes. Estimate the maximum tensile force that would give infinite fatigue life with a safety factor of 1.2.

[Ans.: 229 lb]

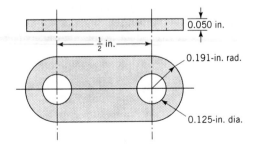

FIGURE P8.39

8.40   Figure P8.40 shows a shaft and the fluctuating nominal stress (in the center of the 50-mm section) to which it is subjected. The shaft is made of steel having $S_u = 600$ MPa and $S_y = 400$ MPa. Estimate the safety factor with respect to eventual fatigue failure if (a) the stresses are bending, (b) the stresses are torsional.

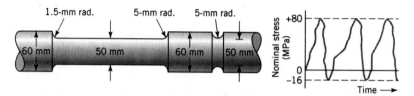

FIGURE P8.40

8.41   Figure P8.41 shows a round shaft and a torque fluctuation to which it is subjected. The material is steel, with $S_u = 162$ ksi and $S_y = 138$ ksi. All critical surfaces are ground. Estimate the safety factor for infinite fatigue life with respect to (a) an overload that increases both mean and alternating torque by the same factor, and (b) an overload that increases only the alternating torque.

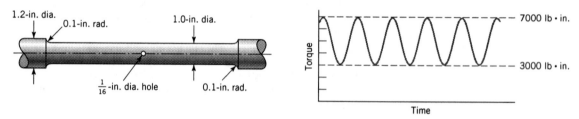

FIGURE P8.41

8.42   A stepped shaft, as shown in Figure 4.35, has dimensions of $D = 10$ mm, $d = 8$ mm, and $r = 0.8$ mm. It is made of steel having $S_u = 1200$ MPa and is finished with a grinding operation. In service, it is loaded with a fluctuating zero-to-maximum torque. Estimate the magnitude of maximum torque that would provide a safety factor of 1.3 with respect to a 75,000-cycle fatigue life.

8.43   The critical portion of a machine part is shaped like the bar in Figure 4.38 with $H = 35$ mm, $h = 25$ mm, $b = 20$ mm, and $r = 2$ mm. The material is steel, of 160 Bhn hardness. All surfaces are machined. The part is loaded in zero-to-maximum cyclic bending. Estimate the value of the maximum bending moment that would give infinite fatigue life with 99 percent reliability (and a safety factor of 1). [Ans.: 300 N · m]

8.44   A solid round shaft has a shoulder (as in Figure 4.35) with $D = 1$ in., $d = 0.5$ in., and r to be determined. The shaft is made of steel, with $S_u = 150$ ksi and $S_y = 120$ ksi. All surfaces are machined. In service the shaft is subjected to a torsional load that fluctuates between 82 and 123 lb · ft. Estimate the smallest fillet radius that would permit infinite life (with safety factor = 1). [Ans.: About 0.040 in.]

8.45 A steel shaft used in a spur gear reducer is subjected to a constant torque together with lateral forces that tend always to bend it downward in the center. These result in calculated stresses of 80 MPa torsion and 60 MPa bending. However, these are nominal values and do not take into account stress concentration caused by a shoulder (as in Figure 4.35), where dimensions are $D = 36$ mm, $d = 30$ mm, and $r = 3$ mm. All surfaces are machined, and the steel has strength values of $S_u = 700$ MPa and $S_y = 550$ MPa. Hardness is 200 Bhn. Estimate the safety factor with respect to infinite fatigue life.

[Ans.: 1.9]

8.46 Figure P8.46 shows a portion of a pump that is gear-driven at uniform load and speed. The shaft is supported by bearings mounted in the pump housing. The shaft is made of steel having $S_u = 1000$ MPa, $S_y = 800$ MPa. The tangential, axial, and radial components of force applied to the gear are shown. The surface of the shaft fillet has been shot-peened, which is estimated to be equivalent to a laboratory mirror-polished surface. Fatigue stress concentration factors for the fillet have been determined and are shown on the drawing. Estimate the safety factor with respect to eventual fatigue failure at the fillet.

[Ans.: 1.9]

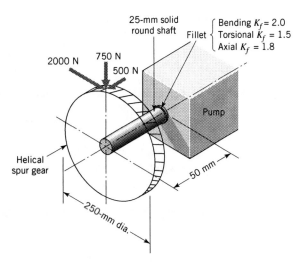

FIGURE P8.46

8.47 Drawing 1 of Figure P8.47 shows a countershaft with helical gear (*B*), bevel gear (*D*), and two supporting bearings (*A* and *C*). Loads acting on the bevel gear are shown. Forces on the helical gear can be determined from equilibrium of moments about the shaft axis plus the given proportions of the helical gear force components. Shaft dimensions are given in drawing 2. All shoulder fillets (at points where diameter changes) have a radius of 5 mm. Note that the shaft is designed so that only bearing *A* takes thrust. The shaft is made of hardened steel, $S_u = 1069$ MPa, $S_y = 896$ MPa. All important surfaces are finished by grinding.

(a) Draw load, shear force, and bending moment diagrams for the shaft in the *xy* and *xz* planes. Also draw diagrams showing the intensity of the axial force and torque along the length of the shaft.

(b) At points *B*, *C*, and *E* of the shaft, calculate the equivalent stresses in preparation for determining the fatigue safety factor. (Note: Refer to Figure 8.16.)

(c) For a reliability of 99% (and assuming a standard deviation of $\sigma = 0.08S_n$), estimate the safety factor of the shaft at points *B*, *C*, and *E*.

[Ans.: (c) 5.0, 6.8, and 5.8, respectively]

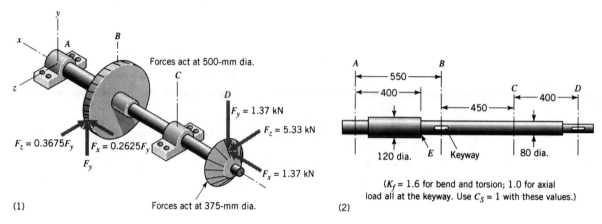

(1)

Forces act at 500-mm dia.

$F_y = 1.37$ kN

$F_z = 5.33$ kN

$F_x = 1.37$ kN

$F_z = 0.3675F_y$ $F_x = 0.2625F_y$

F_y

Forces act at 375-mm dia.

(2)

120 dia.   *E*   Keyway   80 dia.

($K_f = 1.6$ for bend and torsion; 1.0 for axial load all at the keyway. Use $C_S = 1$ with these values.)

FIGURE P8.47

Section 8.12

8.48   A stepped shaft, as shown in Figure 4.35, has dimensions of *D* = 2 in., *d* = 1 in., and *r* = 0.1 in. It was machined from AISI steel of 200 Bhn hardness. The loading is one of completely reversed torsion. During a typical 30 seconds of operation under overload conditions the nominal (*Tc/J*) stress in the 1-in.-diameter section was measured to be as shown in Figure P8.48. Estimate the life of the shaft when operating continuously under these conditions.

[Ans.: Roughly 43 hours]

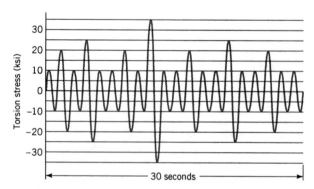

FIGURE P8.48

Section 8.16

8.49   A 1.0-in-diameter aluminum bar is subjected to reversed axial loading of 5000 N at 50 cycles per second. A circumferential crack, 0.004 in. deep, extends radially inward from the outside surface. The axial load is applied remote from the crack. Estimate the crack depth after 100 hours of operation, assuming a Paris exponent of 2.7 and a stress intensity range of 1.5 ksi $\sqrt{\text{in.}}$, corresponding to a growth rate of 0.040 in./10^6 cycles. The configuration factor, Y, may be approximated by $Y = [1.12 + \alpha(1.30\alpha - 0.88)]/(1 - 0.92\alpha)$, where $\alpha = c/w$ and w is the radius of the round bar. The stress intensity factor, $K_1 = \sigma Y \sqrt{\pi c}$, where σ is the uniaxial tensile stress for the gross cross section (see Figure P8.49).

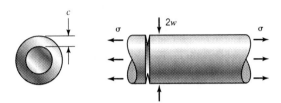

FIGURE P8.49

8.50 A 2.0-in.-diameter aluminum shaft rotates at 3000 rpm and is subjected to a reversed bending moment of 1775 in. lb. A crack, 0.004 in. deep, extends radially inward from the external surface. The reversed bending moment is applied remote from the crack. Estimate the crack depth after 100 hours of operation, assuming a Paris exponent of 2.7 and a stress intensity range of 1.5 ksi $\sqrt{\text{in.}}$, corresponding to a growth rate of 0.040 in./10^6 cycles. The configuration factor Y may be approximated by $Y = [1.12 + \alpha(2.62\alpha - 1.59)]/(1 - 0.70\alpha)$, where $\alpha = c/w$ and w is the radius of the round bar. The stress intensity factor, K_I, is equal to $\sigma Y \sqrt{\pi c}$, where σ is the maximum bending stress for the gross cross section (see Figure P8.50).

FIGURE P8.50

8.51 A component part is axially stressed and made of material that follows the Paris equation with an index $n = 4$ and a crack growth rate of 0.04 in./10^6 corresponding to a stress intensity range of 5.5 ksi $\sqrt{\text{in.}}$. The width of the component is 0.75 in. The configuration factor may be approximated by $Y = 0.85/(1 - \alpha)$, where $\alpha = c/w$. Determine the number of cycles required for a 0.20-in. crack to grow to 0.60 in., if the component is subjected to a cyclically varying uniaxial tensile stress of 0 psi to 6000 psi.

8.52 Repeat Problem 8.51, except the 0.20-in. crack grows to the critical crack length corresponding to $K_{Ic} = 55$ ksi $\sqrt{\text{in.}}$

8.53 Repeat Problem 8.51, except the component is subjected to a cyclically varying uniaxial tensile stress of 15,000 psi to 18,000 psi.

8.54 Derive Eq. 8.6 from Eq. 8.5.

Units

Appendix A-1a *Conversion Factors for British Gravitational, English, and SI Units*

Quantity	British Gravitational and English Units[a]	SI Unit[a]	Conversion Factor Equalities
Length	inch (in. or ″)	meter (m)	*1 in. = 0.0254 m = 25.4 mm
	foot (ft or ′)	meter (m)	*1 ft = 0.3048 m = 304.8 mm
	mile (mi U.S. statute)	kilometer (km)	1 mile = 1.609 km = 1609 m
Volume	gallon (gal U.S.)	meter^3 (m^3)	1 gal = 0.003785 m^3 = 3.785 liters
Force (weight)	pound (lb)	newton[d] (N)	1 lb = 4.448 N
Torque	pound-foot (lb · ft)	newton-meter (N · m)	1 lb · ft = 1.356 N · m
Work, Energy	foot-pound (ft · lb)	joule[c] (J)	1 ft · lb = 1.356 J
Power	foot-pound/second (ft · lb/s)	watt[g] (W)	1 ft · lb/s = 1.356 W
	horsepower[b] (hp)	kilowatt (kW)	1 hp = 0.746 kW
Stress, Pressure	pounds/in.^{2} (psi)	pascal[e] (Pa)	1 psi = 6895 Pa
	thousand pounds/in.^{2} (ksi)	megapascal (MPa)	1 ksi = 6.895 MPa
Mass (British)	slug[f]	kilogram (kg)	1 slug = 14.59 kg
Mass (English)	lbm[h]	kilogram (kg)	1 lbm = 0.454 kg = 454 grams

[a] The *larger* unit is underlined.
[b] 1 hp = 550 ft · lb/s; [c] 1 J = 1 N · m; [d] 1 N = 1 kg · m/s^2; [e] 1 Pa = 1 N/m^2; [f] 1 slug = 1 lb · s^2/ft; [g] 1 W = 1 J/s; [h] 1 slug = 32.2 lbm
* An exact definition.

Appendix A-1b *Conversion Factor Equalities Listed by Physical Quantity*

ACCELERATION
*1 foot/second^2 = 3.048 × 10^{-1} meter/second^2
*1 free fall, standard = 9.806 65 meters/second^2
*1 inch/second^2 = 2.54 × 10^{-2} meter/second^2

AREA
*1 acre = 4.046 856 422 4 × 10^3 meters^2
*1 foot^2 = 9.290 304 × 10^{-2} meter^2
*1 hectare = 1.00 × 10^4 meters^2
*1 inch^2 = 6.4516 × 10^{-4} meter^2
*1 mile^2 (U.S. statute) = 2.589 988 110 336 × 10^6 meters^2
*1 yard^2 = 8.361 273 6 × 10^{-1} meter^2

DENSITY
*1 gram/centimeter^3 = 1.00 × 10^3 kilograms/meter^3
 1 lbm/inch^3 = 2.767 9905 × 10^4 kilograms/meter^3
 1 lbm/foot^3 = 1.601 846 3 × 10^1 kilograms/meter^3
 1 slug/foot^3 = 5.153 79 × 10^2 kilograms/meter^3

ENERGY
 1 British thermal unit (mean) = 1.055 87 × 10^3 joules
*1 erg = 1.00 × 10^{-7} joule
 1 foot-lb = 1.355 817 9 joules
*1 kilowatt-hour = 3.60 × 10^6 joules
 1 ton (nuclear equivalent of TNT) = 4.20 × 10^9 joules
*1 watt-hour = 3.60 × 10^3 joules

FORCE
*1 dyne = 1.00 × 10^{-5} newton
*1 kilogram force (kgf) = 9.806 65 newtons
*1 kilopound force = 9.806 65 newtons
*1 kip = 4.448 221 615 260 5 × 10^3 newtons
*1 lb (pound force, avoirdupois) = 4.448 221 615 260 5 newtons
 1 ounce force (avoirdupois) = 2.780 138 5 × 10^{-1} newton
*1 pound force, lb (avoirdupois) = 4.448 221 615 260 5 newtons
*1 poundal = 1.382 549 543 76 × 10^{-1} newton

LENGTH
*1 angstrom = 1.00 × 10^{-10} meter
*1 cubit = 4.572 × 10^{-1} meter
*1 fathom = 1.8288 meters
*1 foot = 3.048 × 10^{-1} meter
*1 inch = 2.54 × 10^{-2} meter
*1 league (international nautical) = 5.556 × 10^3 meters
 1 light-year = 9.460 55 × 10^{15} meters
*1 meter = 1.650 763 73 × 10^6 wavelengths Kr 86
*1 micron = 1.00 × 10^{-6} meter
*1 mil = 2.54 × 10^{-5} meter
*1 mile (U.S. statute) = 1.609 344 × 10^3 meters
*1 nautical mile (U.S.) = 1.852 × 10^3 meters
*1 yard = 9.144 × 10^{-1} meter

MASS
*1 carat (metric) = 2.00 × 10^{-4} kilogram
*1 grain = 6.479 891 × 10^{-5} kilogram
*1 lbm (pound mass, avoirdupois) = 4.535 923 7 × 10^{-1} kilogram
*1 ounce mass (avoirdupois) = 2.834 952 312 5 × 10^{-2} kilogram
 1 slug = 1.459 390 29 × 10^1 kilograms
*1 ton (long) = 1.016 046 908 8 × 10^3 kilograms
*1 ton (metric) = 1.00 × 10^3 kilograms
 1 ton (short, 2000 pounds mass) = 9.071 847 4 × 10^2 kilograms

Appendix A-1b *(continued)*

POWER
Btu (thermochemical)/second = 1.054 350 264 488 × 10^3 watts
*1 calorie (thermochemical)/second = 4.184 watts
1 foot-lb/minute = 2.259 696 6 × 10^{-2} watt
1 foot-lb/second = 1.355 817 9 watts
1 horsepower (550 foot-lb/second) = 7.456 998 7 × 10^2 watts
*1 horsepower (electric) = 7.46 × 10^2 watts

PRESSURE
*1 atmosphere = 1.013 25 × 10^5 newtons/meter^2
*1 bar = 1.00 × 10^5 newtons/meter^2
1 centimeter of mercury (0°C) = 1.333 22 × 10^3 newtons/meter^2
1 centimeter of water (4°C) = 9.806 38 × 10^1 newtons/meter^2
*1 dyne/centimeter^2 = 1.00 × 10^{-1} newton/meter^2
1 inch of mercury (60°F) = 3.376 85 × 10^3 newtons/meter^2
1 inch of water (60°F) = 2.4884 × 10^2 newtons/meter^2
*1 kgf/meter^2 = 9.806 65 newtons/meter^2
1 lb/foot^2 = 4.788 025 8 × 10^1 newtons/meter^2
1 lb/inch^2 (psi) = 6.894 757 2 × 10^3 newtons/meter^2
*1 millibar = 1.00 × 10^2 newtons/meter^2
1 millimeter of mercury (0°C) = 1.333 224 × 10^2 newtons/meter^2
*1 pascal = 1.00 newtons/meter^2
1 psi (lb/inch^2) = 6.894 757 2 × 10^3 newtons/meter^2
1 torr (0°C) = 1.333 22 × 10^2 newtons/meter^2

SPEED
*1 foot/minute = 5.08 × 10^{-3} meter/second
*1 foot/second = 3.048 × 10^{-1} meter/second
*1 inch/second = 2.54 × 10^{-2} meter/second
1 kilometer/hour = 2.777 777 8 × 10^{-1} meter/second
1 knot (international) = 5.144 444 444 × 10^{-1} meter/second
*1 mile/hour (U.S. statute) = 4.4704 × 10^{-1} meter/second

TEMPERATURE
Celsius = kelvin − 273.15
Fahrenheit = $\frac{9}{5}$ kelvin − 459.67
Fahrenheit = $\frac{9}{5}$ Celsius + 32
Rankine = $\frac{9}{5}$ kelvin

TIME
*1 day (mean solar) = 8.64 × 10^4 seconds (mean solar)
*1 hour (mean solar) = 3.60 × 10^3 seconds (mean solar)
*1 minute (mean solar) = 6.00 × 10^1 seconds (mean solar)
*1 month (mean calendar) = 2.628 × 10^6 seconds (mean solar)
*1 year (calendar) = 3.1536 × 10^7 seconds (mean solar)

VISCOSITY
*1 centistoke = 1.00 × 10^{-6} meter^2/second
*1 stoke = 1.00 × 10^{-4} meter^2/second
*1 foot^2/second = 9.290 304 × 10^{-2} meter^2/second
*1 centipoise = 1.00 × 10^{-3} newton-second/meter^2
1 lbm/foot-second = 1.488 163 9 newton-second/meter^2
1 lb-second/foot^2 = 4.788 025 8 × 10^1 newton-seconds/meter^2
*1 poise = 1.00 × 10^{-1} newton-second/meter^2
1 slug/foot-second = 4.788 025 8 × 10^1 newton-seconds/meter^2

VOLUME
1 barrel (petroleum, 42 gallons) = 1.589 873 × 10^{-1} meter^3
*1 board foot (1 ft × 1 ft × 1 in.) = 2.359 737 216 × 10^{-3} meter^3
*1 bushel (U.S.) = 3.523 907 016 688 × 10^{-2} meter^3
1 cord = 3.624 556 3 meters^3
*1 cup = 2.365 882 365 × 10^{-4} meter^3

Appendix A-1b *(continued)*

*1 fluid ounce (U.S.) = $2.957\,352\,956\,25 \times 10^{-5}$ meter^3
*1 foot^3 = $2.831\,684\,659\,2 \times 10^{-2}$ meter^3
*1 gallon (U.S. dry) = $4.404\,883\,770\,86 \times 10^{-3}$ meter^3
*1 gallon (U.S. liquid) = $3.785\,411\,784 \times 10^{-3}$ meter^3
*1 inch^3 = $1.638\,706\,4 \times 10^{-5}$ meter^3
*1 liter = 1.00×10^{-3} meter^3
*1 ounce (U.S. fluid) = $2.957\,352\,956\,25 \times 10^{-5}$ meter^3
*1 peck (U.S.) = $8.809\,767\,541\,72 \times 10^{-3}$ meter^3
*1 pint (U.S. dry) = $5.506\,104\,713\,575 \times 10^{-4}$ meter^3
*1 pint (U.S. liquid) = $4.731\,764\,73 \times 10^{-4}$ meter^3
*1 quart (U.S. dry) = $1.101\,220\,942\,715 \times 10^{-3}$ meter^3
 1 quart (U.S. liquid) = $9.463\,529\,5 \times 10^{-4}$ meter^3
*1 stere = 1.00 meter^3
*1 tablespoon = $1.478\,676\,478\,125 \times 10^{-5}$ meter^3
*1 teaspoon = $4.928\,921\,593\,75 \times 10^{-6}$ meter^3
*1 ton (register) = $2.831\,684\,659\,2$ meters^3
*1 yard^3 = $7.645\,548\,579\,84 \times 10^{-1}$ meter^3

* An exact definition.
Note: Spaces are sometimes used instead of commas to group numbers. This is to avoid confusion with the practice in some European countries of using commas for decimal points.
Source: E. A. Mechtly, *The International System of Units, Physical Constants and Conversion Factors,* NASA SP-7012, Scientific and Technical Information Office, National Aeronautics and Space Administration, Washington, D.C., 1973.

Appendix A-2a *Standard SI Prefixes*

Category	Name	Symbol	Factor
Recommended, important for this course.	giga	G	$1\,000\,000\,000 = 10^9$
	mega	M	$1\,000\,000 = 10^6$
	kilo	k	$1\,000 = 10^3$
	milli	m	$0.001 = 10^{-3}$
	micro	μ	$0.000\,001 = 10^{-6}$
Not recommended but sometimes encountered.	hecto	h	$100 = 10^2$
	deca	da	$10 = 10^1$
	deci	d	$0.1 = 10^{-1}$
	centi	c	$0.01 = 10^{-2}$
Not encountered in this course.	tera	T	$1\,000\,000\,000\,000 = 10^{12}$
	nano	n	$0.000\,000\,000 = 10^{-9}$
	pico	p	$0.000\,000\,000\,000 = 10^{-12}$
	femto	f	$0.000\,000\,000\,000\,000 = 10^{-15}$
	atto	a	$0.000\,000\,000\,000\,000\,000 = 10^{-18}$

Note: Spaces are sometimes used instead of commas to group numbers. This is to avoid confusion with the practice in some European countries of using commas for decimal points.

Appendix A-2b *SI Units and Symbols*

Quantity	Name	Symbol	Expressed in Other Units
Length[a]	meter	m	
Mass[a]	kilogram	kg	
Time[a]	second	s	
Temperature[a,b]	kelvin	K	
Plane angle[c]	radian	rad	
Acceleration	meter per second squared	m/s^2	
Angular acceleration	radian per second squared	rad/s^2	
Angular velocity	radian per second	rad/s	
Area	square meter	m^2	
Density	kilogram per cubic meter	kg/m^3	
Energy	joule	J	$N \cdot m$
Force	newton	N	$m \cdot kg \cdot s^{-2}$
Frequency	hertz	Hz	s^{-1}
Heat, quantity of	joule	J	$N \cdot m$
Moment of force	newton-meter	$N \cdot m$	
Power	watt	W	J/s
Pressure	pascal	Pa	N/m^2
Specific heat capacity	joule per kilogram kelvin	$J/(kg \cdot K)$	
Speed	meter per second	m/s	
Thermal conductivity	watt per meter kelvin	$W/(m \cdot K)$	
Velocity	meter per second	m/s	
Viscosity, dynamic	pascal-second	$Pa \cdot s$	
Volume	cubic meter	m^3	
Work	joule	J	$N \cdot m$

[a] SI base unit.

[b] Celsius temperature is expressed in degrees Celsius (symbol °C)

[c] Supplementary unit.

Source: Chester H. Page and Paul Vigoureux, eds., *The International System of Units (SI)*, Superintendent of Documents, U.S. Government Printing Office, Washington, D.C. 20402 (Order by SD Catalog No. C13.10 : 330/2), National Bureau of Standards Special Publications 330, 1972, p. 12.

Appendix A-3   *Suggested SI Prefixes for Stress Calculations*

$$\sigma = \frac{P}{A}, \frac{Mc}{I}, \frac{M}{Z}; \; \tau = \frac{P}{A}, \frac{V}{A}, \frac{Tr}{J}, \frac{T}{Z'}, \frac{V}{Ib} \int dA$$

σ, τ	P, V	M, T	A	I, J	c, r, b, y	Z, Z'
Pa	N	$N \cdot m$	m^2	m^4	m	m^3
kPa	kN	$kN \cdot m$	m^2	m^4	m	m^3
MPa	N	$N \cdot mm$	mm^2	mm^4	mm	mm^3
GPa	kN	$N \cdot m$	mm^2	mm^4	mm	mm^3

Appendix A-4   *Suggested SI Prefixes for Linear-Deflection Calculations*

$$\delta = \frac{PL}{AE}^{\text{a}}; \; \delta \propto \frac{PL^3}{EI}^{\text{a}}, \frac{wL^4}{EI}, \frac{ML^2}{EI}^{\text{a}}$$

δ	P	w	M	L	A	E	I
μm	N	N/m	$N \cdot m$	m	m^2	MPa	m^4
μm	N	N/mm	$N \cdot mm$	mm	mm^2	GPa	mm^4
μm	kN	N/m	$kN \cdot m$	m	m^2	GPa	m^4

[a] Illustrated in Table 5.1.

Appendix A-5   *Suggested SI Prefixes for Angular-Deflection Calculations*

$$\theta = \frac{TL}{K'G}^{\text{a}}, \frac{ML}{IE}^{\text{a}}$$

θ	T, M	L	K', I	E, G
rad	$N \cdot m$	m	m^4	Pa
μrad	$N \cdot m$	m	m^4	MPa
mrad	$N \cdot mm$	mm	mm^4	GPa
μrad	$kN \cdot m$	m	m^4	GPa

[a] Illustrated in Table 5.1.

Properties of Sections and Solids

Appendix B-1a *Properties of Sections*

A = area, in.^{2}
I = moment of inertia, in.^{4}
J = polar moment of inertia, in.^{4}

Z = section modulus, in.^{3}
ρ = radius of gyration, in.
$\bar{y}$ = centroidal distance, in.

$A = bh$

$I = \dfrac{bh^3}{12}$

$Z = \dfrac{bh^2}{6}$

$\rho = 0.289h$

$\bar{y} = \dfrac{h}{2}$

Rectangle

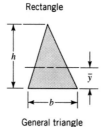

$A = \dfrac{bh}{2}$

$I = \dfrac{bh^3}{36}$

$Z = \dfrac{bh^2}{24}$

$\rho = 0.236h$

$\bar{y} = \dfrac{h}{3}$

General triangle

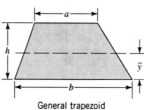

$A = \dfrac{h}{2}(a + b)$

$I = \dfrac{h^3(a^2 + 4ab + b^2)}{36(a + b)}$

$Z = \dfrac{h^2}{12}\dfrac{(a^2 + 4ab + b^2)}{(a + 2b)}$

$\rho = \dfrac{h}{6}\sqrt{2 + \dfrac{4ab}{(a + b)^2}}$

$\bar{y} = \dfrac{h}{3}\dfrac{(2a + b)}{(a + b)}$

General trapezoid

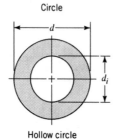

$A = \dfrac{\pi d^2}{4}$

$I = \dfrac{\pi d^4}{64}$

$Z = \dfrac{\pi d^3}{32}$

$J = \dfrac{\pi d^4}{32}$

$\rho = \dfrac{d}{4}$

Circle

$A = \dfrac{\pi}{4}(d^2 - d_i^2)$

$I = \dfrac{\pi}{64}(d^4 - d_i^4)$

$Z = \dfrac{\pi}{32d}(d^4 - d_i^4)$

$J = \dfrac{\pi}{32}(d^4 - d_i^4)$

$\rho = \sqrt{\dfrac{d^2 + d_i^2}{16}}$

Hollow circle

Appendix B-1b *Dimensions and Properties of Steel Pipe and Tubing Sections*

A = area, in.^{2} Z = section modulus, in.^{3}
I = moment of inertia, in.^{4} ρ = radius of gyration, in.

**Standard Weight Pipe
Dimensions and Properties**

Dimensions				Properties				
Nominal Diameter (in.)	Outside Diameter (in.)	Inside Diameter (in.)	Wall Thickness (in.)	Weight per Foot (lb) Plain Ends	A (in.^{2})	I (in.^{4})	Z (in.^{3})	ρ (in.)
$\frac{1}{2}$	.840	.622	.109	.85	.250	.017	.041	.261
$\frac{3}{4}$	1.050	.824	.113	1.13	.333	.037	.071	.334
1	1.315	1.049	.133	1.68	.494	.087	.133	.421
$1\frac{1}{4}$	1.660	1.380	.140	2.27	.669	.195	.235	.540
$1\frac{1}{2}$	1.900	1.610	.145	2.72	.799	.310	.326	.623
2	2.375	2.067	.154	3.65	1.07	.666	.561	.787
$2\frac{1}{2}$	2.875	2.469	.203	5.79	1.70	1.53	1.06	.947
3	3.500	3.068	.216	7.58	2.23	3.02	1.72	1.16
4	4.500	4.026	.237	10.79	3.17	7.23	3.21	1.51
5	5.563	5.047	.258	14.62	4.30	15.2	5.45	1.88

Appendix B-1b *(continued)*

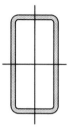

Square and Rectangular Structural Tubing Dimensions and Properties

Dimensions			Properties[b]							
Nominal[a] Size (in.)	Wall Thickness (in.)	Weight per Foot (lb)	A (in.²)	I_x (in.⁴)	Z_x (in.³)	ρ_x (in.)	I_y (in.⁴)	Z_y (in.³)	ρ_y (in.)
2 × 2	$\frac{3}{16}$	4.32	1.27	0.668	0.668	0.726			
	$\frac{1}{4}$	5.41	1.59	0.766	0.766	0.694			
2.5 × 2.5	$\frac{3}{16}$	5.59	1.64	1.42	1.14	0.930			
	$\frac{1}{4}$	7.11	2.09	1.69	1.35	0.899			
3 × 2	$\frac{3}{16}$	5.59	1.64	1.86	1.24	1.06	0.977	0.977	0.771
	$\frac{1}{4}$	7.11	2.09	2.21	1.47	1.03	1.15	1.15	0.742
3 × 3	$\frac{3}{16}$	6.87	2.02	2.60	1.73	1.13			
	$\frac{1}{4}$	8.81	2.59	3.16	2.10	1.10			
4 × 2	$\frac{3}{16}$	6.87	2.02	3.87	1.93	1.38	1.29	1.29	0.798
	$\frac{1}{4}$	8.81	2.59	4.69	2.35	1.35	1.54	1.54	0.770
4 × 4	$\frac{3}{16}$	9.42	2.77	6.59	3.30	1.54			
	$\frac{1}{4}$	12.21	3.59	8.22	4.11	1.51			
	$\frac{3}{8}$	17.27	5.08	10.7	5.35	1.45			
	$\frac{1}{2}$	21.63	6.36	12.3	6.13	1.39			
5 × 3	$\frac{3}{16}$	9.42	2.77	9.1	3.62	1.81	4.08	2.72	1.21
	$\frac{1}{4}$	12.21	3.59	11.3	4.52	1.77	5.05	3.37	1.19
	$\frac{3}{8}$	17.27	5.08	14.7	5.89	1.70	6.48	4.32	1.13
	$\frac{1}{2}$	21.63	6.36	16.9	6.75	1.63	7.33	4.88	1.07
5 × 5	$\frac{3}{16}$	11.97	3.52	13.4	5.36	1.95			
	$\frac{1}{4}$	15.62	4.59	16.9	6.78	1.92			
	$\frac{3}{8}$	22.37	6.58	22.8	9.11	1.86			
	$\frac{1}{2}$	28.43	8.36	27.0	10.8	1.80			

[a] Outside dimensions across flat sides.
[b] Properties are based upon a nominal outside corner radius equal to two times the wall thickness.
Source: Manual of Steel Construction, American Institute of Steel Construction, Chicago, Illinois, 1980.

Appendix B-2 *Mass and Mass Moments of Inertia of Homogeneous Solids*

ρ = mass density

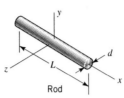

Rod

$$m = \frac{\pi d^2 L \rho}{4}$$

$$I_y = I_z = \frac{mL^2}{12}$$

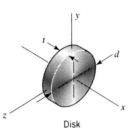

Disk

$$m = \frac{\pi d^2 t \rho}{4}$$

$$I_x = \frac{md^2}{8}$$

$$I_y = I_z = \frac{md^2}{16}$$

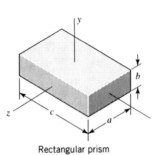

Rectangular prism

$$m = abc\rho$$

$$I_x = \frac{m}{12}(a^2 + b^2)$$

$$I_y = \frac{m}{12}(a^2 + c^2)$$

$$I_z = \frac{m}{12}(b^2 + c^2)$$

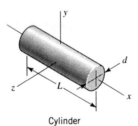

Cylinder

$$m = \frac{\pi d^2 L \rho}{4}$$

$$I_x = \frac{md^2}{8}$$

$$I_y = I_z = \frac{m}{48}(3d^2 + 4L^2)$$

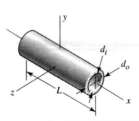

$$m = \frac{\pi L \rho}{4}(d_o^2 - d_i^2)$$

$$I_x = \frac{m}{8}(d_o^2 + d_i^2)$$

$$I_y = I_z = \frac{m}{48}(3d_o^2 + 3d_i^2 + 4L^2)$$

Material Properties and Uses

Appendix C-1 Physical Properties of Common Metals

Metal	Modulus of Elasticity, E		Modulus of Rigidity, G		Poisson's Ratio, ν	Unit Weight, w (lb/in.³)	Density, ρ (Mg/m³)	Coefficient of Thermal Expansion, α		Thermal Conductivity		Specific Heat	
	Mpsi	GPa	Mpsi	GPa				10⁻⁶/°F	10⁻⁶/°C	Btu/h-ft-°F	W/m-°C	Btu/lbm-°F	J/kg-°C
Aluminum alloy	10.4ᵃ	72	3.9	27	0.32	0.10	2.8	12.0	22	100	173	0.22	920
Beryl. copper	18.5	127	7.2	50	0.29	0.30	8.3	9.3	17	85	147	0.10	420
Brass, Bronze	16	110	6.0	41	0.33	0.31	8.7	10.5	19	45	78	0.10	420
Copper	17.5	121	6.6	46	0.33	0.32	8.9	9.4	17	220	381	0.10	420
Iron, gray castᵇ	15	103	6.0	41	0.26	0.26	7.2	6.4	12	29	50	0.13	540
Magnesium alloy	6.5	45	2.4	17	0.35	0.065	1.8	14.5	26	55	95	0.28	1170
Nickel alloy	30	207	11.5	79	0.30	0.30	8.3	7.0	13	12	21	0.12	500
Steel, carbon	30	207	11.5	79	0.30	0.28	7.7	6.7	12	27	47	0.11	460
Steel, alloy	30	207	11.5	79	0.30	0.28	7.7	6.3	11	22	38	0.11	460
Steel, stainless	27.5	190	10.6	73	0.30	0.28	7.7	8.0	14	12	21	0.11	460
Titanium alloy	16.5	114	6.2	43	0.33	0.16	4.4	4.9	9	7	12	0.12	500
Zinc alloy	12	83	4.5	31	0.33	0.24	6.6	15.0	27	64	111	0.11	460

ᵃ Values given are representative. Exact values may vary with composition and processing, sometimes greatly.
ᵇ See Appendix C-3 for more detailed elastic properties of cast irons.
Note: See Appendix C-18 for physical properties of some plastics.

Appendix C-2 Tensile Properties of Some Metals

Material	Ultimate Strength, S_u		Yield Strength, S_y		σ_0[a]		m[a]	ϵ_{Tf}[a]
	ksi	MPa	ksi	MPa	ksi	MPa		
Carbon and alloy steels								
1002 A[b]	42	290	19	131	78	538	0.27	1.25
1010 A	44	303	29	200	82	565	0.23	1.20
1018 A	49.5	341	32	221	90	621	0.25	1.05
1020 HR	66	455	42	290	115	793	0.22	0.92
1045 HR	92.5	638	60	414	140	965	0.14	0.58
1212 HR	61.5	424	28	193	110	758	0.24	0.85
4340 HR	151	1041	132	910	210	1448	0.09	0.45
52100 A	167	1151	131	903	210	1448	0.07	0.40
Stainless steels								
302 A	92	634	34	234	210	1448	0.48	1.20
303 A	87	600	35	241	205	1413	0.51	1.16
304 A	83	572	40	276	185	1276	0.45	1.67
440C A	117	807	67	462	180	1241	0.14	0.12
Aluminum alloys								
1100-0	12	83	4.5	31	22	152	0.25	2.30
2024-T4	65	448	43	296	100	690	0.15	0.18
7075-0	34	234	14.3	99	61	421	0.22	0.53
7075-T6	86	593	78	538	128	883	0.13	0.18
Magnesium alloys								
HK31XA-0	25.5	176	19	131	49.5	341	0.22	0.33
HK31XA-H24	36.2	250	31	214	48	331	0.08	0.20
Copper alloys								
90-10 Brass A	36.4	251	8.4	58	83	572	0.46	—
80-20 Brass A	35.8	247	7.2	50	84	579	0.48	—
70-30 Brass A	44	303	10.5	72	105	724	0.52	1.55
Naval Brass A	54.5	376	17	117	125	862	0.48	1.00

[a] Defined in Section 3.4.

[b] A = annealed, HR = hot-rolled.

Note: Values are from single tests and believed typical. Actual values may vary through small differences in composition and processing; hence, some values here do not agree with values in other Appendix C tables.

Source: J. Datsko, *Materials in Design and Manufacturing*, Mallory, Inc., Ann Arbor, Mich. 1977.

Appendix C.3a Typical Mechanical Properties and Uses of Gray Cast Iron[a]

ASTM Class[a]	Tensile Strength		Torsional Shear Strength		Compressive Strength		Reversed Bending Fatigue Limit		Brinell Hardness, H_B	Tensile Modulus		Torsional Modulus		Typical Uses
	MPa	ksi[a]	MPa	ksi	MPa	ksi	MPa	ksi		GPa	10^6 psi	GPa	10^6 psi	
20	152	22	179	26	572	83	69	10	156	66 to 97	9.6 to 14.0	27 to 39	3.9 to 5.6	Miscellaneous soft iron castings
25	179	26	220	32	669	97	79	11.5	174	79 to 102	11.5 to 14.8	32 to 41	4.6 to 6.0	Cylinder heads and blocks, housings
30	214	31	276	40	752	109	97	14	210	90 to 113	13.0 to 16.4	36 to 45	5.2 to 6.6	Brake drums, clutch plates, flywheels
35	252	36.5	334	48.5	855	124	110	16	212	100 to 119	14.5 to 17.2	40 to 48	5.8 to 6.9	Heavy-duty brake drums, clutch plates
40	293	42.5	393	57	965	140	128	18.5	235	110 to 138	16.0 to 20.0	44 to 54	6.4 to 7.8	Cylinder liners, camshafts
50	362	52.5	503	73	1130	164	148	21.5	262	130 to 157	18.8 to 22.8	50 to 55	7.2 to 8.0	Special high-strength castings
60	431	62.5	610	88.5	1293	187.5	169	24.5	302	141 to 162	20.4 to 23.5	54 to 59	7.8 to 8.5	Special high-strength castings

[a]Minimum values of S_u (in ksi) are given by the class number.

Appendix C-3b *Mechanical Properties and Typical Uses of Malleable Cast Iron*[a]

Specification Number	Class or Grade	Tensile Strength MPa	ksi	Yield Strength MPa	ksi	Brinell Hardness, H_B	Elongation[b] (%)	Typical Uses
Ferritic								
ASTM A47, A338; ANSI G48.1; FED QQ-1-666c	32510	345	50	224	32	156 max	10	General purpose at normal and elevated temperatures; good machinability, excellent shock resistance
	35018	365	53	241	35	156 max	18	
ASTM A197	—	276	40	207	30	156 max	5	Pipe flanges, valve parts
Pearlitic and Martensitic								
ASTM A220; ANSI G48.2; MIL-I-11444B	40010	414	60	276	40	149-197	10	General engineering service at normal and elevated temperatures
	45008	448	65	310	45	156-197	8	
	45006	448	65	310	45	156-207	6	
	50005	483	70	345	50	179-229	5	
	60004	552	80	414	60	197-241	4	
	70003	586	85	483	70	217-269	3	
	80002	655	95	552	80	241-285	2	
	90001	724	105	621	90	269-321	1	
Automotive								
ASTM A602; SAE J158	M3210[c]	345	50	224	32	156 max	10	Steering gear housing, mounting brackets
	M4504[d]	448	65	310	45	163-217	4	Compressor crankshafts and hubs
	M5003[d]	517	75	345	50	187-241	3	Parts requiring selective hardening, as gears
	M5503[e]	517	75	379	55	187-241	3	For machinability and improved induction hardening
	M7002[e]	621	90	483	70	229-269	2	Connecting rods, universal joint yokes
	M8501[e]	724	105	586	85	269-302	1	Gears with high strength and good wear resistance

[a] Condensed from *ASM Metals Reference Book*, American Society for Metals, Metals Park, Ohio, 1981.
[b] Minimum in 50 mm (2 in.).
[c] Annealed.
[d] Air quenched and tempered.
[e] Liquid quenched and tempered.

Appendix C-3c *Average Mechanical Properties and Typical Uses of Ductile (Nodular) Iron*

Grade[a]	Brinell Hardness, H_B	Elongation (%) (in 50 mm)	Tensile Modulus		Poisson's Ratio	Typical Uses
			GPa	10^6 psi		
60-40-18	167	15.0	169	24.5	0.29	Valves and fittings for steam and chemicals
65-45-12	167	15.0	168	24.4	0.29	Machine components subject to shock and fatigue
80-55-06	192	11.2	168	24.4	0.31	Crankshafts, gears, rollers
120-90-02	331	1.5	164	23.8	0.28	Pinions, gears, rollers, slides

Grade	Tensile Strength				Compressive Strength: Ultimate		Torsional Strength			
	Ultimate		Yield				Ultimate		Yield	
	MPa	10^6 psi	MPa	10^6 psi	MPa	10^6 psi	MPa	10^6 psi	MPa	10^6 psi
60-40-18	461	66.9	329	47.7	359	52.0	472	68.5	195	28.3
65-45-12	464	67.3	332	48.2	362	52.5	475	68.9	297	30.0
80-55-06	559	81.8	362	52.5	386	56.0	504	73.1	193	28.0
120-90-02	974	141.3	864	125.3	920	133.5	875	126.9	492	71.3

[a]The first two sections of grade number indicate minimum values (in ksi) of tensile ultimate and yield strengths.
Source: ASM Metals Reference Book, American Society for Metals, Metals Park, OH, 1981.

Appendix C-1a Mechanical Properties of Selected Carbon and Alloy Steels

I: AISI Number[a]	Treatment	Tensile Strength		Yield Strength		Elongation (%)	Reduction in Area (%)	Brinell Hardness, H_B	Izod Impact Strength	
		MPa	ksi	MPa	ksi				J	ft·lb
1015	As-rolled	420.6	61.0	313.7	45.5	39.0	61.0	126	110.5	81.5
	Normalized	424.0	61.5	324.1	47.0	37.0	69.6	121	115.5	85.2
	Annealed	386.1	56.0	284.4	41.3	37.0	69.7	111	115.0	84.8
1020	As-rolled	448.2	65.0	330.9	48.0	36.0	59.0	143	86.8	64.0
	Normalized	441.3	64.0	346.5	50.3	35.8	67.9	131	117.7	86.8
	Annealed	394.7	57.3	294.8	42.8	36.5	66.0	111	123.4	91.0
1030	As-rolled	551.6	80.0	344.7	50.0	32.0	57.0	179	74.6	55.0
	Normalized	520.6	75.5	344.7	50.0	32.0	60.8	149	93.6	69.0
	Annealed	463.7	67.3	341.3	49.5	31.2	57.9	126	69.4	51.2
1040	As-rolled	620.5	90.0	413.7	60.0	25.0	50.0	201	48.8	36.0
	Normalized	589.5	85.5	374.0	54.3	28.0	54.9	170	65.1	48.0
	Annealed	518.8	75.3	353.4	51.3	30.2	57.2	149	44.3	32.7
1050	As-rolled	723.9	105.0	413.7	60.0	20.0	40.0	229	31.2	23.0
	Normalized	748.1	108.5	427.5	62.0	20.0	39.4	217	27.1	20.0
	Annealed	636.0	92.3	365.4	53.0	23.7	39.9	187	16.9	12.5
1095	As-rolled	965.3	140.0	572.3	83.0	9.0	18.0	293	4.1	3.0
	Normalized	1013.5	147.0	499.9	72.5	9.5	13.5	293	5.4	4.0
	Annealed	656.7	95.3	379.2	55.0	13.0	20.6	192	2.7	2.0
1118	As-rolled	521.2	75.6	316.5	45.9	32.0	70.0	149	108.5	80.0
	Normalized	477.8	69.3	319.2	46.3	33.5	65.9	143	103.4	76.3
	Annealed	450.2	65.3	284.8	41.3	34.5	66.8	131	106.4	78.5

I: AISI Number[a]	Treatment	Tensile Strength		Yield Strength		Elongation (%)	Reduction in Area (%)	Brinell Hardness, H_B	Izod Impact Strength	
		MPa	ksi	MPa	ksi				J	ft·lb
3140	Normalized	891.5	129.3	599.8	87.0	19.7	57.3	262	53.6	39.5
	Annealed	689.5	100.0	422.6	61.3	24.5	50.8	197	46.4	34.2
4130	Normalized	668.8	97.0	436.4	63.3	25.5	59.5	197	86.4	63.7
	Annealed	560.5	81.3	360.6	52.3	28.2	55.6	156	61.7	45.5
4140	Normalized	1020.4	148.0	655.0	95.0	17.7	46.8	302	22.6	16.7
	Annealed	655.0	95.0	417.1	60.5	25.7	56.9	197	54.5	40.2
4340	Normalized	1279.0	185.5	861.8	125.0	12.2	36.3	363	15.9	11.7
	Annealed	744.6	108.0	472.3	68.5	22.0	49.9	217	51.1	37.7
6150	Normalized	939.8	136.3	615.7	89.3	21.8	61.0	269	35.5	26.2
	Annealed	667.4	96.8	412.3	59.8	23.0	48.4	197	27.4	20.2
8650	Normalized	1023.9	148.5	688.1	99.8	14.0	40.4	302	13.6	10.0
	Annealed	715.7	103.8	386.1	56.0	22.5	46.4	212	29.4	21.7
8740	Normalized	929.4	134.8	606.7	88.0	16.0	47.9	269	17.6	13.0
	Annealed	695.0	100.8	415.8	60.3	22.2	46.4	201	40.0	29.5
9255	Normalized	932.9	135.3	579.2	84.0	19.7	43.4	269	13.6	10.0
	Annealed	774.3	112.3	486.1	70.5	21.7	41.1	229	8.8	6.5

[a] All grades are fine-grained except for those in the 1100 series, which are coarse-grained. Heat-treated specimens were oil-quenched unless otherwise indicated.
Note: Values tabulated are approximate median expectations for 1-in. round sections. Individual test results may differ considerably.
Source: ASM Metals Reference Book, American society for Metals, Metals Park, Ohio, 1981.

Appendix C-4b *Typical Uses of Plain Carbon Steels*

Carbon (%)	Typical Uses
0.05–0.10	Stampings, rivets, wire, cold-drawn parts
0.10–0.20	Structural shapes, machine parts, carburized parts
0.20–0.30	Gears, shafts, levers, cold-forged parts, welded tubing, carburized parts
0.30–0.40	Shafts, gears, connecting rods, crane hooks, seamless tubing (This and higher hardnesses can be heat-treated.)
0.40–0.50	Gears, shafts, screws, forgings
0.60–0.70	Hard-drawn spring wire, lock washers, locomotive tires
0.70–0.90	Plowshares, shovels, leaf springs, hand tools
0.90–1.20	Springs, knives, drills, taps, milling cutters
1.20–1.40	Files, knives, razors, saws, wire-drawing dies

Appendix C-5a *Properties of Some Water-Quenched and Tempered Steels*

Steel	Diameter Treated (in.)	Diameter Tested (in.)	Normalized Temperature (°F)	Reheat Temperature (°F)	As Quenched, H_B
1030	1.0	0.505	1700	1600	514
1040	1.0	0.505	1650	1550	534
1050	1.0	0.505	1650	1525	601
1095	1.0	0.505	1650	1450	601
4130	0.53	0.505	1600	1575	495

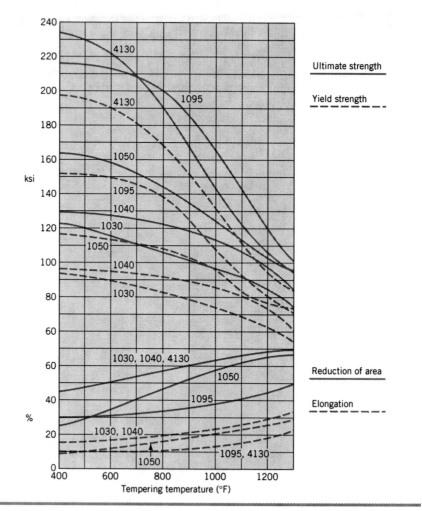

Source: Modern Steels and Their Properties, Bethlehem Steel Corporation, Bethlehem, Pa., 1972.

Appendix C-5b *Properties of Some Oil-Quenched and Tempered Carbon Steels*

Steel	Diameter Treated (in.)	Diameter Tested (in.)	Normalized Temperature (°F)	Reheat Temperature (°F)	As Quenched, H_B
1040	1.0	0.505	1650	1575	269
1050	1.0	0.505	1650	1550	321
1095	1.0	0.505	1650	1475	401

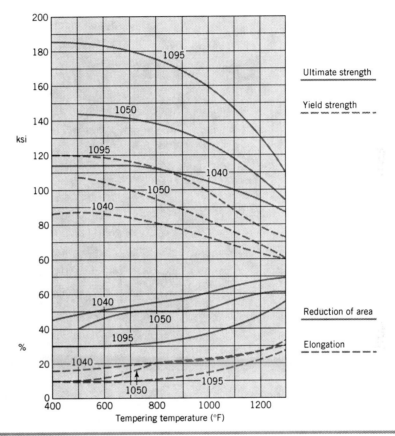

Source: Modern Steels and Their Properties, Bethelehem Steel Corporation, Bethlehem, Pa., 1972.

Appendix C-5e *Properties of Some Oil-Quenched and Tempered Alloy Steels*

Steel	Diameter Treated (in.)	Diameter Tested (in.)	Normalized Temperature (°F)	Reheat Temperature (°F)	As Quenched, H_B
4140	0.53	0.505	1600	1525	555
4340	0.53	0.505	1600	1550	601
9255	1.0	0.505	1650	1625	653

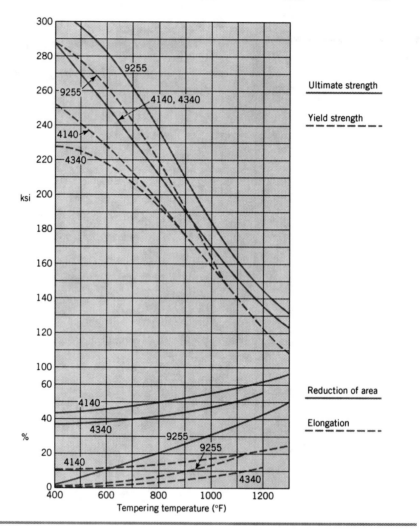

Source: Modern Steels and Their Properties, Bethlehem Steel Corporation, Bethlehem, Pa., 1972.

Appendix C-6 *Effect of Mass on Strength Properties of Steel*

All specimens oil-quenched and tempered at 1000°F (538°C)

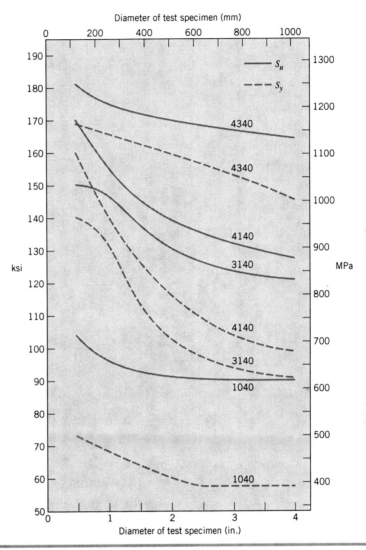

Source: Modern Steels and Their Properties, Bethlehem Steel Corporation, Bethlehem, Pa., 1972.

Appendix C-7 Mechanical Properties of Some Carburizing Steels

	Core									Case		
		Tensile Strength				Ductility		Impact Strength Izod			Thickness	
Steel AISI	Hardness, H_B	Ultimate, S_u		Yield, S_y		Elongation in 2 in. (%)	Reduction of Area (%)			Hardness, R_C		
		ksi	MPa	ksi	MPa			ft·lb	J		in.	mm
1015[a]	149	73	503	46	317	32	71	91	123	62	0.048	1.22
1022[a]	163	82	565	47	324	27	66	81	110	62	0.046	1.17
1117[a]	192	96	662	59	407	23	53	33	45	65	0.045	1.14
1118[a]	229	113	779	76	524	17	45	16	22	61	0.065	1.65
4320[b]	293	146	1006	94	648	22	56	48	65	59	0.075	1.91
4620[b]	235	115	793	77	531	22	62	78	106	59	0.060	1.52
8620[b]	262	130	896	77	531	22	52	66	89	61	0.070	1.78
E9310[b]	352	169	1165	138	952	15	62	63	85	58	0.055	1.40

[a] 1-in. round section treated, 0.505-in. round section tested. Single quench in water, tempered 350°F (177°C).

[b] 0.565-in. round section treated, 0.505-in. round section tested. Double quench in oil, tempered 450°F (232°C). (Tempering at 300°F gives greater case hardness but less core toughness.)

Note: Values tabulated are approximate median expectations.

Source: Modern Steels and Their Properties, Bethlehem Steel Corporation, Bethlehem, Pa., 4th ed., 1958, and 7th ed., 1972.

Appendix C-8 Mechanical Properties of Some Wrought Stainless Steels (Approximate Median Expectations)

AISI Type	Ultimate Strength, S_u (ksi) An.	CW	H&T	Yield Strength S_y (ksi) An.	CW	H&T	Elongation (%) An.	CW	H&T	Izod Impact (ft·lb) An.	CW	H&T	Drawability	Machinability	Weldability	Typical Uses
Austenitic																
302	85	110		35	75		60	35		110	90		VG	P	G	General purpose; springs
303	90	110		35	80		50	22		85	35		G	G	P	Bolts, nuts, rivets, aircraft fittings
304	85	110		35	75		60	55		110	90		VG	P	G	General purpose; welded construction
310, 310S	95			45			50			110			G	P	G	Turbine, furnace, heat exchanger parts
347, 348	90	110		35	65		50	40		110			VG	P	G	Jet engine, nuclear energy parts
384 (wire)	75			35			55						E			Severely cold-worked parts; fasteners
Martensitic																
410	75	105	115	40	85	85	35	17	23	90	75	80	F	F–	F	Machine parts, shafts, bolts, cutlery
414	115	130[a]	160	90	110[a]	125	20	15[a]	17	50		45		F	F	Machine parts, springs, bolts, cutlery
416, 416Se	75	100[b]	110	40	85[b]	85	30	13[b]	18	70	20[b]	25	P	G	P	Cutlery, fasteners, tools, screw machine parts
431	125	130[a]	165	95	110[a]	125	20	15[a]	17	50		40		P–	F	High-strength bolts, aircraft fittings
440 A,B,C	105	115[a]	260	60	90[a]	240	14	7[a]	3	2	2[a]	2	P	VP	P	Balls, bearing parts, nozzles, cutlery (highest H&T hardness of any stainless)
Ferritic																
430, 430F	75	83		43	63		27	20					G	F–G	F	Decorative trim, mufflers, screw machine parts
446	83	85		53	70		23	20		2			P	F	F	Parts subjected to high-temperature corrosion

[a] Annealed and cold-drawn.
[b] Tempered and cold-drawn.

Note: An., CW, H&T mean annealed, cold-worked, and hardened and tempered, respectively.

E, VG, G, F, P, VP mean excellent, very good, good, fair, poor, very poor, respectively.

Sources: *Metal Progress Databook 1980*, American Society for Metals, Metals Park, Ohio, Vol. 118, No. 1 (mid-June 1980); *ASME Handbook Metal Properties*, McGraw-Hill, New York, 1954; *Materials Engineering*, 1981 Materials Selector Issue, Penton/IPC, Cleveland, Vol. 92, No. 6 (Dec. 1980); *Machine Design*, 1981 Materials Reference Issue, Penton/IPC, Cleveland, Vol. 53, No. 6 (March 19, 1981).

794

Appendix C-9 *Mechanical Properties of Some Iron-Based Superalloys*

AISI Grade	Ultimate Strength, S_u (ksi)		Yield Strength S_y (ksi)		Elongation (%)		Rupture Strength, 100 h @ 1000°F (ksi)	Creep Strength, 0.0001%/h @ 1000°F (ksi)	Charpy Impact Strength, @ 70°F (ft·lb)
	70°F	1000°F	70°F	1000°F	70°F	1000°F			
Martensitic									
604 (Chromalloy)	125–138	110	95–108	85	7	—	75	—	—
610 (H-11)	135–310	180	100–240	140	3–17	11	95–115	—	10–32
Austenitic									
635 (Stainless W)	220–225	75–80	215–290	37–50	1–5	47–58	32	—	4–106
650 (16-12-G)	110–140	90	50–100	33	20–45	58	78	26	15
653 (17-24 CuMo)	86–112	65	40–90	29	30–45	37	48	10	8–26
665 (W-545)	176–187	154	123–142	120	19	13	120	—	—

Note: Values tabulated are approximate median expectations.
Source: Machine Design, 1981 Materials Reference Issue, Penton/IPC, Cleveland, Vol. 53, No. 6 (March 19, 1981).

Appendix C-10 Mechanical Properties, Characteristics, and Typical Uses of Some Wrought Aluminum Alloys

Alloy	Brinell Hardness, H_B	Tensile Strength Ultimate, S_u ksi	Ultimate, S_u MPa	Yield, S_y ksi	Yield, S_y MPa	Elongation in 2 in. (%)	Corrosion Resistance	Cold Work	Machine	Braze	Gas Weld	Arc Weld	Resistance Weld	Typical Uses
1100-0	23	13	90	5	34	45	A	A	E	A	A	A	B	Spinnings, drawn shapes, heat exchangers, cooking utensils, tanks
-H14	32	18	125	17	115	20	A	A	D	A	A	A	A	
-H18	44	24	165	22	150	15	A	B	D	A	A	A	A	
2011-T3	95	55	380	43	295	15	D	C	A	D	D	D	D	Screw machine parts
-T8	100	59	405	45	310	15	D	D	A	D	D	D	D	
2014-0	45	27	185	14	97	18	—	—	D	D	D	D	B	Heavy-duty forgings, aircraft structures and fittings, truck frames
-T4	105	62	425	42	290	20	D	C	B	D	D	B	B	
-T6	135	70	485	60	415	13	D	D	B	D	D	B	B	
2024-0	47	27	185	11	76	22	—	—	D	D	D	D	D	Aircraft structures, truck wheels, screw machine parts
-T4	120	68	470	47	325	19	D	C	B	D	B	B	B	
6061-0	30	18	125	8	55	30	B	A	D	A	A	A	B	Boats, rail cars, pipe, flanges, trailers
-T6	95	45	310	40	275	17	B	C	C	A	A	A	A	
6063-0	25	13	90	7	48	—	A	A	—	A	A	A	A	Furniture tube, doors, windows, pipe, fuel tanks
-T6	73	35	240	31	215	12	A	C	C	A	A	A	A	
7075-0	60	38	230	15	105	16	—	—	D	D	D	C	B	Aircraft structures and skins, skis, railings
-T6	150	83	570	73	505	11	C	D	B	D	D	C	B	

Note: Values are approximate median expectations for sizes about $\frac{1}{2}$ in. The H_B values were obtained from 500-kg load and 10-mm ball. Letters A, B, C, D indicate relative ratings in decreasing order of merit.

Source: ASM *Metals Reference Book.* American Society for Metals, Metals Park, Ohio, 1981.

Appendix C-11   *Tensile Properties, Characteristics, and Typical Uses of Some Cast-Aluminum Alloys*

Alloy	Casting Type	Tensile Strength Ultimate, S_u MPa	ksi	Yield, S_y MPa	ksi	Elongation (%)	Corrosion Resistance	Machining	Weldability	Anodized Appearance	Typical Uses
201-T4	Sand	365	53	215	31	20					Aircraft components
-T6	Sand	485	70	435	63	7					
208-F	Sand	145	21	97	14	2.5	4	3	2	3	Manifolds, valve bodies, pressure tight parts
295-T4	Sand	220	32	110	16	8.5	4	3	2	2	Crankcases, wheels, housings, spring hangers, fittings
-T6	Sand	250	36	165	24	5.0					
355-T6	Sand	240	35	175	25	3.0	3	3	1	4	Cylinder heads, water jackets, housings, impellers, timing gears, meter parts
-T6	Permanent mold	290	42	190	27	4.0					
356-T6	Sand	230	33	165	24	3.5	2	3	1	4	Automotive housings, aircraft and marine fittings, general-purpose castings
-T6	Permanent mold	265	38	185	27	5.0					
A390-F	Sand	180	26	180	26	<1.0					Automotive engine blocks, pumps, pulleys, brake shoes
-T6	Sand	280	40	280	40	<1.0					
-F	Permanent mold	200	29	200	29	<1.0					
-T6	Permanent mold	310	45	310	45	<1.0					
520-T4	Sand	330	48	180	26	16	1	1	4	1	Aircraft fittings, levers, brackets, parts requiring shock resistance

Note: Values are approximate median expectations for sizes about $\frac{1}{2}$ in. Characteristics are comparably rated from 1 to 5; 1 is the highest or best possible rating.
Sources: ASM Metals Reference Book, American Society for Metals, Metals Park, Ohio, 1981. *1981 Materials Selector, Materials Engineering,* Penton/IPC, Cleveland, Vol. 92, No. 6 (Dec. 1980).

Appendix C-12 *Temper Designations for Aluminum and Magnesium Alloys*

Temper	Process
F	As cast
0	Annealed
Hxx	Strain-hardened. First digit indicates the specific combination of operations, second digit indicates the degree of strain hardening; thus H18 indicates a greater degree of hardening than does H14 or H24
T3	Solution-heat-treated, cold-worked, and naturally aged
T4	Solution-heat-treated and naturally aged
T5	Cooled from an elevated-temperature shaping process and artificially aged
T6	Solution-heat-treated and artificially aged
T8	Solution-heat-treated, cold-worked, and artificially aged

Appendix C-13 Mechanical Properties of Some Copper Alloys

	UNS Designation	Composition	Tensile Strength				Elongation in 2 in. (%)
			Ultimate, S_u		Yield, S_y		
Alloy			ksi	MPa	ksi	MPa	
Wrought Alloys							
Leaded beryllium copper	C17300		68–200	469–1379	25–178	172–1227	43–3
Med leaded brass	C34000	(65Cu–34Zn)	50–55	345–379	19–42	131–290	60–40
Free cutting brass	C36000		49–68	338–469	18–45	124–310	53–18
Leaded phos bronze	C54400	(88Cu–4Zn)	68–75	469–517	57–63	393–434	20–15
Aluminum silicon-bronze	C64200	(91Cu–7Al–2Si)	75–102	517–703	35–68	241–469	32–22
Silicon bronze	C65500	(97Cu–3Si)	58–108	400–745	22–60	152–414	60–13
Manganese bronze	C67500		65–84	448–579	30–60	207–414	33–19
Cast Alloys							
Leaded red brass	C83600	(85Cu–5Zn–5Sn–5Pb)	37	255	17	117	30
Leaded yellow brass	C85200		38	262	13	90	35
Manganese bronze	C86200		95	655	48	331	20
Navy M bronze	C92200		40	276	20	138	30
Leaded Ni–Sn bronze	C92900		47	324	26	179	20
Bearing bronze	C93200		35	241	18	124	20
Aluminum bronze	C95400		85–105	586–724	35–54	241–372	18–8
Copper nickel	C96200	(90Cu–10Ni)	45	310	25	172	20

Note: Values tabulated are approximate median expectations.

Source: Machine Design, 1981 Materials Reference Issue, Penton/IPC, Cleveland, Vol. 53, No. 6 (March 19, 1981).

Appendix C-14 *Mechanical Properties of Some Magnesium Alloys*

Alloy	Form	Tensile Strength				Elongation in 2 in. (%)
		Ultimate, S_u		Yield, S_y		
		ksi	MPa	ksi	MPa	
AZ91B-F	Die casting	34	234	23	159	3
AZ31B-F	Extrusion	38–53	262–365	28–44	193–303	11–15
ZK60A-T5						
AZ31B-F	Forging	34–50	234–345	22–39	152–269	6–11
HM21A-T5						
AZ80A-T5						
ZK60A-T6						
AZ31B-H24	Sheet, plate	33–42	228–290	21–32	145–221	9–21
HK31A-H24						
HM21A-T8						

Note: Values tabulated are approximate median expectations.
Source: Machine Design, 1981 Materials Reference Issue, Penton/IPC, Cleveland, Vol. 53, No. 6 (March 19, 1981).

Appendix C-15 *Mechanical Properties of Some Nickel Alloys*

Alloy	Form	Tensile Strength Ultimate, S_u (MPa)	Ultimate, S_u (ksi)	Yield, S_y (ksi)	Yield, S_y (MPa)	Creep Strength, 0.0001%/h (ksi)	Creep Strength (MPa)	Elongation in 2 in. (%)	Impact Strength Notched Charpy (ft·lb)	(J)
Wrought nickel	CD annealed bar	379–552	55–80	15–30	103–207	12	83	55–40	228	309
Duranickel 301	CD annealed bar	621–827	90–120	30–60	207–414			55–35		
	CD aged bar	1172–1448	170–210	125–175	862–1207			25–15		
Monel 400	Annealed bar	483–621	70–90	25–50	173–345	24	165	60–35	216	293
	Hot-rolled bar	552–758	80–110	40–100	276–690	25	172	60–30	219	297
Monel K-500	Aged bar		140–190	110–150		87		30–20	39	53
Hastelloy B[a]	As-cast bar	924	134	67	462			52		
Udimet HX[a]	Sheet (0.109 in.)	786	114 (70°F)	52 (70°F)	359			43 (70°F)		
		89	13 (2000°F)	8 (2000°F)	55			50 (2000°F)		
Unitemp HK[a]										
Hastelloy X[a]										
Rene 95[a]	Forging	1620	235 (70°F)	190 (70°F)	1310			15 (70°F)		
		1551	225 (1000°F)	182 (1000°F)	1255			13 (1000°F)		
Inconel 600[a]	Annealed bar	662	96 (70°F)	41 (70°F)	283	40 (800°F)	276	45 (70°F)	180	244
		255	37 (1400°F)	25 (1400°F)	172	2.0 (1600°F)	14	68 (1400°F)		
Inconel 625[a]	Annealed bar	965	140 (70°F)	71 (70°F)	490	12 (1400°F)	83	50 (70°F)	49	66
		538	78 (1400°F)	61 (1400°F)	421	3.9 (1600°F)	27	45 (1400°F)		
Inconel X-750[a]	Aged bar	1269	184 (70°F)	126 (70°F)	869	63 (1200°F)	434	25 (70°F)	37	50
		986	143 (1200°F)	110 (1200°F)	758			7 (1200°F)		
Incoloy 800[a]	Annealed bar	600	87 (70°F)	43 (70°F)	296	6.0 (1400°F)	41	44 (70°F)	107	145
		228	33 (1400°F)	23 (1400°F)	159	3.5 (1600°F)	24	84 (1400°F)		

[a] "Superalloys," noted for high-temperature strength and corrosion resistance. Used in jet engines, turbines, and furnaces.

Note: Values tabulated are approximate median expectations. CD means cold-drawn.

Source: Machine Design, 1981 Materials Reference Issue, Penton/IPC, Cleveland, Vol. 53, No. 6 (March 19, 1981).

Appendix C-16 *Mechanical Properties of Some Wrought-Titanium Alloys*

| Alloy | Designation | Tensile Strength | | | | Elongation in 2 in. (%) | Charpy Impact Strength | |
| | | Ultimate, S_u | | Yield, S_y | | | | |
		ksi	MPa	ksi	MPa		ft·lb	J
Commercially pure alpha Ti	Ti-35A	35	241	25	172	24	11–40	15–54
Commercially pure alpha Ti	Ti-50A	50	345	40	276	20	11–40	15–54
Commercially pure alpha Ti	Ti-65A	65	448	55	379	18	11–40	15–54
Alpha alloy	Ti-0.2Pd	50	345	40	276	20	—	—
Alpha–beta alloy	Ti-6Al-4V	130–160[a]	896–1103[a]	120–150[a]	827–1034[a]	10-7	10–20	14–27
Beta alloy	Ti-3Al-13V-11Cr	135–188[a]	931–1296[a]	130–175[a]	896–1207[a]	16-6	5–15	7–20

[a] Depending on heat treatment.

Note: Values tabulated are approximate median expectations.

Source: Machine Design, 1981 Materials Reference Issue, Penton/IPC, Cleveland, Vol. 53, No. 6 (March 19, 1981).

Appendix C-17 *Mechanical Properties of Some Zinc Casting Alloys*

| Alloy Designation | | | Tensile Strength | | | | Elongation in 2 in. (%) | Charpy Impact Strength | | Brinell Hardness, H_B |
| | | | Ultimate, S_u | | Yield, S_y | | | | | |
ASTM	SAE	ADCI	ksi	MPa	ksi	MPa		ft·lb	J	
AG40A[a]	903	No. 3	41	283			10	43	58	82
AC41A[a]	925	No. 5	47	324			7	48	65	91
ZA-12										
Sand-cast			40–45	276–310	30	207	1–3			105–120
Permanent mold			45–50	310–345	31	214	1–3			105–125
Die-cast			57	393	46	317	2			110–125

[a] Die-cast.

Note: Values tabulated are approximate median expectations.

Sources: Machine Design, 1981 Materials Reference Issue, Penton/IPC, Cleveland, Vol. 53, No. 6 (March 19, 1981); *Metal Progress, Databook 1980*, American Society for Metals, Metals Park, Ohio, Vol. 118, No. 1 (mid-June, 1980).

Appendix C-18a Representative Mechanical Properties of Some Common Plastics

Plastic	Tensile Strength, S_u		Elongation in 2 in. (%)	Izod Impact Strength		Friction Coefficient	
	ksi	MPa		ft · lb	J	With Self	With Steel
ABS (general purpose)	6	41	5–20	6.5	8.8		
Acrylic (standard molding)	10.5	72	6	0.4	0.5		
Cellulosic (cellulose acetate)	2–7	14–48		1–7	1.4–9.5		
Epoxy (glass-filled)	10–20	69–138	4	2–30	2.7–41		
Fluorocarbon (PTFE)	3.4	23	300	3	4.1		0.05
Nylon (6/6)	12	83	60	1	1.4	0.04–0.13	
Phenolic (wood–flour-filled)	7	48	0.4–0.8	0.3	0.4		
Polycarbonate (general purpose)	9–10.5	62–72	110–125	12–16	16–22	0.52	
Polyester (20 to 30 percent glass-filled)	16–23	110–90	1–3	1.0–1.9	1.4–2.6	0.12–0.22	0.39
Polypropylene (unmodified resin)	5	34	10–20	0.5–2.2	0.7–3.0		0.12–0.13

Note: Values shown are typical; both higher and lower values may be commercially obtainable. Also see Appendix C-18b.

Sources: Machine Design, 1981 Materials Reference Issue, Penton/IPC, Cleveland, Vol. 53, No. 6 (March 19, 1981); *Materials Engineering,* 1981 Materials Selector Issue, Penton/IPC, Cleveland, Vol. 92, No. 6 (Dec. 1980).

Appendix C-18b Properties of Some Common Glass-Reinforced and Unreinforced Thermoplastic Resins

Base Resin ASTM Test →	Tensile Strength, ksi D638	Flexural Modulus, Mpsi D790	Izod Impact Strength, ft·lb/in.		Specific Gravity D792	Mold Shrinkage (%) D955	Water Absorption (in 24 h) D570	Thermal Expansion, 10^{-5}/°F D696	Deflection Temperature, °F (264 psi) D648
			Notched D256	Unnotched D256					
ABS	14.5 (6.0)	1.10 (0.32)	1.4 (4.4)	6–7	1.28 (1.05)	0.1 (0.6)	0.14 (0.30)	1.6 (5.3)	220 (195)
Acetal	19.5 (8.8)	1.40 (0.40)	1.8 (1.3)	8–10 (20)	1.63 (1.42)	0.3 (2.0)	0.30 (0.22)	2.2 (4.5)	325 (230)
Fluorocarbon } PTFE	14.0 (6.5)	1.10 (0.20)	7.5 (>40)	17–18	1.89 (1.70)	0.3 (1.8)	0.20 (0.02)	1.6 (4.0)	460 (160)
Nylon 6/12	22.0 (8.8)	1.20 (0.295)	2.4 (1.0)	20	1.30 (1.06)	0.4 (1.1)	0.21 (0.25)	1.5 (5.0)	41 (194)
Polycarbonate	18.5 (9.0)	1.20 (0.33)	3.7 (2.7)	17 (60)	1.43 (1.20)	0.1 (0.6)	0.07 (0.15)	1.3 (3.7)	300 (265)
Polyester[a]	19.5 (8.5)	1.40 (0.34)	2.5 (1.2)	16–18	1.52 (1.31)	0.3 (2.0)	0.06 (0.08)	1.2 (5.3)	430 (130)
Polyethylene[b]	10.0 (2.6)	0.90 (0.20)	1.1 (0.4)	8–9	1.17 (0.95)	0.3 (2.0)	0.02 (0.02)	2.7 (6.0)	260 (120)
Polypropylene[c]	9.7 (4.9)	0.55 (0.18)	3.0 (0.4)	11–12	1.12 (0.91)	0.4 (1.8)	0.03 (0.01)	2.0 (4.0)	295 (135)
Polystyrene	13.5 (7.0)	1.30 (0.45)	1.0 (0.45)	2–3	1.28 (1.07)	0.1 (0.4)	0.05 (0.10)	1.9 (3.6)	215 (180)

[a] Polybutylene terephthalate (PBT) resin.
[b] High density (HD).
[c] Impact-modified grade.

Note: Values in parentheses pertain to unreinforced resins. Other values are typical of 30 percent glass reinforcement formulas. All values shown are typical; both higher and lower values may be commercially obtainable.

Source: Machine Design, 1981 Materials Reference Issue, Penton/IPC, Cleveland, Vol. 53, No. 6 (March 19, 1981).

805

390

Application	Thermoplastic																		Thermoset		
	ABS	Acetal	Acrylic	Cellulosics	Fluoroplastics	Nylon	Phenylene oxide	Polycarbonate	Polyester	Polyethylene	Polyimide	Polyphenylene sulfide	Polypropylene	Polystyrene	Polysulfone	Polyurethane	Polyvinyl chloride	Phenolic	Polyester	Polyurethane
Structural, mechanical — gears, cams, pistons, rollers, valves, pump impellers, fan blades, rotors, washing machine agitators		X				X						X						X		
Light-duty mechanical and decorative — knobs, handles, camera cases, pipe fittings, battery cases, auto steering wheels, trim moldings, eyeglass frames, tool handles	X		X	X						X				X	X		X	X		
Small housings and hollow shapes — phone and flashlight cases, helmets; housings for power tools, pumps, small appliances	X			X			X	X	X					X	X		X	X		
Large housings and hollow shapes — boat hulls, large appliance housings, tanks, tubs, ducts, refrigerator liners	(Foam)					(Foam)			(Foam)	(H.D. Foam)				(Foam)	(Foam)		(Foam)	(Glass-filled)	(Foam)	
Optical and transparent parts — safety glasses, lenses, safety and vandals-resistant glazing, snowmobile windshields, signs, refrigerator shelves			X	X				X						X	X					
Parts for wear applications — gears, bushings, bearings, tracks, chute liners, roller skate wheels, wear strips		X			X	X				(UHMW)	X	X				X		X	X	

Note: H.D. means high-density; UHMW means ultrahigh molecular weight.

Source: Machine Design, 1987 Materials Reference Issue, Penton/IPC, Cleveland, Vol. 59, No. 8 (April 16, 1987).

Appendix C-19 *Material Classes and Selected Members of Each Class*

Class	Members	Abbreviation
Engineering Alloys (Engineering metals and alloys)	Aluminum alloys	Al alloys
	Cast irons	Cast irons
	Copper alloys	Cu alloys
	Lead alloys	Lead alloys
	Magnesium alloys	Mg alloys
	Molybdenum alloys	Mo alloys
	Nickel alloys	Ni alloys
	Steels	Steels
	Tin alloys	Tin alloys
	Titanium alloys	Ti alloys
	Tungsten alloys	W alloys
	Zinc alloys	Zn alloys
Engineering Polymers (Engineering thermoplastics and thermosets)	Epoxies	EP
	Melamines	MEL
	Polycarbonate	PC
	Polyesters	PEST
	Polyethylene, high density	HDPE
	Polyethylene, low density	LDPE
	Polyformaldehyde	PF
	Polymethylmethacrylate	PMMA
	Polypropylene	PP
	Polytetrafluorethylene	PTFE
	Polyvinylchloride	PVC
Engineering Ceramics (Fine ceramics capable of load-bearing application)	Alumina	Al_2O_3
	Diamond	C
	Sialon	Sialon ($Si_{6-x}Al_xO_xN_{8-x}$)
	Silicon carbide	SiC
	Silicon nitride	Si_3N_4
	Zirconia	ZrO_2
Engineering Composites (A distinction is drawn between the properties of a ply—"UNIPLY"—and of a laminate—"LAMINATES")	Carbon fiber reinforced polymer	CFRP
	Glass fiber reinforced polymer	GFRP
	Kevlar fiber reinforced polymer	KFRP
Porous Ceramics (Traditional ceramics, cements, rocks, and minerals)	Brick	
	Cement	
	Common rocks	
	Concrete	
	Porcelain	
	Pottery	
Glasses (Ordinary silicate glass)	Borosilicate glass	B-glass
	Soda glass	Na-glass
	Silica	SiO_2
Woods (Separate envelopes describe properties parallel to the grain and normal to it, and wood products)	Ash	
	Balsa	
	Fir	
	Oak	
	Pine	
	Wood products (plywood, etc.)	